PORCELAIN *for* PALACES

—— The Fashion for Japan in Europe: 1650-1750 ——

THIS EXHIBITION AND CATALOGUE HAVE BEEN MADE POSSIBLE
BY THE GENEROUS SPONSORSHIP OF

THE GLOBAL COMPUTER AND COMMUNICATIONS COMPANY

PORCELAIN *for* PALACES

The Fashion for Japan in Europe

―――― 1650-1750 ――――

John Ayers, Oliver Impey, J. V. G. Mallet

WITH CONTRIBUTIONS BY

Anthony du Boulay and Lawrence Smith

AN EXHIBITION ORGANISED JOINTLY WITH THE
BRITISH MUSEUM IN THE NEW JAPANESE GALLERIES
6TH JULY TO 4TH NOVEMBER 1990

ORIENTAL CERAMIC SOCIETY

© Oriental Ceramic Society, 1990

Distributed by Philip Wilson Publishers Limited
26 Litchfield Street, London WC2H 9NJ

ISBN 0 903421 24 0
LC 90-060779

Designed by Langley Iddins
Printed and bound by Balding & Mansell,
Wisbech, Cambridgeshire

Photographic Acknowledgements

Reproduced by gracious permission of Her Majesty the
   Queen: Nos 71, 137, 139, 151, 152, 221, 235, 236,
   249, 250, 252
Amsterdam, Rijksmuseum: Fig. 7 and No. 53
Amsterdam, Rijksprentenkabinet: Nos 5 and 6
Arnhem, Gemeentemuseum: Nos 273 and 274
Ashmolean Museum, Oxford: Nos 18, 19, 20, 21, 23, 27,
   28, 32, 39, 43, 50, 57, 58, 67, 70, 75, 80, 81, 82, 84,
   88, 90, 91, 92, 95, 96, 97, 102, 105, 106, 107, 110, 111,
   112, 113, 115, 118, 121, 122, 123, 125, 130, 134, 145,
   150, 203, 205, 206, 212, 213, 214, 243, 259, 262, 263,
   266, 270, 304, 305, 347, 351, 354, 356, 359, 360, 365
Berlin, Staatliche Museen Preussischer Kulturbesitz,
   Kunstbibliothek: Fig. 14
The British Library: Nos 8, 10, 11, 12
The British Museum: Fig. 12, Nos 3, 13, 14, 15, 155,
   183, 186, 192, 193, 195, 198, 200, 201, 284, 291, 292,
   297, 298, 299, 301, 307, 313, 326, 330, 332, 339, 341,
   342, 343, 344, 345, 349, 353, 355, 358, 363, 368, 370,
   371
Brussels, Musées Royaux d'Art et d'Histoire: Nos 141,
   293, 295, 310
Cecil Higgins Art Gallery and Museum, Bedford:
   No. 294, 366, 367
Christie's: Fig. 3 and Nos 99, 168, 333
Delft, Museum Het Prinsenhof: No. 278
Lucinda Douglas-Menzies: Fig. 17 and Nos 2, 16, 17, 30,
   34, 37, 38, 48, 49, 51, 52, 55, 60, 62, 63, 64, 65, 68,
   69, 78, 87, 89, 104, 114, 120, 127, 128, 131, 132, 135,
   136, 138, 140, 143, 153, 156, 157, 158, 160, 162, 163,
   167, 169, 170, 171, 172, 175, 179, 182, 188, 197, 199,
   208, 209, 210, 216, 217, 220, 225, 227, 228, 232, 233,
   251, 254, 260, 267, 268, 296, 300, 315, 317, 318, 328,
   334, 335, 336, 337, 338, 348, 357, 361
Dresden, Porzellansammlung: Fig. 6 and No. 191

Dresden, Staatsarchiv: Figs 11 and 16
Royal Worcester Porcelain Ltd: No. 356 (drawing)
Frankfurt am Main, Historisches Museum: Fig. 5
Fitzwilliam Museum, Cambridge: Nos 54, 98, 148, 159,
   165, 177, 178, 180, 189, 219, 271, 275, 276, 308, 311,
   321, 322
The Hague, Algemeen Rijksarchief: No. 9
The Hague, Gemeentemuseum No. 272, 282, 283
Brian Morgan: Nos 22, 24, 25, 26, 29, 33, 35, 41, 42, 44,
   45, 47, 59, 61, 66, 72, 73, 74, 76, 79, 83, 85, 86, 100,
   109, 117, 119, 133, 142, 144, 164, 173, 184, 187, 194,
   196, 204, 207, 211, 215, 226, 234, 237, 239, 242, 277,
   279, 280, 281, 285, 286, 287, 288, 289, 290, 302, 303,
   306, 309, 312, 316, 319, 325, 327, 329, 331, 340, 346,
   350, 352, 364, 369, 372
Munich, Bayerisches Nationalmuseum: No. 244
Munich, Residenzmuseum: Nos 146, 147, and 190
National Maritime Museum, Greenwich: No. 7
New York, Metropolitan Museum of Art Library:
   No. 172 (drawing)
Paris, Bibliothèque Nationale: Fig. 8
Paris, Musée du Louvre: Fig. 4 and No. 149
Pommersfelden, Graf von Schönborn Kunstsammlungen:
   Fig. 15
John Stoel, Haren, The Netherlands: Nos 31, 36, 40, 46,
   56, 108, 126, 174, 176, 181, 218, 230, 231, 241, 323,
   324
Vienna, Hofsilber- und Tafelkammer: Nos 245, 246, 247,
   248
Victoria and Albert Museum: Fig. 10 and Nos 1, 4, 77,
   93, 94, 103, 116, 154, 161, 166, 185, 202, 222, 223,
   224, 238, 253, 255, 256, 257, 258, 261, 264, 265, 269
Victoria B. C. Art Gallery: Nos 124 and 129
Michael Wheeler: Nos 101 and 240

Contents

6

LENDERS TO THE EXHIBITION

Her Majesty the Queen

Amsterdam, Rijksmuseum

Amsterdam, Rijksprentenkabinet

Arnhem, Gemeentemuseum

The Ashmolean Museum, Oxford

The British Library, India Office Library and
Records, Oriental Collections and Map Library

The British Museum

Brussels, Musées Royaux d'Art et d'Histoire

The Burghley House Collection, Stamford,
Lincolnshire

The Cecil Higgins Art Gallery and Museum,
Bedford

Delden, Stichting Twickel

Delft, Museum het Prinsenhof

Drayton House

Dresden, Porzellansammlung

Lord Egremont, Petworth House

The Fitzwilliam Museum, Cambridge

Grimsthorpe and Drummond Castle Trust

Groningen, Groninger Museum

The Hague, Algemeen Rijksarchief

The Hague, Gemeentemuseum

The Methuen Collection, Corsham Court

Munich, Bayerisches Nationalmuseum

Munich, Residenzmuseum

National Maritime Museum, Greenwich

The National Trust: Belton House, Clandon Park
and Erddig

Paris, Musée du Louvre

Sherborne Castle Estates

The Victoria and Albert Museum

Vienna, Hofsilber- und Tafelkammer

Mr Philip N. Allen

Mr J. G. Ayers

Mr Richard Barker

Mr Peter Barlow

Mr and Mrs A. J. H. du Boulay

Mr H. A. Daendels

Mr Valentine Dawnay

Mr J. W. van Diepen

Mr and Mrs Myron S. Falk, Jr

Sir John and Lady Figgess

Miss Irene Finch

Mr Gerald First

Mr and Mrs Henry Hayter

Dr and Mrs O. R. Impey

Mr R. G. Jenyns

Mr R. W. Lawrence

Lady Victoria Leatham

Mr K. Main

Mr J. V. G. Mallet

Mr B. S. McElney

Professor David McMullen

Mr Hugo Morley Fletcher

Brigadier and Mrs J. M. Neilson

Lady Cynthia Postan

Mr A. S. Reynolds

Mr Adrian Sassoon

Mr Ahmad Sheikhi

Mr Tony Stevenson

Mr and Mrs M. J. Webb

Mrs G. F. Wingfield Digby

Mr and Mrs Stephen Winkworth

Marquess of Zetland

Foreword

More than three decades have elapsed since the Oriental Ceramic Society last turned its full attention to Japanese ceramics with the pioneer exhibition of Japanese porcelain in the spring of 1956. That exhibition, which was largely the inspiration of that great scholar and collector, the late Soame Jenyns, marked the starting point of a reawakened interest in Japanese export porcelain not only in Europe and America but also avidly in Japan where, until then, it had been all but overlooked. By the 1980s a rising enthusiasm for Japanese art was evident and, in 1986 the Council of the Society decided to examine the prospect for mounting an exhibition on an altogether larger scale than that of 1956 and, in particular, to widen the scope to demonstrate the influence which the great charm and appeal of the Japanese porcelains had on the development and production of porcelain in Europe. It was felt that this would attract connoisseurs of English and Continental ceramics and would also be likely to interest the general public, since it is a romantic story which has not been fully told.

The import of Japanese porcelain into Europe began in the middle of the 17th century when the previously dominant Chinese trade temporarily collapsed. The bold decoration and brilliant colours of the new imports, especially of the Kakiemon types, soon captivated Europeans who had not seen their like before. Collecting rare Oriental porcelains had long been a princely pursuit; now their palaces and pavilions began to fill up and they adopted special, often spectacular measures to display their treasures. All this is encompassed in the exhibition which also explores how the fashion for things Japanese spurred European potters and their patrons to great efforts to reproduce the Japanese wares. When the secret of true porcelain was at last re-discovered (at Meissen in 1709) the Kakiemon style in particular emerged as a significant element in the shapes and decoration of the production. The fashion spread throughout Europe, especially to France, Holland and England. In certain forms the popularity of Japanese styles continues today.

From the start it was clear that an exhibition of the scale envisaged could not be mounted from the unaided resources of the Society and that it would be essential to seek collaboration and to find a sponsor. Fortunately, the new Japanese galleries at the British Museum were due for completion early in 1990, and Sir David Wilson, the Director of the Museum, who from an early stage had indicated his enthusiastic support for the kind of exhibition we had in mind, very kindly agreed that it could be mounted as the first loan exhibition in the new galleries. We are most grateful to the Trustees of the Museum and to Sir David for this beneficence and I must also express our gratitude for the close and congenial collaboration that followed, and especially for the cooperation of the Department of Japanese Antiquities, under its Keeper, Lawrence Smith. We are no less indebted to many other departments involved.

The need for a sponsor to shoulder the very heavy costs to be met was paramount, and the Society is infinitely grateful to Sir Michael Butler who, through his banking connections, effected an introduction to Fujitsu, a leading Japanese computer and communications company who most generously agreed to sponsor the exhibition.

There are over three hundred and seventy exhibits in all, borrowed from lenders in this country and abroad, to all of whom the Society is profoundly indebted. First I must acknowledge our gratitude to Her Majesty The Queen, by whose gracious permission a number of rare pieces, some not previously shown in public, have been lent from the Royal Collection. The difficult task of selection has been eased by sizeable loans from the principal museums, notably the British Museum itself, and from such great and worthy institutions as the Victoria and Albert Museum, Ashmolean Museum, Oxford, and the Fitzwilliam Museum, Cambridge; we are much indebted to their respective Directors and Trustees.

Many great houses, including a number belonging to the National Trust have agreed to release their treasures, and that outstanding storehouse of 17th century wares, Burghley House, has been extraordinarily generous, even lending their unique inventory of 1688. We are immensely grateful for this.

The greatest princely collections of the past are to be found on the Continent of Europe, and we are fortunate to have been given such willing help from some of the most prominent of these, notably the *Porzellanzimmer* of the Staatliche Kunstsammlungen in Dresden, where much of the collection formed early in the 18th century by Augustus the Strong of Saxony is still kept. We are deeply indebted to its Director and no less to the Directors of the Residenzmuseum and the

Bayerisches Nationalmuseum in Munich; the Ehemalige Hofsilber- und Tafelkammer, Vienna; and the Musée du Louvre in Paris; all of which have lent rare treasures of historic value. A very warm response was received also to our requests for loans from the Netherlands, the early home of so many collections, and we are especially grateful to the staff of several Dutch museums. Members of the Society from the Netherlands and the USA as well as in the United Kingdom have lent pieces from their private collections, and to all we are grateful for their participation.

An immense amount of time and energy was devoted to their task by all the experts charged with the selection of objects to be shown; John Ayers, the Coordinator and the driving force behind the entire project, Dr Oliver Impey of the Ashmolean Museum, Oxford, whose specialist knowledge of the subject has been invaluable, John Mallet, the acknowledged authority on European ceramics, formerly in charge of the collections at the Victoria and Albert Museum, Lawrence Smith whose valuable support cannot be overstressed and Anthony du Boulay whose special contribution stems from his wide knowledge, his acquaintance with collections and his connection with the National Trust, to whom we are indebted for a number of important loans from great houses in their charge. That the efforts of the Committee were successfully brought to fruition is largely due to the quite remarkable support provided by the Organising Secretary for the exhibition, Jean Martin, who was tireless in travelling the country, following up loan requests, maintaining records, organising all the photography, managing correspondence, and generally maintaining control.

It is a source of very great pleasure to us that our Patron, His Royal Highness the Duke of Gloucester, kindly consented to open the exhibition.

Lastly, I would like to pay tribute to Fujitsu Limited without whose generous sponsorship, the exhibition could not have taken place.

SIR JOHN FIGGESS, K.B.E., C.M.G.
PRESIDENT, ORIENTAL CERAMIC SOCIETY

Editorial Preface

This catalogue, like the exhibition itself, is the product of concerted endeavour in many quarters. The selection of the exhibits, which has taken shape through a long process of appraisal and re-appraisal, is the work of the Exhibition Committee, while in practice responsibility for it has devolved chiefly on those here named as members of the Catalogue Committee. It is their individual contributions also, combined and edited, which make up the body of the catalogue. Much of the foundation work was done by Oliver Impey, Anthony du Boulay and Lawrence Smith. Oliver Impey and J. V. G. Mallet undertook to explore and develop the themes of the exhibition in four longer Introductions, and in bringing their scholarship to bear they have, I believe, succeeded in presenting the matter in ways that are fresh and authoritative. That this many-sided collaboration has been held together and brought to an effective conclusion is owing more than anything to the tireless enthusiasm and skill of our Organising Secretary, Jean Martin.

Work on the catalogue and on mounting the exhibition itself have been largely inseparable, and many institutions and individuals have earned our thanks. The active association of the British Museum has from an early stage contributed to shape the project and, as the effective borrowing agent for loans, the Department of Japanese Antiquities, under its Keeper, Lawrence Smith, has been continuously involved. We are very conscious of the debt owing to his efficient and hard-working staff: Victor Harris, Tim Clark, Greg Irvine, Sarah Jones, Sally Martin and Catherine Edwards.

The exhibition display was undertaken by the Design Office and our gratitude goes to its Head, Margaret Hall and to the very gifted designer Andy Creed-Miles, also to Andrea Easey and Judith Simmons for their work, the fruits of which are now evident. The Department of Medieval and Later Antiquities has lent many exhibits. We are grateful both to the Keeper, Neil Stratford and to Aileen Dawson, who has been unstinting with practical help and advice. The Department of Oriental Antiquities, also, has assisted generously and we would particularly like to thank its Keeper Jessica Rawson, Jane Portal, and Sheila Vainker. In the British Library we have reason to be grateful to Hilary Williams, of the Print Room, Geoffrey Armitage of the Map Room and Yuying Brown of Oriental Manuscripts and Printed Books. The staff of the Press and Public Relations Office played a significant part in launching the exhibition; here we should particularly thank Geoffrey House and Andrew Hamilton for their skill and counsel. Invaluable services were performed by the Ceramics and Glass Section of the Conservation Department, notably in the persons of Nigel Williams and Denise Ling.

The list of those elsewhere whose help calls for acknowledgement is substantial. At the Victoria & Albert Museum, another major source of loans, we must especially thank, in the Far Eastern Department, Rose Kerr and Rupert Faulkner; in the Department of Ceramics, Michael Archer, Ann Eatwell and Judith Bradfield; and in the Department of Furniture, Simon Jervis. The Ashmolean Museum, Oxford contributed largely in both loans and expertise and here we are much indebted to Mary Tregear, of the Department of Eastern Art, and Dr John Whiteley, of the Department of Western Art for their compliance with our many requests. At the Fitzwilliam Museum, Cambridge, Robin Crighton gave us exemplary help. Anthony Farrington of the India Office Library and Dr Eric Kentley of the National Maritime Museum both gave much-needed advice in their respective fields. In connection with the loans from the Royal Collection, Sir Geoffrey de Bellaigue and his colleagues supplied valuable information about mounts. At Burghley House, Lady Victoria Leatham gave much encouragement and agreed to our every loan request; the help of Jon Culverhouse was also invaluable. At the National Trust we were much aided by Joanna Rickards. From New York, Linda Shulsky provided important information relating to her research into the collecting of Queen Mary II. In Tokyo, Haruo Igaki was uncommonly helpful. Mark Hinton, of Christie's and Gordon Lang of Sotheby's both gave much useful advice. We are grateful to Michiko MacIver for reading the Japanese text. For much-appreciated help in a variety of ways we wish to thank also Noel Anderson, Leonore Stuart and John Martin, Margaret Sisley, Judy Smith and Catharine Reynolds.

Many loans have come from abroad; and here a special debt must be acknowledged to C. J. A. Jörg, Curator at the Groninger Museum, who has been tireless in supplying ideas and information; likewise A. L. den Blauuwen, formerly of the Rijksmuseum, Amsterdam; Pauline Scheurleer and Dr Vroom, Curators in that institution; Frits Scholten, Curator at the Gemeentemuseum, The Hague, and the curators of the Museés d'Art et d'Histoire, Brussels. Cooperation of the greatest value was received from Dr Klaus-Peter Arnold, Director and Dr Friedrich Reichel, Curator of

the Porzellansammlung, Dresden; Dr Peter Parenzan, in respect of the Ehemalige Hof- und Tafelzimmer; Vienna; Dr Gerhard Hojer, regarding the Residenzmuseum and Dr Lorenz Seelig of the Bayerisches Nationalmuseum in Munich; Dr Katharine Bott, concerning Schloss Pommersfelden; and Daniel Alcouffe, of the Musée du Louvre in Paris.

At the same time we wish to acknowledge the essential contribution of those many other individuals, including curators and private lenders, who have so willingly assisted at one stage or another; their names figure largely in the list of Lenders to the Exhibition.

As acknowledged elsewhere, the greatest number of photographs reproduced here are the work of Lucinda Douglas-Menzies; for a substantial number more, however, we are much indebted to Brian Morgan, a devoted member of the Society, who has once again given most generously of his time and special skill. In the design of the 'Porcelain Room' invaluable help was provided by Edward Impey. We also much appreciate the expert and friendly collaboration of the editorial staff of Philip Wilson Publishers Ltd, especially Mary Osborne and Sally Prideaux, and the designer Langley Iddins, in producing this volume.

As regards the arrangement of the catalogue, it is hoped this may largely speak for itself. The aim has been to present, firstly, a brief overview of the circumstances of the porcelain trade, followed by a systematic presentation of the main classes of exported Japanese wares, as they appear in the exhibition. An interlude is provided by Section V, which deals with the more spectacular side of their impact on the European scene: their use as room decoration in important houses and palaces, and the concomitant practice of furnishing them with fine metal mounts. Subsequent sections detail the remarkable effect of the Japanese styles on the development of European ceramics and in particular, on the nascent porcelain industry.

The style of the catalogue entries follows a pattern that must now be familiar. Each section is prefaced by a brief introduction, the authorship of which is indicated by the following initials:

J. G. A.   John Ayers
A. du B.   Anthony du Boulay
O. R. I.   Oliver Impey
J. V. G. M.   John Mallet
L. R. H. S.   Lawrence Smith

JOHN AYERS
EDITOR

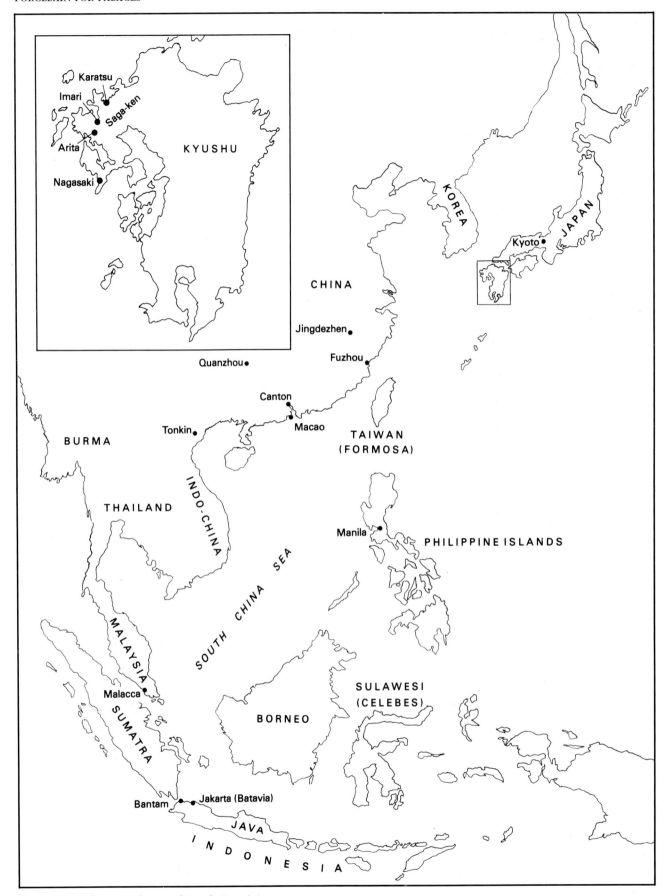

FIG. 1 Map of Japan, China and South-East Asia.

The Trade in Japanese Porcelain

OLIVER IMPEY

Porcelain from China seems to have become available in Europe by the late 14th century, but was exceedingly rare until the early 15th century. Then it would have filtered through into Europe from Mamluk Egypt either as expensive trade goods or as diplomatic presents. It was, at first, rare, precious and mysterious; neither its origin nor its composition was known. We still do not know for sure the origin of the word 'porcelain'. This was, of course, mostly blue-and-white porcelain from Jingdezhen in China (see Fig. 1); such pieces can be seen depicted in Renaissance paintings, most famously in *The Feast of the Gods* by Giovanni Bellini, which was finished by Titian in 1514.[1] This, perhaps, gives some clue to the value placed upon porcelain in the West – would one not have expected the Gods to eat off massy gold, or at least silver gilt? To protect it and to enhance its decorative effect, porcelain could be mounted in precious metal mounts, as was the 'Beckford vase', a Yuan dynasty white porcelain (*yingqing*) bottle vase with mounts (now lost) dateable to 1381;[2] and the celadon bowl called the *Katzenelnbogischer Willkomm* with mounts dateable to about 1435.[3] This mounting of porcelain in metal is a practice that we shall see later.

Contemporary inventories can give us some indication of the amounts of porcelain that then would have been owned by grandees; the Medici Inventories of 1553 list some 400 pieces of porcelain, including 59 celadons and 289 pieces of blue-and-white.[4]

Direct access to the trade in porcelain was gained by the Portuguese after Vasco da Gama had rounded the Cape of Good Hope and reached Calicut in 1498. Porcelain could then be bought from Chinese merchants direct, cutting out the middlemen and the overland transhipment through Egypt. By the middle of the 16th century porcelain was being made to order in Jingdezhen for the Portuguese market, and was to be found offered for sale in the shops of the Rua dos Mercadores in Lisbon.

This porcelain was of a different type from those made before, and much of it was made in shapes in current use in Europe; in other words, it was considerably adapted to European usage and to European taste. By the end of the century a very definite style of this porcelain, specifically made for export, had emerged; this was during the Wanli period of the late Ming dynasty. Nearly all of this was a relatively coarsely-made though thinly-potted ware then, and now, called *kraak porselein* or 'carrack ware', an incorrect Dutch language interpretation, and it was almost all blue-and-white. A small quantity of enamelled wares did filter through to Europe, but this was exceptional. White wares (*blanc-de-Chine*) were reaching Europe by the end of the century, from the southern kilns of China, to be followed later

---

1. Now in the National Gallery, Washington. See Arthur Spriggs, 'Oriental porcelain in Western paintings', *Transactions of the Oriental Ceramic Society*, 36, 1964–66, pp. 73–87.
2. Arthur Lane, 'The Gaignières-Fonthill Vase; a Chinese porcelain of about 1300', *Burlington Magazine*, 103, 1961, pp. 124–33.

3. Franz Adrian Dreier, 'The *Kunstkammer* of the Hessian Landgraves in Kassel' in Oliver Impey and Arthur MacGregor (eds), *The Origin of Museums*, Oxford, 1985, pp. 102–109.
4. R. W. Lightbown, 'Oriental Art and the Orient in Late Renaissance and Baroque Italy', *Journal of the Warburg and Courtauld Institutes*, 32, 1969, pp. 228–79.

by the brown Yixing wares, also from the South.

The Portuguese monopoly ensured that porcelain was not so widely known outside Iberia and thus references to the possession of porcelain are rare in northern Europe before about 1600. The monopoly also excited jealousy, particularly after the extent (and profitability) of the trade was demonstrated when the contents of two Portuguese ships captured by the Dutch, the *St Iago* and the *Sta Catharina* were sold at auction in Middleburg in 1602 and 1604.[5] The Honourable East India Company of London had been founded in 1600 and the Vereenigde Oost-Indische Compagnie (the Dutch East India Company, 'V.O.C.') in 1602. It was the Dutch who first competed in Eastern waters with the Portuguese, so successfully challenging their monopoly that by the middle of the century they had virtually supplanted the Portuguese as the main purveyors of oriental cargoes.[6]

Profitable though the trade in porcelain was, it was not the basis of the eastern trade, but was one of a series of interlocking trade movements in which various commodities were bought in one eastern port and sold for a profit in another in order to buy there other commodities to be sold in yet other ports. Thus a sort of circle of trade built up a profit and a profitable cargo suitable for shipping on the long and hazardous trip back to Europe. The main profits were, at first, upon spices (cloves, pepper, nutmeg, cinnamon), precious metals and silk, with other things such as cottons, lacquer and porcelain, which were more bulky, affording a smaller percentage profit.[7]

Japan only really comes into this pattern of trade, which the Portuguese had inherited from the Chinese and from the Arabs, in the mid 16th century when the Portuguese, as the first

Europeans to arrive in Japan, began a limited trade in gold (later, silver and copper) and other things including lacquer, but not including porcelain which was not made in Japan until the early 17th century. The Dutch and the English only arrived in Japan in the first years of the 17th century. The English withdrew their 'factory' in 1623, and by 1639 the Japanese, partly with the connivance of the Dutch, expelled the Portuguese. In the period after this expulsion (*sakoku* in Japanese) the country of Japan was rigidly excluded by its *de facto* rulers, the Tokugawa Shoguns from all contact with the outside world, with the important exception of the severely controlled trade allowed to the Dutch East India Company and the Chinese. Thus the subsequent monopoly the Dutch held of the direct Japanese trade was always shared with the Chinese, an important factor that we shall discuss later. The Japanese themselves were forbidden to leave the country, but were allowed to trade through these outlets, both the Shogunate and many great lords investing in Dutch and Chinese ventures.

By the 1640s, the amount of Chinese porcelain shipped by the Dutch each year was to be counted in hundreds of thousands of pieces.[8] Not all of this was for Europe, in fact the greater proportion was retained in Asia and traded by the Dutch from their 'factories' in South-East Asia, India and the Islamic lands of the Near East. It was, therefore, a major if not the most profitable commodity of their trade. But Jingdezhen, where most of this porcelain was made, was badly affected by the struggles of the civil war that led to the fall of the Ming dynasty to the Manchus, who set up the Qing dynasty after 1644. Little porcelain seems to have been produced in Jingdezhen during a period of perhaps twenty years. Certainly by the late 1640s the Dutch stockpiles in Taiwan of Jingdezhen porcelain were running low. Porcelain from the southern

5.   T. Volker, 'Porcelain and the Dutch East India Company', *Mededelingen van het Rijksmuseum voor Volkenkunde, Leiden*, 11, 1954, p. 22.
6.   C. R. Boxer, *The Dutch Seaborne Empire*, London, 1965.
7.   C. R. Boxer, *The Portuguese Seaborne Empire*, London, 1969.
8.   Volker, 1954, op. cit.

kilns of Fujian was still available and accessible and was shipped in large quantities to the Dutch 'factories', mostly by the Chinese, throughout the mid century. While some of this southern porcelain was of a quality suitable for shipment to Europe, much was of lesser quality and was intended for South-East Asia. Clearly the Dutch had less control over what was made, and had to buy what was available if they wanted to buy anything at all. The shapes made to order had come from Jingdezhen. If the V.O.C. wished to continue to have porcelain made to specification they had to look elsewhere. So the Dutch turned to Japan.

This was not all that strange, for the Dutch had been importing Chinese porcelain (the so-called Tianqi wares) into Japan since the 1630s;[9] this, made for the Japanese domestic market, was made in shapes and decorated in styles based on locally available wares, the *shoki-Imari* wares of Arita. The Dutch must also have been aware of the relatively small export trade of Arita wares, mostly large celadon dishes made in imitation of those of Zhejiang in China, to Borneo and Sulawesi.[10] The Dutch were, then, familiar with the porcelain market in Japan as well as with the domestic manufacture of porcelain in Arita, even though the Arita porcelain industry was less than half a century old.

It was logical, therefore, to look to Japan to supply the porcelain to substitute for that of Jingdezhen. This early Dutch trade in Japanese porcelain – the official trade, that is – is very well documented in the records of the V.O.C.[11] What we do not know is the extent to which these records tell the entire story; as we shall see, later, the private trade, legal but mostly undocumented, often greatly surpassed in volume the official

trade. However, we are probably fairly safe in assuming that the general picture of Dutch participation at this early stage is as recounted in the official documents of the Company. We do not know, however, the extent of the involvement of the Chinese in the purchase of Japanese porcelain at this time. As we shall see, Chinese buying of Arita porcelain was to become very important later.

The headquarters of the Dutch East India Company was in Batavia, modern Jakarta, on Java (No. 9). By the 1640s the 'factory' of the Dutch in Japan was on a small fan-shaped island, a reclaimed mud-flat called Deshima Island in Nagasaki harbour (Nos 11 and 12); the Chinese, similarly restricted, had a 'factory' nearby. The merchants on Deshima (each was allowed a tour of one year only) received instructions from Batavia, which in turn received instructions from the 'Chamber of Seventeen', the 'board' of the V.O.C. in Amsterdam. Of course, a considerable extent of freedom of action was allowed to the men on the spot who were presumed, usually with justification, to have a good knowledge of local conditions. And Deshima was only one of the 'factories' of the Dutch throughout South-East Asia. It is worth remembering that the Dutch never obtained the concession for a 'factory' in China.

Documentation of the trade begins in 1650[12] when 145 coarse porcelain dishes were bought for Tonkin in Indochina. The word used for coarse here was '*grove*', the word that had been used to describe the Chinese porcelains imported into Japan from China in the 1630s and 1640s, the so-called Tianqi wares. It seems possible, then, that these 145 pieces were the Japanese equivalent, *shoki-Imari* wares. It is difficult to see why Tonkin

9.   Oliver Impey, 'Shoki-Imari and Tianqi; Arita and Jingdezhen in competition for the Japanese market in porcelain in the second quarter of the seventeenth century', *Mededelingenblad nederlandse vereniging van vrienden van de ceramiek*, 116, 1984, pp. 15–29.

10.   Oliver Impey, 'Celadon porcelain from Arita', *Mededelingenblad nederlandse vereniging van vrienden van de ceramiek*, 130/31, 1988, pp. 29–42.
11.   Volker, 1954, op. cit.
12.   Manuscript in the Algemeen Rijksarchief in The Hague, *Factorij Japan*, 774.

should have wanted *shoki-Imari*. In 1651, 176 assorted plates, dishes and bottles, not described as '*grove*', but probably so all the same, were sent to Tonkin.[13] 1652 was the date of the first shipment to Batavia, 1,265 large and small medical pots; as these were apparently not specially ordered we cannot be sure of what shape they were.[14] The first pieces actually ordered, in 1653,[15] were made from models supplied in 1652;[16] 1,200 small porcelain bottles and pots and 1,000 pots for medical salve. These latter were probably of the standard *albarello* shape (No. 30) so widely used in Europe as medical containers. Sherds of *albarello* that imitate Dutch originals have been found at two kiln sites in Arita, Sarugawa and Shimoshirakawa. The bottles were by no means as certainly of the so-called 'gallipot' shape as Volker would have us believe.

The orders for 1654 (3,745 pieces), 1655 (3,209 pieces), 1656 (4,149 pieces) and 1657 (3,040 pieces) were not much different;[17] all were for small bottles and small pots for the surgeons or the apothecaries in Batavia. They were for use, not for resale. In 1657, however, there was an additional item, a chest of unknown size containing an unknown number of porcelain samples for Holland.[18] This is the first shipment to Holland, even if it was only of samples. No samples were shipped in 1658, only 457 un-described pieces went to Bengal and 4,800 medicine pots and bottles to Batavia.[19] Pre-sumably the samples were found satisfactory, for in 1659 came the first really large order for Japanese porcelain, for some 64,866 pieces. This is the beginning year of the true export trade.[20]

The question must be asked – what was in the case of samples? As the Dutch had been aware of the Japanese trade to South-East Asia of the 1640s–60s, they must have known of the enamelled porcelain of Arita. The early enamels were dark in colour and somewhat opaque; they were not more interesting than the enamels of late Ming China. But one may presume that their quality was improving to the extent that it was worth including enamelled ware in the 1657 case of samples to be sent to Holland.

Most of the vast order of 1659 was for Mocha (in Arabia) and was made to conform to models sent from Holland. Of the 56,700 pieces for Mocha, all were to be blue-and-white except for 5,000 coffee cups which were to be white and, more importantly, 50 large porcelain bottles with red and green painting. Note that only 50 pieces were to be enamelled, but that Mocha was to continue to prefer blue-and-white later. The complete order for Mocha is listed by Volker. What Volker never saw, however, were the invoices for this and for the other destinations for this year's order for porcelain.[21] From these we can see that only 4,320 small white cups were shipped and only 37 bottles with leaf decoration in red and green. Of the 500 pieces for Surat on the west coast of India, some had red decoration, others gold decoration – was this over underglaze blue? Of the 1,048 pieces for Bengal, 100 were 'round table dishes with red flower design' among other enamelled wares. Among the 870 pieces for Coromandel there were small round plates with red and green decoration inside. But with the pieces for Batavia and Holland we come to the main point; most of the pieces were enamelled, including such items as '100 white-sided cups with red and green decoration' and '90 butter dishes with blue, red and gold decoration'. It must be evident that the samples of 1657 had mostly been enamelled and that it was this

13. *Factorij Japan*, 775.
14. *FJ*, 776.
15. *FJ*, 286, 852.
16. *FJ*, 284.
17. *FJ*, 776, 781 852, 853, 855.

18. *FJ*, 781.
19. *FJ*, 782 857.
20. Volker, 1954, op. cit, pp. 129–31.
21. *FJ*, 783.

enamelled ware that was to be bought for Holland. Asia may have preferred blue-and-white (indeed in 1670 the Persian factory ordered 16,500 pieces 'all of them with blue painting, the red colour being unwanted here'); Holland wanted the brilliant enamel colours.

These enamelled wares were a revelation to Europe, where the less bright late Ming enamelled wares were little known. Heretofore porcelain had, basically, been celadon or blue-and-white; now it could rival the brilliance of maiolica.

Now most of these pieces were to be made in shapes unfamiliar to the Japanese, to be decorated in styles of painting virtually unknown in Japan (where very few Wanli-style and Transitional porcelains seem to have arrived) and many of them were of sizes larger than had been made before. It is hardly surprising that the porcelain industry of Arita, although drastically reorganised, was unable to cope with this order and was only able to supply half the 1659 order in 1660. However, it is from this time that the full export trade in Japanese porcelain begins.

In 1659 the Opperhoofd in Deshima, Zacharias Wagenaer wrote[22] that he had been collecting pieces for Holland, presumably not all ordered shapes but some Japanese shapes as well, for among the salts, mustard pots, ink pots and the indeterminate cups, plates and bowls were also saké kettles and *sioubacken* (probably a transliteration of *jubako* meaning a stacking, layered box) and also 'assorted dolls' and three pairs of figures of cranes. It was also in 1659 that Wagenaer wrote of porcelain left unsold as it was 'too sparsely flowered' and how he had devised a decoration of small silver tendril-work on a blue ground (No. 35).

1660 was a busy year for Arita;[23] 57,173 pieces

were shipped to Malacca but of more interest here are the 11,530 pieces sent to Holland. These included wares in new combinations of colours: blue and red; red, blue and green; blue, black and gold. New shapes include square bowls and octagonal plates. Among 902 pieces sent to Batavia were 20 very expensive wash basins; these were probably large and may well have resembled the large blue-and-white bowl shown here as No. 44.

In 1661,[24] among 76,000 pieces, barbers' bowls are mentioned and in 1662, incense bowls (very profitable), *kendis*, beer jugs, blue beer jugs with gold and silver (these sound like the 'silver tendril work on a blue ground' of 1659, see No. 35); beakers and large boxes. From this year onwards, the trade continues to expand both in quantity and in the variety of the shapes demanded; much of it was enamelled[25] (*pace* Volker, who thought it was mostly blue-and-white) and some of it was in non-European shapes, makeweights.

It must be remembered that the Dutch never held a total monopoly of the direct trade with Japan; the monopoly was always shared with the Chinese. Exactly how much Japanese porcelain the Chinese bought is not known; but it was bought for resale to the European nations other than the Dutch who were venturing into the China Sea. The quantities must have been very considerable, but we have almost no information on the subject. It should be borne in mind that the figures we have even of the Dutch trade, the figures quoted by Volker from the trade documents of the V.O.C., are always of the official trade only; they do not take into account the private trade allowable to servants of the Company. As we shall see, the discrepancy (when we can measure it) between the quoted figures and the true figures was sometimes, possibly always, vast.

However, we do know from Dutch sources that in 1658 there were Chinese junks at Nagasaki

22. Volker, 1954, op. cit., pp. 136.
23. Volker, 1954, op. cit., pp. 136–37.
24. Volker, 1954, op. cit., pp. 140–46.
25. *FJ*, 783.

that were to ship porcelain from Japan.[26] In 1661 a Chinese junk carried 7,000 Japanese porcelains to Batavia, and in 1664, another carried 83,090 pieces, in a year when the Dutch themselves shipped 68,682 pieces to Batavia.

These pieces were for Batavia; in other words the Chinese were then selling Japanese porcelain to the Dutch. Later they were to sell elsewhere. In 1667, for instance, a Chinese junk sailed from Nagasaki with 'coarse porcelain' for Taiwan. The Dutch had difficulty in obtaining such information; the Japanese interpreters were expressly forbidden by the Governor of Nagasaki to inform the Dutch of the amounts of porcelain sold to the Chinese. Volker has suggested that the Chinese bought about twice the amount by value bought by the Dutch; it may well have been more. The trade, therefore, was large and though it is undocumented, it must have continued well into the 18th century. Possibly it was only with the beginning of the lower quality of Chinese Imari, perhaps in the early 1720s or a little earlier, that the Chinese began to cut back on their purchases of Japanese porcelain. This may have been a contributory factor to the rising price of Japanese porcelain that finally forced the Dutch out of the market shortly before 1750.

Meanwhile, however, in the 1670s, Japanese porcelain, especially the innovative coloured ware, was as highly desirable to all other nations as it was to the Dutch. Instead of buying Japanese porcelain from the Dutch in Europe, they bought from the Chinese in various ports in South China. The result of this is, or was, visible in old collections in Holland, England, Germany and France. Old collections in Holland are rich in coloured Imari and in blue-and-white; they tend to lack the coloured Kakiemon wares, though many do have quantities of Kakiemon-style blue-and-white. English, German and French collections, on the other hand, have Kakiemon as well as Imari. A curious feature of this differential is that German collections tend to be rich in *kenjo-Imari* wares, the so-called 'presentation wares' of formal design, which are poorly represented elsewhere.

A possible explanation for this may lie in the taste of the Dutch and the Chinese buyers. There is plenty of evidence to show that the Dutch demanded, and got, richly decorated wares. But the Kakiemon style is much closer to Chinese taste than is the Imari, and it seems more than probable that the Chinese bought Kakiemon wares for preference. This would, in turn, have influenced the production at the Kakiemon kiln, as well as stimulating competition from other kilns, and Kakiemon wares would have tended to develop more and more into Chinese taste, making pieces suitable for the Chinese market. While the Chinese buyer had the European buyer in mind, the Japanese would not have been interested in the ultimate destination of the porcelain, but only in the actual first sale.

Nor is it so strange that the Chinese bought Japanese porcelain even after the 1670s, when Jingdezhen was back in production and was producing the late phase of Transitional pieces that led into the fully-fledged Kangxi style. By this date the enamels used on Chinese porcelain, the so-called *famille verte, famille jaune* and *famille noire*, were of fine quality, rivalling that of the Kakiemon. But in Europe in the late 17th and early 18th centuries it was the Kakiemon that was in demand. This can be verified simply by considering what styles of porcelain were most imitated (and adapted) by the new porcelain factories at Chantilly, Meissen, Chelsea or Bow. For a discussion of this, see pp. 44–55. Japanese porcelain was also far more expensive than the Chinese. This is evident in the prices quoted in the sale catalogues of the auctions held by the East India Company in London in the early 18th century.[27]

26. Volker, 1954, op. cit., pp. 128 ff.

27. Geoffrey Godden, *Oriental Export Market Porcelain*, London, 1979 quotes many of these.

It is, of course, almost impossible to be certain that one is comparing like with like, and one has to choose shapes that sound precise. In 1703, for instance, the contents of the East Indiaman *Dashwood*, carrying both Chinese and Japanese porcelain, was sold at auction in London. Chinese blue-and-white chocolate cups (with saucers) had a presale valuation of 4*d.* each, while Chinese 'red chocolate cups' varied in value from 4*d.* to 8*d.* In the same sale, Japanese chocolate cups were valued at 1*s.* or 3*s.* each. The most expensive Chinese items in that sale were '12 large painted bowls' which sold at 16*s.* 6*d.* each, while '2 Japanese basons' were sold for £5.4*s.*0*d.* each. The most expensive items in the sale were '4 Jappan jars' at £9.11*s.*0*d.* each.

The 'Japanese basons' were items of private trade and were bought at the sale by the owner, the ship's captain Marmaduke Rawdon, for the rules stated that everything had to be sold by the Company, even if it only acted as agent; they were, in effect, bought in. Thus the extent of the private trade can, to some extent, be measured for imports into England, but this does not help us with exports from Japan. It is only when we have Japanese documents to check against the Dutch official papers that we can surely judge the extent of this private trade. We can then see the inadequacy of the official documents of the V.O.C. as records of the numbers of Japanese porcelains imported into Europe. Such documents have survived, apparently uniquely, for the years 1709–11.[28] As the amounts of what the Dutch say they bought from the Japanese are so at variance with the amounts the Japanese say they sold to the Dutch – a difference in one year of fourteen-fold – it is worth recording this in full (see table, p. 22). The lists of the shapes sold to the Dutch are also interesting.

Some of these shapes sound unfamiliar; all are inadequately described for identification with known shapes, let alone pieces. It would, for instance, be more than rash to attempt to identify the *onna ningyo* (figures of women) of 1711 with the known Kakiemon-style figures such as No. 165 or No. 166.

The first two decades of the 18th century may well have been the high point of the Japanese export trade in porcelain, at least in terms of numbers of items shipped and in total value. Even at this time far more Chinese porcelain was imported and it was, we have seen, on average much cheaper.

Volker's figures,[29] dangerous to use as they are, suggest that after the peak years of the early 1660s (when the figures are probably unnaturally high as most of the trade would have been official) and the great year of 1683 (when some half million pieces may have been exported), the year 1720 may have been the highest. We have already noted high totals in the supposedly low total years 1709–11. Volker comments on the variability of the trade after 1720 and it may have been this almost as much as the increased competition from Jingdezhen (and possibly from Meissen) that was a major factor in the decline of the trade. Volker quotes a relatively high yield year in 1735 (approx. 15,000 pieces) declining to about 2,800 pieces in 1745 as the next highest year, with nothing officially exported after 1747.

However, as we have seen, these numbers may be so inaccurate as to be thoroughly misleading, so it would be unwise to attempt to quantify the extent of the trade in the late 17th and early 18th centuries, nor chart the annual fluctuations in numbers. But the documents do give us some fascinating insights into the problems faced by the Dutch in order to carry on this highly profitable (at least at first) trade. Not only were the restrictions placed on the Dutch almost

28. *Toban Kamotsu Cho 1709–1711*, published by Naikaku Bunko, Tokyo, 1971, 2 vols.
29. Volker, 1954, op. cit., and T. Volker, 'The Japanese porcelain trade of the Dutch East India Company after 1683', *Mededelingen van het Rijksmuseum voor Volkenkunde, Leiden*, 13, 1959.

Comparison of Dutch and Japanese records of export of porcelain from Japan for the years 1709–11

1. The Dutch records
   Extracts from the *Dagh* registers taken by Volker:

	1709	1710	1711
	9,820	10,940	16,614

2. The Japanese records
   Extracts from the *Toban kamotsu cho*:

	Kanei 6 Sept 21 4 Dutch ships	Shotoku 1 Sept 1 4 Dutch ships	Shotoku 2 Sept 21 4 Dutch ships
Imari *yakimono*			
Hachi/deep bowl	17,294	26,198	8,820
Tokkuri/bottle	3,606	2,234	2,607
Hanaike/flower vase	1,286	4,076	1,490
Kaku tokkuri/square bottle	100		
Futachawan/bowl with lid	413 (sets)	6,107	500
Kiridame/rounded jar	2,119	550	1,190
Hina-dogu/miniatures	5,334 (sets)	5,580	
Bonyama	1		
Fudekago/writing box	45		
Konafuri tokkuri/bottle for powder	2,174		
Chokozara/small saucer	49,196	90,012	158,644
Tsubo/jar	2,256	9,619	2,180
Tetsuki chaire/[?] jar with handle	200		
Tetsuki kame/jar with one handle	1,324	5,984	6,486
Futachawan/bowl with lid	1,269		
Haifuki/cylindrical jar	151	362	
Karako onna ningyo/figure of woman and child	1,285		
Koro/incense burner	2	81	
Suzuri/inkstone	15		
Koyakuire/ointment box		2,300	
Chawan/tea bowl		5,081	
Mizuire onna karako ningyo/ water jar [as] woman & child		394	
Onna ningyo/figure of woman			13
Totals	88,070	158,578	181,930

Difference between Japanese and Dutch numbers:

	78,250	147,638	165,316

FIG. 2 'Nécessaire', offered to Marie Leczinska on the birth of the Dauphin in 1729, and formerly in her Grand Cabinet at Versailles. Silver-gilt objects, with dolphins, by Henri-Nicolas Cousinet; the porcelain Chinese, Japanese and Meissen. Musée du Louvre, Paris.

intolerable, but the Japanese merchants employed a gamesmanship of considerable sophistication. They would, for instance, deliver the ordered porcelain to the quayside one day before the Dutch ships would be obliged to leave Deshima if they were to catch the favourable monsoon. It was therefore a gamble whether to unpack the porcelain from its straw wrappings and check it, in which case there was inadequate time for it to be wrapped properly again or, to hope that the Japanese had delivered what was ordered and what they declared they had delivered, even then hoping that not too much was already broken.

Curiously, the porcelain seems to have been wrapped at the port of Imari, rather than in Arita;

recent excavations in Imari found huge piles of broken-off spurs from the bases of dishes and plates.[30] Presumably the packing in Arita was for the manual transportation to Imari (no horses), but for the ship journey to Nagasaki this was inadequate and special packing was required.

Possibly the last gasp of the regular Japanese export trade in porcelain can be seen in the story of the sending of designs drawn in Holland to Japan and to China to be copied onto porcelains, the forms and sizes of which were also specified. This was quite different from the ordering of decoration to be taken after prints or engravings or even after coats-of-arms bookplates; this was instructing the orientals in oriental design! We are referring here, of course, to the drawings of Cornelis Pronk.[31]

30. Koji Ohashi, personal communication.
31. C. J. A. Jörg, *Pronk porcelain; porcelain after designs by Cornelis Pronk*, Groningen, 1980.

These were ordered in March 1734, arrived in
Batavia in 1735 and were sent on to China and
Japan in 1736. The most famous is of 'the lady
with the parasol' who walks with her attendant
among identifiable Dutch wading birds (No. 70).
This design is the only one of several that was, as
far as we know, copied both in Japan and in China.
In Japan it occurs as blue-and-white or in enamels;
curiously, it is the former that is by far the less
common of the two. Several other drawings by
Pronk were used on Chinese porcelain only, the
best known being 'the arbour' and 'the doctors'.

After the 1740s, Japanese porcelain was not
exported in quantity to Europe, though small
amounts do appear to have been shipped
spasmodically. Arita suffered considerably from
the loss of trade, barely recovering in the 1770s as
a maker of domestic wares for an unsophisticated
market.

The period of the exportation of Japanese
porcelain to Europe, then, can be seen to have
lasted only about 85-odd years, from 1659 until
about 1745. During the major part of this time,
Japanese porcelain was in great demand and was
comparatively expensive. It was sought by
collectors during its period of production, for
instance, in France (Fig. 2), by Queen Mary of
England and by Augustus the Strong, and after its
cessation, for example by Margaret, 2nd Duchess
of Portland and by William Beckford. No great
house in Europe lacked its impressive garnitures
of Imari jars and trumpet vases; many houses had
innumerable ornamental wares scattered through
public and private rooms alike. Just as had
Japanese lacquer cabinets, so Japanese porcelain
became a standard requisite of a great house; and
in both cases decoration and even furniture was
adapted to display it. If some houses had more
than others, this was merely a quantitative and
not a qualitative difference. Japanese porcelain has
always been used in Europe for grand decoration:
'Porcelain for Palaces'.

Japanese Export Porcelain

OLIVER IMPEY

Arita porcelain is made from a porcelain stone low in alumina, but quite strong and relatively easy to work. As it was not as plastic as many Chinese clays, it was necessary to make the products thicker in body than were the Chinese equivalents, though this meant that tall shapes such as bottles or jars could be thrown in one piece and not in the two pieces normal for the Chinese. The porcelain 'clay', actually a decayed granite porcelain stone, was found at Izumiyama (Fig. 3), in North-East Arita. Here both external and internal weathering (due to hot springs) decreased the quartz content in favour of the kaolinite and sericite content, making it the more easily workable. The stone therefore varied considerably according to its location in the mountain and even in the 17th century certain pockets of stone were recognised as superior. The iron in the stone ensured that the fired body was bluish in colour. There was always a tendency towards underfiring in the industry and much Arita body, especially in the earlier periods was grey and opaque. The glaze was a mixture of woodash and clay from another outcrop of the same granite as that of Izumiyama. Izumiyama clay is now of insufficient quality for use for anything but drainpipes and rooftiles; the glaze clay is still sometimes used for glaze material. The glaze, too, was imperfectly transparent and all Arita wares, save the fine white *nigoshide* of the Kakiemon kiln and its rivals and successors, have a blue cast to them.

FIG. 3 Izumiyama: the source of the porcelain stone used in Arita.

The porcelain stone was pounded into clay by means of water-powered drop-hammers and refined by levigation in water. For this reason, most early kilns were built near running water. The body was thrown on the Kyushu kick-wheel and turned, or press-moulded and turned. Cast moulds were not used until the 19th century. Almost all Arita wares were fired only once in the kiln; there was no biscuit firing and the pots were raw-glazed. There is a school of thought which contests this, claiming that everything made in the late 17th century, or later, was twice-fired. The almost total absence of biscuit sherds at kiln sites does not support this view.

Underglaze blue was therefore painted onto the raw ('green') body, with a thick but pointed brush that allowed complete control over the amount of the pigment that could flow through the brush onto the pot. This was done by tightening or relaxing the grip the hand had on the bristles. The pigment was a suspension of cobalt oxide in water. The longer the pigment was in contact with the body, the more colour was absorbed, and the darker the result; overlaps caused a line between two areas of paint to be darker. This limit to the possibilities of painting was later exploited by the Chinese to make the 'cracked ice' patterns. Onto the body, whether decorated or not, the glaze would be applied, either by pouring or by dipping. The total amount of glaze on the pot had to be controlled, for if there was too much it would run when melted; the glazer had therefore to be skilled. His, or more likely, her finger-marks are often visible at the base of jars or bowls.

Although the body was relatively strong, the well of dishes had to be supported during firing once the ratio of foot diameter to overall diameter had reached one half. Earlier wares had had smaller feet in relation to the overall diameter. Small cones of clay, broken off after firing, left the characteristic spur marks, sometimes as many as seven, often only one.

The *noborigama* kiln, though far superior to the preceding *ogama* was not easy to use, and great skill was required so to arrange the pots in the packing of the kiln as to exploit or to alleviate the particular characteristics of each kiln chamber. A partial down-draught was created in the chambers, for better circulation of the heat, by the interconnection of each chamber with the next up the slope of the hill. This was done by means of flue holes at the base of the firing wall of the upper chamber, which were about one third of the way up the upper wall of the lower chamber of the two. The kilns were built on a hillside with a slope of between 10° and 20°. The chambers were fired sequentially, uphill, with wood thrown into a space left for it in the packing, as each one reached the temperature of about 850°C from the firing of the chamber below. On reaching 1280°C each chamber was sealed to eliminate oxygen and allowed to cool slowly. The temperature was judged by the colour of the incandescent pots. There was considerable wastage, though this was partly due to the relatively unsophisticated kiln furniture that was used. At the beginning of the export period, the majority of pieces were not even fired in seggars, and the stands for the new, large shapes were thick and crude. With time, the kiln furniture improved and was more carefully used, with a consequent lessening of waste. Even today, when every piece is biscuit-fired and usually fired in a gas kiln, a top quality factory will still expect a fifty percent wastage rate from the very beginning of making pieces to the final display in the showroom.

The colour of the underglaze blue on the fired pot depended not only on the quality of the source of the cobalt, usually the mineral erythrite, but also upon total exclusion of oxygen during the course of firing and cooling (reduction). Colour of the blue is of little help in attempts to date Arita porcelain. The glaze was also much affected by the cooling period and could be crackled or smooth. There was never the fritting at the edges caused by slight incompatibility between body and glaze (*mushikui* in Japanese, 'worm-eaten') that is characteristic of so much Chinese porcelain of the same period.

Pieces that were to be enamelled may then have been taken to the Aka-e-machi, the enamellers' quarter of Arita to be enamelled and fired again to about 950°C in a muffle kiln. Quite when the enamellers' quarter was set up is a matter of some argument, but it seems certain that it was functioning by the last quarter of the 17th century; before that time there may have been muffle kilns elsewhere, possibly close to a *noborigama*, though there is no evidence of this. Porcelain that had survived firing up to 1280°C in a *noborigama* was rarely damaged in a muffle kiln and sherds of enamelled pieces are very rare at kiln sites. It has always been assumed that the Kakiemon kiln alone had its own muffle kiln after the 1680s and there is some rather tenuous evidence for this.

Recent excavation of a small part of the Aka-e-machi suggests that not only was a very wide range of wares covering a wide time scale enamelled there, but also that the muffle kilns were used for the biscuit firing of some complex pieces. Moulds for the making of figures have been found, as well as some pulls from these moulds; sherds of figures are conspicuously absent from kiln sites. Some of the sherds of pulls at the site were of standard Imari figures, with underglaze blue; a figure of the drinking Dutchman sitting on a barrel (No. 72) has been found. The suggestion is that these figures were, unusually, biscuit-fired and then sent to *noborigama* to be glaze-fired; they would then be sent back to the Aka-e-machi to be enamelled. Total absence of pulls of the figure of a *bijin* ('beautiful woman') which is found in the West decorated in Kakiemon enamels (No. 165), of which at least two sets of moulds were found at the Aka-e-machi site, suggests that these figures did not return there to be enamelled, but were enamelled at a Kakiemon muffle kiln.

The *noborigama* kilns were usually large, sometimes of more than twenty chambers, each of which may have been three metres wide by two metres deep, while muffle kilns must all have been small. Thus, the twelve-odd export porcelain kilns would have been served by a large number of enamelling workshops and kilns, possibly hundreds. Differences between the products of such workshops can sometimes be detected today, forming the basis for classification of the Imari wares and of the Early Enamelled wares that we use here. Enamel colours are merely glazes that will only tolerate low-temperature firing and therefore could have been available in varieties of tones to each individual workshop. It is on the total palette of the various types that such classification depends. It must be admitted that this is a very imperfect criterion for judgement, particularly as we know so little of the organisation within the industry as a whole, but it does provide some basis for discussion and, indeed, forms the criterion upon which the whole division of the export porcelains depends. These divisions, Early Enamelled ware, Imari and Kakiemon provide the beginnings of a taxonomy that we shall see is sufficiently useful for us to retain even though we shall be charting its limitations.

Perhaps because of their origin in the Karatsu stoneware kilns, the earliest *shoki-Imari* pieces tended to be underfired; the body was very grey and opaque. By the mid century firing techniques had improved and only the low-quality-producing outlying kilns of Arita were making a grey-bodied ware.

By the time of the earliest export orders, there were several kilns making highly sophisticated shapes, many of which were skilfully painted with individual designs. Clearly there was a Japanese market for high quality, and expensive, blue-and-white porcelain. Possibly there was an internal market for enamelled ware, too. Below this, the lower levels of the market, right down to the mass produced, continued as ever. The industry was capable, theoretically, of coping with the vast Dutch order of 1659; practically there were difficulties and, as we have seen, the order took two years to fulfil.

Much of the order was for enamelled ware. We recognise the early pieces by the comparatively dark and opaque colour of the enamels. Compare, for instance, the figure of a man on a tortoise (No. 158) from Burghley House with the elephants (No. 160) from the same house. The latter is identifiable in the 1688 Inventory (No. 17), but the tortoise, which may well have been part of a shipload of 1665, has early dark enamels, while the elephants have the developed Kakiemon-style enamels. Although yellow was a standard colour for the early 'Kutani' style, there was a tendency among some groups of Early Enamelled wares to avoid the use of yellow; these may be the groups the most closely ancestral to the Kakiemon line, as opposed to the Imari line. See, for instance, the bowl No. 83 where there is no yellow but there is overglaze blue. On the small jar No. 84 there is no yellow but both overglaze and underglaze blue. Other pieces in this lineage do have yellow, but it is much more apparent in the Imari line.

In contrast, some groups seem to have specialized in yellow. Most obvious of these are the dark blue and dark yellow wares. This palette is only found on a type of jar, but of more than one size, and on narrow-necked bottles on which, almost invariably, the decoration includes a garden viewed from a verandah. This suggests the work of a single workshop. Another type with a strong yellow is the green-and-yellow palette group that seems to have specialized in the decoration of round-bodied jars (No. 73), a shape that also occurs in underglaze blue only wares. Yet another palette is found on small round-bodied jars (No. 80) where the decoration is always of birds flying through or sitting in dense foliage; the colours are dark. This shape and pattern is also found in underglaze blue only wares. How close was the link between the two?

Geometrical patterns had been a feature of the *shoki-Imari*; in Early Enamelled wares they were commonly used on bottles (No. 75), often of tea-whisk shape (No. 76) which sometimes, but not invariably also bore pictorial designs. These seem closely related to the bottles with dense foliage including arrow-leaf on a red ground (No. 78); they have both in the past been called *ko-Kutani*, now they are part of the ancestry of Imari.

The early blue-and-white export wares seem to fall into three major styles. Firstly there was the continuation of the late *shoki-Imari* style for large pieces; the most obvious is the large basin No. 44 where the scale of the decoration is particularly bold. Sherds of these have been found at the Cho-kichi-dani kiln, a kiln which seems to have stopped production in the 1670s. Related to these are large bottles (No. 43). The same kiln also made both of the other two early export styles, those based on the newly imported Chinese styles, the Wanli and the Transitional; these were also made at other kilns. The Japanese seem to have used the Transitional for closed shapes (Nos 38 and 39) and the Wanli for open shapes (Nos 31 and 32) and both styles ran parallel for many years, degenerating or being adapted more and more to Japanese styles as time went on.

The controversy over the origin of the Transitional style in Japanese blue-and-white and in Delft tin-glaze, whether the Japanese took it from the Delft or *vice versa*, will be discussed by John Mallet. From the Japanese point of view, it seems most likely that the models sent to Arita to be copied (in, for example 1661) were either wooden, as had been the ones sent to China, in which case they had probably been painted by Delft pottery-painters, or they may have been actual pieces of delftware. Sherds of porcelain decorated in the Transitional style that pre-date the export trade do not seem to have been found at any Arita kiln site. If it was the Japanese who introduced a variation of the Transitional style to the Dutch, one would expect it to have been used in Japan fairly soon after its origin in, perhaps, the late 1630s and before the 1650s. This does not appear to have been the case. Nor are the Chinese Transitional pieces found either in old Japanese collections or as sherds in excavations of consumer sites.

The Kakiemon palette was settled by 1688 – evidence of examples at Burghley House. In all probability the Kakiemon kiln had only begun shortly before this date, though the elephants are unlikely to have been made there. The Kakiemon, whoever they were, were enamellers before they either started their own kiln or specialized in decorating the products of the kiln we now call the Kakiemon kiln, in Nangawara. Even here, they did not make all their own wares, for no sherds of closed shapes have been found at the kiln site. The Kakiemon had to order them from elsewhere (Nos 112 and 120). There seems to have been an evolution towards the white body *nigoshide* that became characteristic of the Kakiemon kiln (with some small rivalry from other kilns), for such pieces as the dish No. 97, an Early Enamelled piece, has an exceptionally white body. This body seems never to have been used with underglaze blue.

Kakiemon enamelled decoration leans noticeably toward the Chinese taste rather than toward the European. The *nigoshide* dishes tend to run in standard patterns nearly all of which are Japanese versions of Chinese-style painting and depict subjects in the Chinese canon. Flower and bird patterns predominate, landscape is a poor second. Figure subjects are rare; when they occur they do so in Chinese terms: 'Hob-in-the-well' (No. 122) is the English name (see Nos 192 and 193) for the Chinese story of Sima Guang, while most other figures are of Chinese boys ('*karako*'). One such pattern, by way of variety, is of Japanese origin; the lady by the verandah

(No. 127), the 'lady' pattern of Chelsea (No. 328) obviously derives from Japanese painting in the Tosa or Machi-Kano style. It is emphatically not European in origin. The obvious exception to this non-European 'rule' is the great jar decorated with figures, some of whom hold umbrellas, in cartouches (No. 138), where the pattern is clearly influenced by European taste, though probably not from a European model. This is not the work of the Kakiemon enamellers and will be discussed below.

Certain motifs appear to be characteristic of the Kakiemon. Most famous, perhaps, is the 'banded hedge' (No. 121), usually misunderstood in Europe as a wheatsheaf (No. 201). In fact 'wheatsheaves', really bundles of rice or millet, are not uncommon on Kakiemon and other wares (No. 126). A curious, apparently random scattering of certain small patterns over the surface of a plate or a jar (No. 145) may be the 'house style' of a group of enamellers close to the Kakiemon. The patterns include *shishi*, crickets, butterflies, sprays of flowers, a bird with a sickle-like object and a boy (a Chinese boy) apparently standing on a raft. A plate of this pattern was, in 1786, described as being of 'the lion, butterfly and sprig' pattern. This was a style much imitated at Chantilly (No. 188) but little elsewhere.

Some larger pieces in the Kakiemon palette of enamels will be excluded from the Kakiemon canon – see below. Others may well belong. The great landscape jar No. 93, of which only one other is known, is in a style not unlike that found on some blue-and-white Kakiemon, and not in the European taste. The large bowl No. 92 has different motifs mixed together in a careful arrangement to form a central section and a broad border.

The brown edge, a glaze colour and not an enamel, so prized in 18th century Europe, is found both on the *nigoshide* body and on the ordinary body, where it is standard for the better quality blue-and-white wares (No. 132). Kakiemon wares that have both underglaze blue and overglaze enamels were in all probability a cheaper range of the kiln's production and, of course, they, too, were much imitated elsewhere in Arita. There were several types of this ware, none of which was made of the *nigoshide* body, so that they all have the blue tinge of body and glaze of other Arita wares.

One type of this group was decorated in a manner closely akin to the *nigoshide* wares, with the underglaze blue taking a major role in the colour scheme. Closest to the standard *nigoshide* patterns is the phoenix dish No. 130, though there are bowls and other shapes in similar styles; these are usually of high quality. A little lower down the scale there are dishes with underglaze blue borders of rocks to which flowers are added in enamel and with an empty centre to which the enameller could add a decoration of his choice. Closely related to these are others that have an underglaze blue landscape decoration in the centre and both underglaze blue and overglaze enamel in the border (No. 107).

The *nigoshide* body was not the major product of the Kakiemon kiln; blue-and-white was much more common. Many of the blue-and-white wares have much in common with the enamelled wares; they may share the shapes and sizes, the brown edge and even, remarkably frequently, the decoration (Nos 125 and 126). The better quality pieces were meticulously painted in a style that yet allows considerable vigour and movement (Nos 109 and 132). Borders were sometimes emphasised (No. 133), sometimes absent (No. 134). Not all of the blue-and-white products of the kiln, as confirmed by potsherds found at the site, would fall into our notion of the Kakiemon style (possibly No. 61); few of such types are exhibited here. The extraordinary series of shaped small dishes and boxes in the Burghley House collection include several that are demonstrably

from the Kakiemon kiln, others that may be (No. 62), and yet others that are certainly from other kilns (No. 34, which is from Cho-kichi-dani kiln). Celadon sherds are not uncommon at the Kakiemon kiln site; usually these are of a good even colour, with a relatively translucent glaze. Decoration is usually confined to incised or stamped motifs in the well of dishes, though the border may be moulded and petalled. Celadon dishes similar to these and enamelled in Kakiemon enamels are known in Europe and these may or may not be products of the Kakiemon kiln. Curiously, perhaps, European factories do not seem much to have copied celadon.

Many of the pieces that look at first sight like Kakiemon prove on examination to be different; they were probably the work of rivals to the Kakiemon. Such are the famous 'Hampton Court' jars (No. 151), which bear a brown enamel only found on one other shape, the square bottles and jars derived from the Dutch glass gin-bottle shape (No. 149). It is difficult to envisage the Kakiemon enamellers' not using the brown for other wares, if it were available to them. Nor is it easy to fit the great jars decorated with a lady under an umbrella (No. 138) into the Kakiemon *oeuvre*; the style of painting is so markedly different. The great landscape jars (No. 93) are easier to reconcile with Kakiemon taste, though here there is the complication that certain rather similar jars in the collection at Kassel, while sharing the palette and style of landscape painting, differ in the use of a shoulder decoration which more resembles that on some of the 'Hampton Court' jars (No. 151). Most of the things that we call Kakiemon were made at the Kakiemon kiln, or at least decorated by the decorators of the Kakiemon kiln products; equally, there was more than one group of rival decorators who used a Kakiemon-like style or a Kakiemon-like palette of enamels.

With the Imari wares the problems are even greater, for both the volume of material and the width of variety are so much larger. We have drawn here a major division between those enamelled Imari wares that use underglaze blue and those that do not. This tells us little about production, but something about price; although most kilns probably made both types, the latter tend to be of better quality, as if they were emulating the Kakiemon, and there is clearly much variation in quality and hence in price in each group.

There were some eleven kilns other than the Kakiemon involved in the manufacture of porcelain for export. At least seven of these were in production in the 1660s and at least three of them made dishes marked with the insignia of the V.O.C. (Nos 32 and 33). The output, then, was vast. We are not able to classify the products of these kilns according to which kiln made which pieces; only occasionally are we able with some certainty to ascribe a piece to one kiln only (see No. 44, described above). Some years ago I semi-facetiously coined 'Impey's First Law of Kiln sites' which states that 'Almost everything is made almost everywhere'; it is surely true. It is important to remember that the separation that we use of the coloured wares (Imari) from the blue-and-white (Arita) is one of convenience only; they were made simultaneously in the same kilns throughout the export period and, indeed, later.

There was an increasing tendency with time towards the use of underglaze blue in such a way as to dictate to the enameller exactly what he had to paint, exactly what pattern or flower, implying a close co-operation between potter (who painted the cobalt onto the unfired pot) and the enameller. It also implies a certain stream-lining of factory production methods. Curiously, perhaps, the actual outlining in underglaze blue of areas such as leaves to be enamelled is almost

unknown in any Arita ware, though it was standard practice on the Nabeshima wares of Okawachi. There was also a tendency towards increasingly dense decorated surfaces, to the use of more and more patterns on each individual piece. To this, the pieces that bear no underglaze blue seem an exception; there were some coarse pieces in a somewhat aberrant palette including much black enamel (No. 215) but mostly they were more restrained.

Most Imari wares, whether or not using underglaze blue, are decorated in a rich palette of strong enamels. Some of these are clear and brilliant, resembling some of the Kakiemon colours, others are darker and more opaque. In common use were two yellows, two greens, aubergine, matt red, blue and black; frequently there is much use of gold, involving a third firing, at low temperature. Almost all Imari wares bear black enamel at least as outlining.

Among the wares that used no underglaze blue there were many combinations of colours that may identify individual workshops of enamellers. An early group used green, red, aubergine and black only (No. 202), a late group used pale green, red and gold only (No. 243). Red, gold and black may be found on dishes, much copied at Worcester (Nos 350 and 354), red and gold only, on ewers, gold and black only, on some dishes.

It seems likely that at least after the 1670s, most enamelling was done in the Aka-e-machi, rather than near to the kiln of origin. This does not imply that there was a centrally-controlled enamelling factory, it was simply the area in which, apparently by regulation, the various enamelling workshops were gathered. And various they were, as one can see today by the wide variety of palettes and styles used on the Imari wares. We have pointed out above that enamelled sherds are but rarely found at kiln sites. This means that we have little evidence of the origin of enamelled pieces and justifies our use of the palette of enamels as a means of classification; we can often detect a coherence in colours and styles between porcelains that may mark the output of one enamelling workshop.

Within the colours themselves, there is a tendency towards increased translucency, the better colours becoming available later. Of course, these better colours were often ignored by the makers of the lower-priced wares, and quality is little or no criterion of judgement of date. The major colour innovation seems to have been the introduction of a pink wash. This may be so thin as to shade out into nothingness and it was used to supplement other colours or to tone down the white. Made from colloidal gold, this wash first appeared sometime around 1700–1710 and was much used thereafter. It never appears on Kakiemon porcelain, nor on the non-export Nabeshima.

Sets of dishes, bowls and so on were made in Imari styles in enormous numbers, simply as the standard method of production. Dinner services, with many shapes sharing a common pattern, are rare, though a few are known; consequently certain shapes used for services, such as the sauceboat shape derived from European silver (No. 242) are very rare. Condiment-holders are, on the other hand, more common and pairs of jugs or sets of salts, ewers and small jugs, often marked with a European initial (e.g. 'A' for *azijn*: 'vinegar', 'S' for soy) are frequently found, sometimes even on stands (No. 241); miniature, toy-sized versions are also known. Ewers bearing armorials were made from the 1660s. Some wares bear true armorials (No. 231), in other cases the arms may be spurious, as if they were merely a decorative device and sometimes there is mantling over an empty shield as if in preparation for the addition of arms in Europe (No. 232).

Shaped dishes and other vessels are not uncommon, that is, pieces not round, or shaped as some natural shape such as bamboo (No. 119),

shells, leaves (Nos 34 and 65) or fruit (No. 63), or after other shapes such as fans. Reticulation, either as piercing (see the Porcelain Room p. 136–37, No. 12), as double-wall piercing or as shaped cut-outs (No. 221) probably only occurs after the 1680s or 1690s. One particular pattern of Imari (shown in the Porcelain Room, No. 12), hexagonal, octagonal or decagonal in shape and with alternating panels of reticulation, was much copied at Meissen and elsewhere.

Dishes sometimes have borders moulded in low relief, which may be emphasised by the enameller, or totally ignored. Applied incrustation of flowers in low or high relief (Nos 209 and 211) is relatively common, and coffee pots are known supported by modelled human figures. Figures of men and women (Nos 165 and 174), sometimes specifically European men (No. 72), of birds (No. 156), plants (No. 71), animals (No. 176), fishes (No. 179), tortoises (No. 158), dragons and other mythical beasts, especially *shishi* (No. 167) are quite common. Piece moulding was certainly in use by the 1680s and probably earlier; piece moulds have been found at the Aka-e-machi site (see p. 26). Some of these figures were copied in Europe (No. 342) or were mounted in precious metal or ormolu (No. 146), sometimes in combination with other porcelain (No. 147) not necessarily Japanese, or with lacquer.

The variation of subject matter in the decoration on Imari wares is too wide to be detailed here. Pictorial subjects were common (No. 205), several scenes often occurring in shaped cartouches on one piece (No. 224). These subjects tended to be birds and flowers, landscapes with or without human figures, or animals. Many of these owe a debt to Chinese models, many are purely Japanese (No. 233); comparatively few were taken from European engravings. The most famous of the latter is a scene of a Dutch landscape (No. 67), often ludicrously called Deshima Island, which appears to be an adaptation of two or more Dutch originals. The story of the sending of drawings by the Dutch artist Cornelis Pronk (1691–1759) to be copied in Arita (No. 70) is recounted on pages 23–24.

Not all decoration was scenic; simple patterning was common, much of it based on formalised animal (No. 234) or plant (No. 213) motifs. Commonest of all, perhaps, were those patterns based on the radiating chrysanthemum (No. 238), the petal panels usually including flowers or flowering branches; this was a style much copied at Worcester (No. 353). As happened with the Kakiemon, small motifs could be scattered randomly over a shape to which they might not conform (No. 243). Partitioning of the design into separate areas, again almost regardless of shape, was as arbitrary as it was on the Kodaiji lacquers (No. 215).

Imari wares frequently have an overpainted blue background to all (No. 36) or part (No. 227) of the vessel. This may go back to the blue ground wares with silver tendril-work devised by Zacharias Wagenaer in 1659, when he ordered 200 pieces 'curieus op blauwen grond met kleyn silver ranckagiewerck' (No. 35), later complaining that they had quickly been copied by other factories. Quite possibly this was only later copied in China, and one might suggest that Wagenaer could claim to have originated the 'powder-blue' of Kangxi.

Some of the Imari wares are very large; jars over a metre tall are not uncommon, while no Kakiemon-like pieces seem ever to be taller than about 60-odd centimetres and most are much smaller. Sets of jars and trumpet-shaped vases made garnitures for chimney-pieces or cornices, though some were so large as to have to be placed in fireplaces rather than over them. In some houses, pyramids were built especially to take these large pieces.

Imari jars tend to be narrower than were the Chinese. In the early periods, the lids were flattish in profile, resembling the Chinese and had simple pointed ball knops. Modelled knops, as *shishi*, human figures, birds or animals appeared more commonly in the 1680s, the lids grew taller, eventually having almost vertical sides, and the knops becoming exaggeratedly large during the early years of the 18th century. Occasionally the underside of the flange of the lid of a large jar was decorated.

Equally, very small pieces were not uncommon, from the *poppegoet* of the early days to the miniatures which surrounded the medium sized pieces on the brackets of the *Porzellan-zimmer* and *Spiegel-kabinet*. European shapes predominate, of course, though some purely Japanese shapes do appear to have been imported for their curiosity value; particularly popular was the saké kettle shape (Nos 206 and 207) that was much imitated in Meissen, though not so often elsewhere.

A style that is difficult to define but comparatively easy to recognise is the *kenjo-Imari* style, the so-called 'presentation style' (Nos 216 and 217). Here there is much use of coloured grounds, and some hard colours in red and green. Patterns are usually so formal as to appear Baroque. Usually these are of the highest quality, though they are not always the most attractive to European eyes. They seem to occur more in collections in Germany than elsewhere.

At the cheapest end of the scale of coloured wares were the red, blue and gold wares; these were much copied by the Chinese as 'Chinese Imari' from about 1710 (see Fig. 4), and this copying may well have contributed to the loss of the European market experienced by Arita in the 1740s. In fact the Chinese had also copied the better polychrome wares (Nos 256 and 258) and the copies are often difficult to tell from the originals.

The width of range of Japanese export porcelain has been shown to be very wide; from

FIG. 4 Johann Zoffany, R.A. (1733–1810). A group portrait of John, 14th Lord Willoughby de Broke, and his family in the Breakfast Room at Compton Verney. On the table both Japanese and Chinese Imari porcelain. Thos Agnew & Son Ltd.

the enormous garnitures to the toys for dolls' houses, from the exquisite *nigoshide* Kakiemon dishes to the coarse blue, red and gold Imari, from the leaf-shaped dishes to figures copied from European models. We have not attempted here to be fully representative, but to show the types of Japanese porcelain imported into Europe that had the greatest effect on porcelain production in Europe. If this is a limited aim, it is also a large one, for the effects were so great that often Japanese styles are accepted without question in Europe as being of European origin. By charting them thus we have attempted to trace the ancestry of much European pottery and porcelain.

It says something remarkable about European tastes that it was the Kakiemon style that was so much imitated in the first half of the 18th century and the Imari that was favoured in the second half.

European Ceramics and the Influence of Japan

J.V.G. MALLET

EARLY ITALIAN REACTIONS TO CHINESE PORCELAIN

The development of Europe's tin-glazed earthenwares would be inexplicable unless viewed as a sequence of reactions to the example provided by Far Eastern porcelains.

Tin-glazed earthenwares are variously designated maiolica, faience or delftware not by reason of any significant technical differences between these but rather according to place and time of production and the stylistic tradition to which each belongs. Essentially all three are formed of a soft pottery ranging in colour, after firing, from pale buff to brick-red and covered by a lead glaze opacified with tin-oxide in such a way as to present an outer surface that, in differing degrees, is white.

Whiteness was soon perceived in Europe as one of the desirable qualities of porcelain and, learning from the Islamic potters of the Near East, North Africa and Spain, the Italians began by the early 13th century to be able to imitate this whiteness in tin-glazed earthenware, even if the translucency and hardness of Chinese porcelain still eluded them. By the early 16th century more direct contact with the Far Eastern nations was made possible for Europeans by the opening of the sea route via the Cape of Good Hope. At this time, the influence of Chinese porcelain made itself felt in a search for greater thinness and lightness in the forms of plates and other maiolica vessels.

Meanwhile attempts were being made by the Italians to imitate not just the whiteness of porcelain but also its translucency. A serious effort at porcelain-making seems to have been made at Ferrara around 1561–67, while it is likely that a porcelain-like material was made at Venice around 1504, if not even in 1470. Nonetheless the earliest surviving European ware that is white enough and sufficiently translucent to deserve the name of porcelain was made in Florence around 1573–87 and perhaps later, under the patronage of the Medici Grand Dukes. Although nearly all surviving examples are painted in underglaze blue, often in styles reminiscent of Chinese porcelain, the material itself is an artificial or frit-porcelain technically more akin to Near-Eastern imitations of Ming porcelain than to the Chinese originals. Not until the 18th century, however, did European porcelain represent serious competition to tin-glazed earthenwares.

FAIENCE IN NORTHERN EUROPE AND THE ARRIVAL OF JAPANESE PORCELAIN

By the end of the 16th century, the production of tin-glazed wares had spread to every corner of Europe. A particularly successful variety, distinguished by its brilliant white glaze and sparse decoration, was popularized by the North Italian town of Faenza, whence the term 'faience'. To the impact of Faenza white wares was added, soon after 1600, a growing need to copy the Chinese blue-and-white porcelain which now began to flood into Europe. The sombre palette derived by the North European potters from earlier maiolica began to give ground to wares of a paler white, decorated mainly in blue.

Fig. 5 Still-life, oil painting by Cornelis de Man
(1621–1706) showing a Delft jar of a kind till recently
attributed to Frankfurt am Main. Historisches Museum,
Frankfurt am Main.

Two styles of Chinese blue-and-white export porcelain particularly influenced 17th century European faience: *kraak porselein* and late Ming 'Transitional' wares. The *kraak* wares are characterized by the way their plant and animal decoration is divided into segmental panels. They were soon being copied almost all round the globe: in frit-ware by the Persians; in tin-glaze at Lisbon, Liguria and Delft; even in porcelain at Arita in Japan (No. 31).

The late Ming style 'Transitional' to the blue-and-white porcelain of the succeeding Qing dynasty evolved later than the *kraak* wares, around 1630. In the form most imitated by Europe it was notable for a type of aerial perspective in which the figures and plants of the foreground are separated from the mountainous backgrounds by swirling strands of mist or cloud. Groups of little 'V' shaped brush-strokes indicating grass are another feature that was seized on by makers of European faience, some of the finest derivations being made at Nevers between about 1660–80.

Perhaps even finer, and at times far truer to the oriental prototypes, is the faience belonging to a group that has, since Adolf Feulner's book of 1935,[1] usually been attributed to Frankfurt am Main, but which Dutch scholars are now with ever more overwhelming arguments claiming to have been made at Delft.[2] This category is of considerable interest for our purposes because to it belong what appear to be the earliest European tin-glazed wares related to Japanese porcelain.

In 1935, when making his attributions to Frankfurt, Adolf Feulner sought to distinguish the hand of a particularly able painter whom he designated *der Feinmeister*. Whether or not the wares of the group can be satisfactorily allocated to individuals in this way, it is certainly true that some of the finest pieces are large blue-and-white covered jars with figures and landscapes in 'Transitional' style placed within panels derived, by contrast, from the *kraak porselein* tradition (No. 273).

A vase of this kind is accurately represented in an allegorical still-life oil-painting by Cornelis de Man (1621–1706), who worked at Delft, visited Italy and France, but cannot be shown ever to have been to Frankfurt (Fig. 5).[3] Furthermore we are told that the lid of just such a faience vase has been excavated at Delft, at the site of the potworks known as *De Porceleyne Fles*,[4] whereas excavations at Frankfurt have so far unearthed nothing very comparable.[5] It would indeed be inherently more likely that we should find a close relationship between the porcelain of Japan and the tin-glazed ware of Holland, the country that first imported that ware in any quantity, rather than with an inland centre like Frankfurt am Main.

Having reclaimed for Delft this attractive group of tin-glazed wares, Dutch scholars are now trying to determine more precisely its relationship with Japan. Frits Scholten has seen the Delft pieces, which had initially followed Chinese originals, as beginning to copy Japanese prototypes around 1660, or a little earlier.[6] Jan van Dam, however, interprets the similarities that appear in the 1660s as evidence that, on the contrary, the Japanese were copying the Dutch. The first big consignment of Japanese porcelain sent to Europe, in 1660, probably failed to please because we know that in 1661 'models' were sent back to Japan. Van Dam suggests that these were neither painted wooden models such as those sent

1. A Feulner, *Frankfurter Fayencen*, Berlin, 1935.
2. For the recent literature on the 'Frankfurt' wares and the arguments concerning them, see Jan van Dam, 'Geleyersgoet en Hollants Porseleyn, Ontwikkelingen in de Nederlandse Aardewerk-Industrie, 1560–1660', *Mededelingenblad Nederlandse Vereniging van Vrienden van de Ceramiek*, 108, 1982/4, pp. 13–26; Frits Scholten, 'Vroege Japonaiserie in Delft, 1660–1680', ibid, 128, 1987/3, pp. 17–25; M. Bauer, *Frankfurter Fayencen aus der Zeit des Barock*, exhib. cat., Museum für Kunsthandwerk, Frankfurt am Main, 1988; H. H. Ressing, 'Frankfurter Fayencen aus der Zeit des

Barock', *Mededelingenblad*, 134, 1989/2, pp. 13–18; Frits Scholten, 'Frankfurt Revisited', *Mededelingenblad*, 134, 1989/2, pp. 19–23.
3. A. Feulner, op.cit., p. 8 (no illustration); F. Scholten (1987) pp. 22–23 and Fig. 11; H. Ressing, loc. cit., p. 18 and Fig. 4.
4. F. Scholten (1989) p. 23 and note 12.
5. Kordula Bischoff and Dr Baron Ludwig Döry, *Keramika 2, Frankfurter Fayencen des 18 Jahrhunderts*, exhib. cat., Historiches Museum, Frankfurt am Main, 1984.
6. F. Scholten (1987) p. 18, Fig. 1.

in 1637 by the Dutch from Taiwan to China, nor German stoneware jugs, but Delft blue-and-white in which the forms of German stoneware and the patterns of the Chinese Transitional and *kraak* styles were to be found already commingled. He points also to the occurrence on the Japanese blue-and-white of running border patterns found up to 1660 on Delft pottery with Ming-style painting, but never on the Ming wares themselves.[7] These are strong arguments, but need not exclude the possibility that Delft potters also copied Japanese porcelain: the export trade offers examples of influence travelling back, forth and back again; indeed the evidence of shapes such as the 'double gourd' bottle (No. 180), seems to confirm this was the case.

After 1680, when the marks of the various potworks at Delft were registered and their use became more common, there can be fewer arguments as to the nature of production there. From 1680, too, Chinese porcelain flooded back into Europe and the new wares of the Qing dynasty, whether polychrome or blue-and-white, exerted their influence. But if Japanese blue-and-white porcelain always remained somewhat in the shadow of the Chinese, the Japanese Imari and Kakiemon porcelains from Arita had caused a sensation in Europe and threatened the makers of tin-glazed pottery in a field they had hitherto had virtually all to themselves: polychrome decoration. The reaction, particularly in Holland, was not long delayed.

The iron-red and cobalt blue of the commonest sorts of Imari could be reasonably well imitated by the long familiar techniques of firing the colours at the same time as the white tin-glaze, but gilding, which created such a marketable effect of opulence, and indeed much

of the brilliant palette of the Kakiemon style, demanded at least one additional firing in a low-temperature muffle-kiln. The pioneer of the gilding technique at Delft was a potworks called *Het Jonge Moriaenshooft* ('the Young Moor's Head'), where Rochus Hoppesteyn is believed to have begun gilding his *grand feu* polychrome wares after contact, around 1692–94, with a partnership of outside enamellers working at The Hague.[8]

Only with the introduction around 1700, at a few Delft potworks, of an additional low-temperature firing did more reliable gilding and a range of enamel colours become available. By far the commonest marks found on Delft pottery, enamelled and gilded in the Japanese taste, are the monograms 'PAK' and 'AR'. The first mark is now known to stand for the *Grieksche A* ('Greek A') factory run by Pieter Adriaenson Kocks and his wife and successor, Johanna Heul, giving a date-span from 1701 to 1722 (Nos 279, 280, 283 and the lid of No. 138). Within this period falls the production of several services with blue, red and gold Imari borders and fairly closely dateable coats-of-arms in the centre, including those of Frederick I of Prussia (1701–13) and Nicolas Auguste de la Baume (1705–16).[9]

The 'AR' mark has been said to represent not a potworks but the individual painter, Ary van Rijsselberg who, with two others, signed a contract in 1713 to work for the *Grieksche A* potworks, was later with *De 3 Vergulde Astonekens* and is traceable until 1735.[10] A foreigner should be cautious of dissenting from an opinion that has found favour with recent Dutch writers, yet the argument originally put forward by Dr van Gelder for identifying all 'AR' marked pieces as van Rijsselberg's looks tentative, and pieces so marked seem rather numerous and rather various in style

7. J. D. van Dam, 'Vroege uit Delft (1625–1655) en de Invloed op Japans Porselein (1660–1970)', *Mededelingenblad Nederlandse Vereniging van Vrienden van de Ceramiek*, 135, 1989/3, pp. 4–18 en 29–30.
8. C. H. de Jonge, *Delft Ceramics*, London, 1970, pp. 70–71.
9. H. P. Fourest, *Delftware*, English edition, London, 1980, p. 114, Fig. 109.

10. C. H. de Jonge, op. cit., Chapter X, pp. 109–19; A. R. Lunsingh Scheurleer, *Niederländische Fayence*, Munich, 1984, p. 119; H. E. van Gelder, 'De Kunstenaars van Oud-Delfts Aardewerk', *Mededelingenblad Nederlandse Ceramiek*, 12, 1958, p. 5.

to be the work of a single hand (Nos 281, 282 and 363). Whoever painted them, the 'AR' marked group contains sprightly adaptations of Imari designs, sometimes mingled with motifs proper to the Kakiemon style.

Some other early 18th century Delftware copies of Imari designs showed even wilder variations as the Japanese porcelain themes were taken up not just at Delft but in other centres of production where there were often fewer opportunities to familiarize oneself with the Japanese originals or even with the Chinese Imari copies that began to supplant them. For instance the German covered bowl from Fulda No. 287, while showing undoubted influence from Japan both in the form of its handles and in its decoration, displays an attractively original blend of decorative styles that owes as much to Chinese *famille rose* and to German porcelain from Meissen. This piece has been attributed to the painter C. H. von Löwenfinck who, like his elder brother, A. F. von Löwenfinck, began his career at Meissen.[11]

At the influential faience centre of Rouen in Normandy, had it not been for the example of the Imari wares a strong red would surely never have been combined, just before 1700, with the blue already in use for the lambrequin and radiating patterns disseminated by contemporary ornamentalists. From the mid 18th century, when the asymmetrical mode of the Rococo made itself felt at Rouen, motifs like the banded hedge of the Kakiemon patterns sometimes put in an appearance alongside the more usual *décor à la corne* or 'cornucopia pattern',[12] but in general French faience was very resistant to close copying of Japanese porcelain.

Such traces of Japanese influence as can be found on English delftware seem usually to derive from Dutch tin-glazed wares. From 1669 until the beginning of the 18th century we can find dated examples of English delft bearing simplified versions of late Ming 'Transitional' painting, many of which look as though they reflect the Japanese versions of that style.[13] The fashion for decorating English delftware in blue, green and red that appears in the first decade of the 18th century, but is common in the two succeeding decades, presumably owes more (via Holland) to Chinese *famille verte* than to Japanese Imari.[14] Only rarely on English delftwares do we find echoes of such Japanese motifs as the *mon* or the banded hedge (No. 289).

In Italy the vogue for Imari patterns on tin-glazed wares arrived late and manifested itself particularly at the Clerici and Rubati factories of Milan and at Count Ferniani's at Faenza. Of Kakiemon patterns in Italy there seems scarcely an echo.[15]

A last princely flowering in faience of the Imari style occurred at the Belvedere factory at Warsaw, founded by King Stanislas Poniatowski of Poland, where a service enamelled, lavishly gilt and inscribed in Turkish is said to have been made in 1776 as a gift from the King to Sultan Abdul Hamid I of Turkey (No. 285).[16]

THE DUTCH OUTSIDE DECORATORS

So long as the Europeans had only soft-bodied, opaque, friable faience on which to imitate the Japanese Imari and Kakiemon patterns, they could never hope to compete on level terms with the Far Eastern imports. It is usually assumed that the establishment of soft-paste porcelain factories in France in the late 17th and early 18th century,

11. Konrad Strauss, 'Seltene Deutsche Fayencen in Ausländischen Museen VII, Victoria & Albert Museum, London', *Keramos*, 66, December, 1974, p. 17 and Fig. 8. Strauss dates the piece to *c.* 1740–43.
12. *Faïences Françaises XVIe XVIIIe Siècles*, exhib cat, Grand Palais, Paris, 1980, gives a recent survey and bibliography of its subject. For Rouen see pp. 193–227.
13. Louis L. Lipski and Michael Archer, *Dated English Delftware*, London,

1984, especially Nos 768, 135, 143–44 and 233.
14. Ibid., especially Nos 256, 984 and 1066.
15. For an illustrated survey of Italian 18th century tin-glazed pottery see Saul Levy, *Maioliche Settecentesche*, 2 Vols, Milan, 1962 and 1964.
16. Halina Chojnacka, *Fajanse Polskie XVIII–XIX Wieku*, Warsaw, 1981, p. 36 and Fig. 16.

and more importantly the founding at Meissen in 1710 of the first European factory capable of producing a hard, white porcelain, mark the beginning of something like parity with the East. This view leaves out of account a numerically small but historically important class of wares: oriental porcelains enamelled in Holland.

The Dutch independent enamellers have not yet received the systematic study long since accorded to their equivalents, the *hausmaler* of Germany. Historical documents and dateable pieces are scarce, but a start has been made at grouping the different types of Dutch enamelling found on oriental porcelains.[17]

The earliest category that concerns us here comprises some rather rare Japanese bottles decorated in a palette dominated by red, for the most part in an Imari manner (No. 262);[18] they must be dateable between about 1665 and perhaps a little after 1700. The enamelling may of course be later than the vessels, though it is remarkable that this type of decoration does not occur on Meissen porcelain nor on any ware dateable after, say, 1710. The nearest analogies seem to be with the painting of *Delft dorée* bearing the 'PAK' monogram and thought to date between 1701–22.

A pair of bottles in the British Museum was partly decorated in Japan for the European market, since each bottle bears the initials 'BS' in underglaze blue, but has enamelled onto it, presumably in Holland, what must be one of the earlier European essays in the Kakiemon style. W. B. Honey, who illustrates and discusses one of

these bottles, dates it 'about 1725',[19] though its decoration could well be some five or ten years earlier, and the same could be true of the decoration on a Chinese bottle whose underglaze copper-red mythical beasts are being attacked by Dutch-enamelled Europeans (No. 183).

These bottles provide links with a much larger group of pieces believed to have been decorated in Holland with Kakiemon designs, the earlier-looking examples of which are painted on Chinese porcelain considered to date from the later years of the Emperor Kangxi, who died in 1722. Several saucer-dishes[20] are painted with a Dutch ship on whose stern appears the date 1700, and it is a pity we cannot be sure this is the year of their decoration in Holland, rather than the date of the ship's launching, because in the former case we could have been certain that the enamel colours needful for Kakiemon decoration, including gilding and the peculiar green and turquoise found on the Dutch copies, were available to the enamellers by that year.

It is of interest that the collection of Augustus the Strong at Dresden contains, alongside authentic Japanese pieces, a number of Chinese pieces enamelled in Holland in the Kakiemon style. Indeed we might have been tempted to suppose these were decorated at Meissen or Dresden rather than in Holland, were they not so evidently linked by their palette, and especially by the use of a peculiar, acid-looking, slatey-green enamel, with pieces that bear Dutch subject-matter.[21] Friedrich Reichel's researches suggest

---

17. Apart from the literature cited below, the reader may wish to consult Ernst Zimmermann, 'Nachdekorierung von chinesischen Porzellan in Europa', *Der Kunstwanderer*, 1928–29, pp. 202–207; Minke A. de Visser, 'Chineesh Porselein in Holland met Kakiemon decor vorziern, *Oud-Holland*, Jaargang LXXI, Aflevering I–IV, 1956, pp. 212–16; Masako Shono, *Japanisches Arita Porzellan in sogenannten 'Kakiemonstil' als Vorbild für die Meissener Porzellan Manufactur*, Munich, 1973, also has some useful illustrations and comparisons.
18. See for instance, W. W. Winkworth, 'The Delft Enamellers', *Burlington Magazine*, LII, 1928, Pl. IA, B; W. B. Honey, 'Dutch Decorators of Chinese Porcelain', *Antiques*, February, 1932, p. 76, Fig. 4; *Eastern Ceramics and Other Works of Art from the Collection of Gerald Reitlinger*, Ashmolean Museum, Oxford, 1981, Nos 235–36.

19. Honey, loc. cit., p. 76, Fig. 4 and p. 78. Also illustrated by Winkworth, loc. cit., Pl. IA. British Museum, No. F 939+.
20. In the British Museum, illustrated by W. B. Honey, loc.cit., p. 75, Fig. 2; in the V. & A., No. C. 77–1963; two in the Rijksmuseum, Amsterdam, one of them illustrated by D. F. Lunsingh Scheurleer, *Chinese Export Porcelain, Chine de Commande*, English Edition, London, 1974, p. 179, Pl. 355.
21. E.g. apart from the saucer-dishes with ships, Honey, loc.cit., p. 78, Fig. 11 illustrates a cup and saucer in the V. & A. decorated in this typical palette with the combined arms of Holland and England, presumably in commemoration of the marriage in 1734 of William IV of Orange and Princess Anne of England.

that whenever the Ministers of Augustus the Strong travelled to the Netherlands, they tried to acquire oriental porcelain for their master.[22] If, as Oliver Impey here suggests, the Kakiemon porcelain that Augustus particularly liked was harder than Imari to come by in Holland, then these Ministers are likely to have resorted to the Dutch enamellers, or perhaps to have been duped by their hybrid products. A Dutch-decorated Chinese beaker and saucer, said by Reichel to have been already listed as in the Dresden Collection by 1721, combines *famille verte* motifs with Japanese. The same author illustrates also a Chinese dish bought in 1723 and bearing plant and bird decoration in a rather more convincing imitation of the Kakiemon style, except that the Dutch enamellers could not forbear to add rose pink to the palette.[23]

The Dresden Inventories of 1721 and later may yet yield further information on Dutch enamelling. P. J. Donnelly has already drawn attention to the fact that an octagonal cup 'painted in Europe' is recorded in them as bought in July 1723 'from HE the FM', which makes one wonder if Donnelly is right in considering a Dehua octagonal *blanc-de-Chine* cup he illustrates to have been decorated in China rather than at Delft.[24] In an inventory of the duc d'Orleans, also from 1723, are listed 'Six tasses et six soucoupes porcelaine de Saxe, peinte en Hollande', though we are not told whether the decoration was in the Oriental or in the European manner[25] (No. 266).

At least one piece of Chinese porcelain at Dresden must have been enamelled with its combination of Kakiemon and Imari motifs expressly for the Royal Collection, because it bears additionally a crowned cartouche with a monogram that Reichel reads as 'AR' for 'Augustus Rex' (Fig. 6).[26] If the monogram really does read as 'AR' that would not exclude a date after Augustus the Strong's death in 1733, because his successor also sometimes used it; but there is a slanting stroke across the top of the monogram on this Kangxi vase that makes a reading of 'FAR' possible, which would stand for Friedrich August II (Augustus III of Poland) who ruled from 1733–63. The painter shows a sound grasp of enamelling and gilding techniques, and a fair sense of the details of Japanese style, though not of the way these details were combined in Japan.

The Dutch enamellers were certainly familiar with Japanese styles before 1733. In the winter of 1728–29 a French dealer named Lemaire, of whom we must soon speak again, sent white porcelain, purchased from the Meissen warehouse in Dresden, to be painted in Holland 'in the taste of old Japan with instructions that they should send it back to me here (i.e. Dresden) to serve as a model for the Factory painter and to put him in the taste of the colours of old Japan'.[27] When he wrote this, Lemaire was trying to justify himself in the eyes of Augustus the Strong, but he had no motive to falsify this particular part of his story, which in any case could easily have been checked. Now if the Dutch were capable of enamelling 'in the taste of the colours of old Japan' whilst Meissen, in 1728–29, was not, we can no longer think of the Saxon factory as having originated in Europe the more or less accurate copying of Japanese enamelled patterns on porcelain.

We have little enough documentary evidence as to who in Holland actually did the enamelling, but Havard, without quoting his source, tells us

---

22. Friedrich Reichel, *Early Japanese Porcelain, Arita Porcelain in the Dresden Collection*, English edition, London, 1981, p. 119.
23. F. Reichel, 'Holländische Überdekore auf chinesischem Porzellan', *Dresdner Kunstblätter*, 9 Jahrgang, 1965, Heft 6, Cover Illustration and pp. 82–86. I owe this reference to A. L. den Blaauwen, along with other useful suggestions.
24. P. J. Donnelly, *Blanc de Chine, the Porcelain of Tehua in Fukien*, London, 1969, p. 346 and Pl. 134D.

25. Joseph Marryat, *A History of Pottery and Porcelain*, London, 1863, p. 328.
26. Reichel, (1981), Fig. 99 and p. 153.
27. Claus Boltz, 'Hoym, Lemaire und Meissen, Ein Beitrag zur Geschichte des Dresdner Porzellansammlung', *Keramos*, 88, April 1980, pp. 57–58.

that 'un industriel, nommé Gerrit van der Kaade' opened on 17th October, 1705, a shop in Delft specializing in exotic porcelains decorated in Holland.[28] As we have seen, the profession of outside enameller was already by the late 17th century familiar to the pottery industry at Delft, and it would have seemed sound business to such enamellers in the early 18th century, when the arrival of imported new Japanese porcelain was becoming erratic, to make good the shortage in particular of the expensive Kakiemon wares, which would have offered the largest margin of profit, by decorating in that style any porcelain blanks they could lay hands on.

After 1729, when accurate copies made at Meissen after pieces in the Dresden Royal Collection came on the market, the Dutch decorators were put on their mettle, and Delft copies too became for a time more accurate. A mid 18th century Chinese part tea-service in a somewhat generalised 'Indian' pattern, derived through Meissen from the Japanese Kakiemon, even has the Meissen crossed swords mark on it, but in iron-red, not in blue,[29] suggesting Dutch work.

Dutch decoration on Meissen porcelain rather rarely takes the form of Kakiemon patterns (No. 267) and when it does the date of the ware itself cannot be taken as the date of the enamelling, since Meissen normally resisted selling white wares that might fall into the hands of outside decorators unless it was a question of clearing outmoded stock.

Much the greatest quantity of Dutch enamelling in Japanese styles was done on Chinese ware from Jingdezhen, but occasionally pieces of Fujian ware are found with this type of

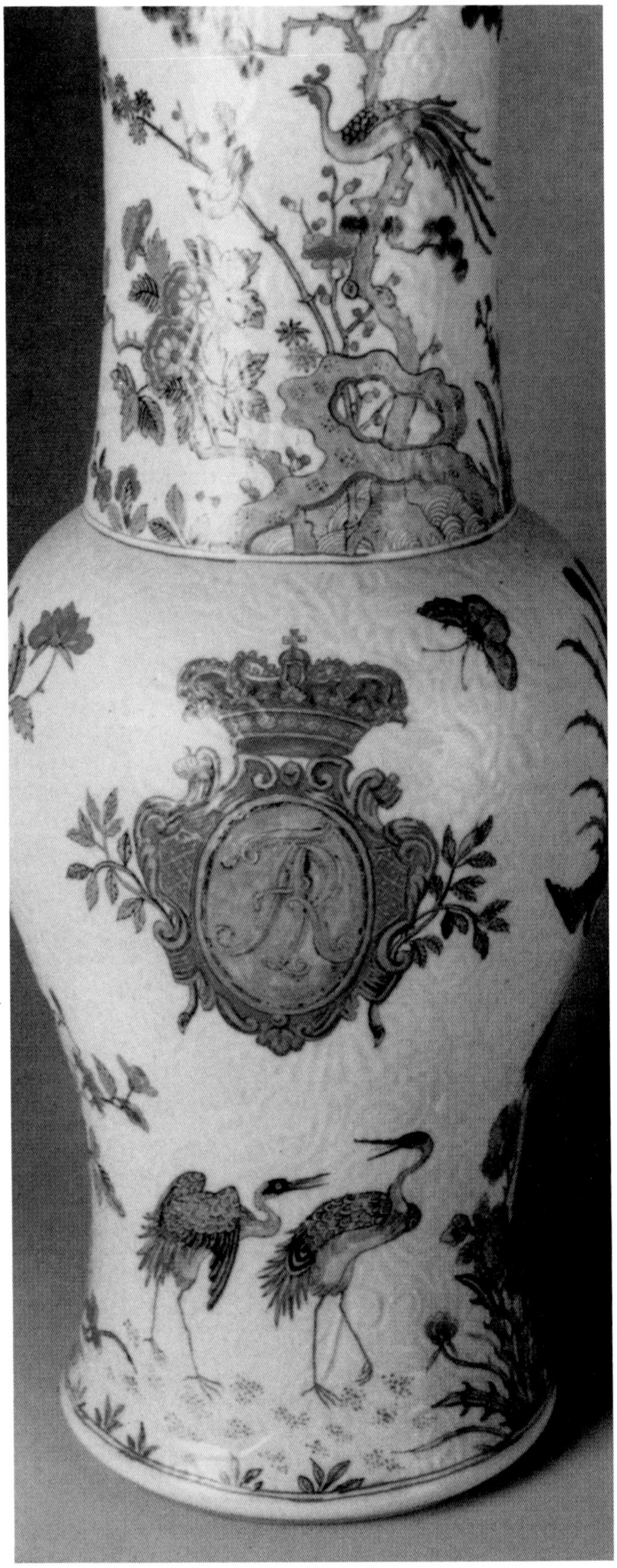

28. Henry Havard, *La Céramique Hollandaise*, 2 Vols, Amsterdam, 1909, p. 144.
29. W. W. Winkworth, 'European Kakiemon', *Antique Collector*, Oct./Nov. 1970, p. 216, Figs 1 and 2; a slop basin from this set, also marked in red, is V. & A., No. C.316–1919. Despite my great respect for this author, I can see no reason to suppose either these pieces or the earlier-looking Kangxi vase in his Fig. 4 were decorated at Meissen or Dresden rather than in Holland.

FIG. 6 Detail of vase, Chinese porcelain of the reign of Kangxi (1662–1722) enamelled at Delft with Kakiemon motifs and with monogram probably intended as that of Friedrich Augustus II of Saxony (ruled 1733–63). Porzellansammlung, Dresden.

enamelling (No. 270). Possibly the fact that such *blanc-de-Chine* porcelain was admired for its whiteness spared it from more frequent use. The dating of Fujian porcelain is usually possible only within broad limits, which makes it exceptionally hard to know what to make of claims that a few pieces, especially those decorated with quail, may have been painted in England.[30] Interesting but inconclusive comparisons are sometimes suggested with the Kakiemon decoration on Chelsea or Bow porcelains, but though there seems no obvious impediment to the idea that English outside decorators may have worked in the Kakiemon style, there is no recognisable reference to enamelling in the Japan taste in the London account book of William Duesbury's retail, repair and enamelling business from 1751 to 1753,[31] and the great age of the English decorators such as James Giles[32] belongs to a period after the mid 1750s, by which time the accurate copying of Japanese patterns was going out of fashion. I am inclined to believe most such pieces Dutch-decorated or, if not, then decorated by Dutchmen working in England.

By the mid 18th century the Dutch enamellers were very active, particularly on sparsely decorated blue-and-white from Jingdezhen, and a Frenchman, Edmé Gersaint, judged their work often very '*mal à propos*' in 1747,[33] a year from which we have a fair number of pieces commemorating William IV of Orange's assumption of the Stadholdership. This later work is known to Dutch collectors as *Amsterdams Bont* ('Amsterdam motley' or parti-coloured

Amsterdam ware), a misnomer because there seems no reason to connect its production with Amsterdam rather than Delft.[34]

Amongst the mid 18th century *Amsterdams Bont* a popular design, related to contemporary or earlier *Delft dorée*, is an Imari pattern with a flower basket within a reserved panel.[35] An example of this pattern, slightly degenerated, is to be seen on a Staffordshire salt-glaze jug bearing the surprisingly late date of 1779.[36] Possibly that piece was actually decorated in Holland, as a number of other Staffordshire salt-glaze and creamware pieces are believed to have been,[37] but Simeon Shaw recorded in 1829 a tradition that some Dutch enamellers were by 1751 active at Hot Lane, Cobridge in the Staffordshire Potteries, and that it was these men who had introduced enamelling to the district.[38]

It is not impossible that, besides some *famille rose* enamelling that seems related to *Amsterdams Bont*, they may be responsible for the rare examples of the Kakiemon style on Staffordshire salt-glaze dateable around 1750 (No. 343). The matter is not clear-cut however, because the export of considerable quantities of Staffordshire ware to Holland can already be documented before 1749.[39]

The Delft enamellers probably exercised considerable influence on the decoration of Staffordshire salt-glaze. They may also have had some impact on the decoration of French soft-paste porcelain because a painter named Antoine Grémy, born at Delft in 1705, is recorded at Chantilly by 1734.[40] The great Meissen factory in Saxony was anticipated by the Delft enamellers in

30. W. W. Winkworth, ibid., Figs 6 and 7.
31. Mrs Donald MacAlister (ed.), *William Duesbury's London Account Book*, London, 1931.
32. Bernard Watney, 'The King, the Nun, and Other Figures', *Transactions of the English Ceramic Circle*, Vol 7, Part I, 1968, pp. 48–58; Gerald Coke, *In Search of James Giles*, Wingham, 1983.
33. W. B. Honey, citing the catalogue of the Fonspertuis Collection, in *Antiques*, February, 1932, p. 77, and *Dresden China*, 1954 edition, p. 160.
34. Elka Schrijver, 'Amsterdams Bont', *Apollo*, November, 1964, pp 396–97; W. J. Rust, 'Een Classificatie van Amsterdams Bont', *Mededelingenblad Vrienden van de Nederlandse Ceramiek*, No. 41, December, 1965, pp. 9–43; D. F. Lunsingh Scheurleer, op.cit., pp. 178–86.

35. Compare Rust, loc. cit., Fig. 2 and C. H. de Jonge, *Delft Ceramics*, London 1970, Pl. XVIII and Figs 118 and 119.
36. Arnold Mountford, *Staffordshire Saltglazed Stoneware*, London, 1971, Pl. 216.
37. Bernard Rackham, *Schreiber Collection*, Vol. II, Victoria and Albert Museum, London, 1930, Nos 223–28.
38. Simeon Shaw, *History of the Staffordshire Potteries*, Hanley, 1929, pp. 177–79.
39. J. V. G. Mallet, 'John Baddeley of Shelton Part I', *Transactions of the English Ceramic Circle*, Part 2, 1966, pp. 125–27.
40. Xavier de Chavagnac and Gaston de Grollier, *Histoire des Manufactures françaises de Porcelaine*, Paris, 1906, p. 71.

its efforts to emulate the Kakiemon style: perhaps we have underestimated not only their historic importance but also the aesthetic interest of their best work.

MEISSEN AND NORTH EUROPEAN HARD-PASTE PORCELAIN

The first European factory to produce hard-paste porcelain not unlike that of China and Japan was Meissen, which owed its existence in large measure to the enthusiasm of an extravagant ruler, Augustus the Strong of Saxony and Poland. Augustus was an ardent collector of Far Eastern porcelains, including the Japanese 'Imari' and 'Kakiemon' varieties from Arita, but it has recently been suggested that he was not truly seized by the passion for porcelain-collecting until about 1715 – i.e. only after the founding of his own porcelain factory at Meissen. That he regarded his accumulated oriental porcelain as a 'collection' is attested not just by the elaborate plans he made to transform the Dutch Palace at Dresden into a Japanese Palace for its display, but also by the extreme reluctance with which he was persuaded to allow pieces from there to be used at table even for so important a political event as the *Zeithain Campement*.[41]

With such an owner and patron as Augustus we may wonder why wholesale copying of Japanese porcelain at Meissen was deferred until nearly twenty years after the factory's formal establishment in 1710. The reasons must in part have been technical. The off-white colour of the lime-porcelain produced before about 1728, the only gradually acquired mastery over underglaze blue and the unsatisfactory nature of the enamels before J. G. Höroldt joined the factory in 1720 must have discouraged premature attempts to

FIG. 7 Jar, porcelain enamelled with oriental figures, Meissen, *c*.1735. Rijksmuseum, Amsterdam. Compare the Chelsea jar, No. 197.

copy Kakiemon, the most expensive – and hence the most desirable – of the Eastern porcelains at that time known in Europe. At first the brown stonewares of Yixing or the plain white wares and figures of Dehua were more susceptible of copying by the infant factory, that is when it was not engaged in a scramble to produce in its newly-mastered material Baroque forms created by the self-confident Dresden court-silversmiths and sculptors.

During the first, or Böttger Period (1710–19) copies were made of the Japanese *koro* form (used in Germany for broth)[42] and of square-sectioned

---

41. For Augustus as a collector see Friedrich Reichel, op.cit. (1981), p. 119.
42. E.g. Dresden Staatliche Kunstsammlungen, *Meissen, Frühzeit und Gegenwart, Johann Friedrich Böttger zu Ehren*, Dresden, 1982, No. I/69.

43. Ibid. Nos I/4; I/10; I/68. This shape continued in production for some years after the Böttger period, when an alternative of octagonal section was also introduced.

saké bottles and covers.[43] Both these shapes had probably undergone Dutch influence before they reached Europe in the form of Arita porcelain, and continued to evolve at Meissen. The square-sectioned saké bottle was at first furnished at Meissen with a foot, and is found both in Böttger's brown stoneware, in which case the bottle could be faceted or otherwise cut and polished in ways unknown in Japan, and in early white porcelain, in which case European moulded ornament was sometimes applied before the factory possessed the skill to paint adequately in underglaze blue (No. 290) or in overglaze enamels.

The early 1720s were remarkable at Meissen above all for the development in J. G. Höroldt's enamelling workshop of a style of decoration consisting of fantastic figures (Fig. 7) such as we today call chinoiseries, but which are described in a document signed in 1731 by Höroldt himself as 'mit Japanischen Figuren'.[44] However the impulse to reproduce in quantity truly Japanese styles of porcelain at Meissen resulted from the dubious activities of an outsider, a business man called Rodolphe Lemaire;[45] in view of the near-contemporary essays in the Kakiemon style at Chantilly, it is of some interest that this man came from Paris.

As mentioned above, when Lemaire first came to Dresden at the end of 1728 he sent glazed white specimens of Meissen porcelain back to Holland to have them enamelled 'in the taste of the colours of old Japan' as models from which the Meissen factory could make copies for him. Obtaining an introduction to Graf von Hoym, who had recently been ambassador to France and had then become First Minister to Augustus and

Senior Director of the Meissen porcelain factory, Lemaire secured in September 1729, through Hoym's influence, a most favourable contract with the factory.[46] In correspondence with Augustus the Strong leading up to the signing of this contract, Lemaire suggested that through his marketing skills Saxon porcelain could take the place of Japanese and Chinese imports and that, by executing the designs and models that he could deliver, Meissen 'could surpass all the porcelain today being landed in Europe, and be similar to that of old Japan'.[47]

It is worth noticing that 'old' Japanese porcelain was already, in 1728, implied to be superior to any imports at that time reaching Europe. A patent granted in 1735 to the Chantilly factory likewise refers to imitating the porcelain 'qui se faisait antérieurement au Japon',[48] while the Chelsea sale catalogue of 1755 is full of references to 'Old Japan pattern' or simply, for short, 'Old pattern'.[49] Oliver Impey argues persuasively (pp. 21–23) that imports of porcelain from Japan continued to reach Europe in some quantity until the 1740s, but if so the late arrivals were evidently judged inferior to the antique Japanese wares that the European porcelain factories most sought to emulate.

From the beginning of his dealings with Meissen, Lemaire attached importance to having the crossed swords factory mark, based on the Saxon coat-of-arms, omitted from ware supplied to him, though he was happy to accept a pseudo-oriental mark or other indeterminate sign. The factory officials were immediately and probably rightly suspicious that he hoped to pass such goods off as 'old Indian *kraak* ware',[50] but though the factory resisted putting any clause into the contract specifically allowing Lemaire latitude in

44. 30th May, 1731. Printed in Richard Seyffarth, *Johann Gregorius Höroldt,* Dresden, 1981, p. 134.
45. For a general outline of Lemaire's brief connection with Meissen see Otto Walcha, *Meissen Porcelain*, English edition, Dresden, 1981, pp. 7ff. For full documentation and further comment see Claus Boltz, 'Hoym, Lemaire und Meissen, ein Beitrag zur Geschichte der Dresdner Porzellansammlung', *Keramos*, 88, April, 1980, pp. 3–101.

46. Boltz, loc.cit., pp. 7–8.
47. Boltz, loc.cit., p. 4, letter dated 17th December, 1728.
48. See below, p. 50.
49. See below, p. 53.
50. 'Altes indianisches crak Guth'. See Boltz, loc. cit., p. 3, document dated 17th December, 1728. The term 'crak gut' seems often to be applied, in the Dresden archives, not to late Ming export ware but to Kakiemon.

this question of the marks, in practice Hoym and his officials seem much of the time to have condoned production of wares evidently intended by Lemaire to deceive. Even today experts may be excused for mistaking some of the more accurate Meissen copies of 'Kakiemon' for the real thing. Cups made for the Turkish market were sometimes marked with the 'caduceus' on the principle that Mohammedans might mistake the more usual Meissen mark for a Christian cross,[51] but Augustus and most of his factory officials did not want Meissen to lose the credit for wares sold without the usual mark. Lemaire, however, was a 'fixer',and he is known to have had the 'caduceus' mark placed on ware made for him even before he had received his contract.[52] After that he sometimes contrived, through Hoym's influence, to have the crossed swords painted not in underglaze- but in overglaze-blue, so that it could be removed with acids or by abrasion; failing that, Lemaire sometimes arranged for enamelling or gilding to cover up the crossed swords.[53] By way of a rather ineffectual control on what Lemaire might be doing with the factory's porcelain it was proposed at the beginning of 1730 that wares made for him should, in addition to the usual marks, be incised almost imperceptibly and in a manner unknown to Lemaire himself with two or three scratches made in the unfired paste with the fingernail, in some inconspicuous place on the underside.[54]

Under Lemaire's contract of 1729, renewed the following year, the Frenchman was to take porcelain, against a monthly security, and to sell it on commission in France and Holland though not in Saxony. Amongst other clauses, Lemaire was precluded from arranging to have ware decorated outside the factory, while for the duration of the contract he was to have exclusive use of any models or patterns he introduced.[55]

Lemaire's method of introducing new models and patterns to the Meissen factory was simple:

some 220 pieces from the King's own collection were, with the agreement of Augustus, taken from his Dutch Palace near Dresden to be copied at Meissen 'Exactement tant pour les forme [sic] que pour les pinturs'.[56] Without the impulse generated by the pushy Frenchman and his large orders, the twelve miles' distance between Meissen and Dresden might have remained a severe impediment to the Royal factory's making copies of porcelain in the Royal Collection. As it was, by the time Augustus ordered the return of his porcelain, copies had been made of more than 120 pieces.

The fall of Graf von Hoym in the spring of 1731 put an end to Lemaire's profitable connection with Meissen. Hoym's disgrace was due partly to his leaking of diplomatic secrets to the French, partly to the discovery that he was implicated with Lemaire in trying to obtain the manufacturing secrets of Meissen porcelain. Hoym was imprisoned and some years later committed suicide; Lemaire, characteristically, talked his way out of worse trouble than deportation. Though another Frenchman, Huet, in part continued the trade, it appears that Meissen's production of copies and adaptations of Kakiemon patterns, though it continued for many years, never again resumed the dominant importance it had had in 1729–31, when Lemaire's orders absorbed a large part of the Meissen factory's creative and productive capacity.

Lists of the oriental porcelain withdrawn from the King's Dutch Palace in November to December 1729 and in 1730 survive,[57] and since these include the so-called 'Johanneum' numbers, it is possible to identify some of the surviving

51. Ibid., p. 13.
52. Ibid., p. 51.
53. Ibid., pp. 35, 37, 50, 51.
54. Ibid., p. 10.
55. Ibid., pp. 7–8.
56. Ibid., p. 58.
57. Ibid., pp. 16–19; pp. 20–21.

pieces, which bear these numbers cut into their undersides. The often fuller descriptions made in the Dresden Inventory of 1770 of the pieces so numbered are an additional aid to identification, as also is a specification of 24th February, 1731, made in Höroldt's own hand, of pieces to be copied further.[58]

As for the Meissen porcelain made for Lemaire, we can form some idea of it by means of a number of documents which Klaus Boltz has published, including an inventory drawn up on 7th April, 1731 of the pieces which Lemaire was storing in Hoym's palace.[59] Thus, included in an undated delivery to Lemaire, we find 'Coppgen zuruck 12 paar grosse caffè schälgen a perdrix' and octagonal plates 'mit den Hahn', surely versions of Kakiemon patterns with quail and with hens.[60] Among items set by for Hoym and Lemaire in the factory's warehouse at Dresden in February, 1731 were '2 grosse Vogel in Form eines Adlers', presumably the type of eagles modelled by J. G. Kirchner[61] after a Japanese prototype (Nos 172 and 191). From a price list we learn that a pair of such eagles would have cost Lemaire 20 Thalers; they are the second most expensive item on the list,[62] though it is not clear whether the price refers to white examples or coloured, since a pair of each were found in Hoym's palace when it was searched and inventoried in April 1731, the latter in a part of the list specifically designated as belonging to Lemaire.[63]

The lists prepared in April 1731 during the investigation of Hoym and Lemaire contain a number of other items recognisably copied from Japanese prototypes. We find mention of patterns with 'lions', both blue and yellow; there are three plates with the red dragon (No. 296) and no less

than 502 knife-handles of the same pattern, showing that Lemaire did not limit himself to forms known in Japan; there are plates 'mit Bajotten', that is with Pagods, in this context more likely to have been Japanese than Chinese; there is a pattern 'mit Korn Ehren' or wheat-sheaves, as the representations of banded hedges on Kakiemon porcelain were mistakenly thought to be; there are scalloped dishes 'with green dragons and flames' and scalloped dishes with storks; further patterns are designated 'à Lions gris' and 'Dessein à Pertrix' in French, as though in deference to Lemaire and the predominantly French-speaking market he served.

After Lemaire's deportation and the return of the King's oriental porcelain from the Meissen factory to his Japanese Palace in Dresden, the pressure and the ability to produce accurate copies of Kakiemon patterns decreased. But the Meissen painters had become familiar with the style and their customers had acquired the taste for it. There was no longer any attempt to make Meissen copies that could be passed off as Japanese originals, and Kakiemon patterns were deployed, often very effectively, to decorate European shapes in the Rococo style, to which their asymmetry was not inappropriate (No. 302).

We can trace the use of Kakiemon patterns through a whole series of porcelain services, including two sets of about 1730 with the tiger pattern known as *gelber Löwe*, one with the Saxon Electoral Arms, the other with the Royal Arms of Poland.[64] The Sulkowski Service of 1735– 37 had an influential ozier-moulded border to its plates, perhaps suggested by certain basket-moulded Kakiemon wares.[65] It has moreover been suggested that the wavy rims with brown edges

58. Klaus Boltz, ibid., *Anhang*, 2, pp. 79–101 gives a useful concordance of these lists.
59. Ibid., pp. 42–47.
60. Ibid., p. 24.
61. Carl Albiker, *Die Meissner Porzellantiere im 18. Jahrhundert*, Berlin, 1959, No. 23.
62. Boltz, loc.cit., p. 31.

63. Ibid., pp. 42 and 45.
64. Rainer Rückert, *Meissener Porzellan 1710–1810: Ausstellung im Bayerischen Nationalmuseum*, Munich, 1966, Nos 451 and 452; Boltz, loc.cit., p. 72 says that the Gelber Löwe services for Dresden and Warsaw were delivered in 1738, but the two armorial services look earlier.
65. Cf. a dish at Burghley House illustrated by M. Hinton and O. Impey, 1989, No. 13.

that were so widely distributed throughout European mid 18th century porcelains, derive from those of Japanese Kakiemon plates.[66] On the Sulkowski Service Kakiemon flowers and wheat-sheaves (there is no question of their being banded hedges) are scattered over such surfaces as remain between the basket-moulding and the dominant coat-of-arms.[67] The even more heavily moulded Swan Service made for Count Brühl in 1737–41 treats its Kakiemon flowers, now reverting to a more generalised 'Indian' type, in a yet more casual manner.[68] By the time of the Möllendorf Service, in some sense 'designed' by Frederick the Great of Prussia in 1761, vaguely 'Indian' flowers in iron-red monochrome were used alongside the scrollwork and *Mosaik* of the Rococo decorative repertoire.[69] The rise of Neoclassicism soon afterwards extinguished such frivolities.

Pieces for a service with the so-called 'red dragon' pattern (No. 296), first recorded in 1731, were delivered to the royal household at Dresden in 1733–39,[70] and at Meissen the design seems to have become accepted, right into the succeeding century, as exclusive to the Electoral Court of Saxony, though Chantilly examples also exist. Though not so rare in Arita porcelain as Shono supposed, this tightly mustered design, consisting of rearranged oriental symbols, is so un-Japanese that it has been suggested that its conception, at least, was European even if, as Oliver Impey has suggested to me, the Europeans were merely reassembling motifs used in different ways in Japan.[71] It has been pointed out that the Chinese rather than Japanese symbolism of the Dragon for the Emperor and the Phoenix for the Empress would have been especially suitable for a Court

Service,[72] but if that was the idea it would indeed be a rare example of the Meissen painters knowing or caring about the symbolism of the oriental forms they copied. In general, when not making an accurate copy from a Japanese original, Meissen mingled different motifs with a total disregard for their symbolism or for the way they would have been combined in Japan. Nor was it just that the Europeans mistook banded hedges for wheat-sheaves and quail for partridges; they had no idea that the flowers and plants on Kakiemon porcelain represented particular species and were no mere flowers of fancy.

Sometimes the two Arita genres, Kakiemon and Imari, were confused at Meissen on a single piece, as occurs with happy effect on some dishes from the mid 1730s on which a zig-zag line divides a clean white area, sparsely painted in the Kakiemon taste, from a densely enamelled and gilt chequer pattern in the Imari manner (No. 185). Nor did straightforward Imari patterns fall out of fashion at Meissen any sooner than the Kakiemon, some of the finest dating from the 1740s.

At the other North European hard-paste factories Imari designs in blue, red and gold predominated over Kakiemon. At Vienna during the Du Paquier period (1718–44) the painters showed comparatively slight acquaintance with the Japanese originals, which enabled them to improvise cheerfully in either style (No. 311). Later, when the State had taken over the factory, some more solemn versions of Imari were produced (No. 310).

In the main, the hard-paste North European porcelain factories took their lead from Meissen, so it is surprising that, with the exception of Ludwigsburg (No. 322) very few wares in the

66. Rückert, op. cit., pp. 84 and 85.
67. Ibid., Nos 487–90.
68. Ibid., Nos 508–17.
69. Ibid., No. 469.
70. This date is given by Boltz, loc.cit., p. 72, citing the Dresden State archives, but Rückert, op.cit., No. 305 says the pattern is first mentioned in the Meissen *Preisverzeichnis in* 1731, and that the royal service was

delivered in 1734, with supplementary deliveries in 1736 and 1739.
71. Masako Shono, op.cit., pp. 25–26, Pls 31–33; Rainer Rückert and Johann Willsberger, *Meissen, Vienna* etc., 1977, No. 48.
72. Hermann Jedding, *Meissner Porzellan des 18 Jahrhunderts in Hamburger Privatbesitz*, Museum für Kunst und Gewerbe, Hamburg, 1982, pp. 135–36, No. 124.

Japanese styles were produced, though more generalised oriental flower painting was popular.

In Holland, where we might have expected copies of Japanese porcelain, there are rather few on porcelains apart from the short-lived Loosdrecht factory; it is striking that in a recent scholarly publication on the factory's products, all the pieces in Kakiemon and Imari style are assigned to the 'middle period', around 1778–82,[73] and that most of them look as though they derive more from Meissen than from Japan direct.

Italy, too, showed a rather belated interest in the Japanese Imari style and virtually none in the Kakiemon. Capodimonte had early on sported oriental flowers on its vases and coffee-sets, but they are more a development of Meissen's *indianische Blumen* than of anything directly from the Far East. The orientalizing patterns of Doccia seem similarly non-specific and the cockerel pattern (*a galletto*) and the peony pattern, misnamed *a tulipano*, seem more Chinese than Imari in derivation. Only at the Cozzi factory at Venice, around the 1780s, does there seem to have been any sizeable production in the Japanese taste (No. 321), and here it was often more a question of the Imari palette than the Imari style. Far more interesting were the imitations of Japanese porcelain produced in France and in England.

JAPANESE INFLUENCE AT CHANTILLY AND ON OTHER FRENCH SOFT-PASTE PORCELAIN FACTORIES

Curiosity about Far Eastern artefacts, including porcelain, was greatly stimulated in France by the arrival in 1686 of ambassadors from the King of Siam bearing gifts to Louis XIV and others at the court of Versailles. To Louis himself came no less than 1,500 to 1,550 pieces of porcelain 'des plus belles, des plus curieuses de toutes les Indes', a term that included Japanese as well as Chinese porcelain. Some of the porcelain was said to be more than 250 years old, and the gift consisted of 'des tasses et assiettes, petits plats et grand vases de toutes sortes de façons et grandeurs'. M. de Coustance also took the opportunity of ingratiating himself with Louis by means of a gift including 'un oiseau de proye, du Japon' and '2 oiseaux de proye de porcelaine', perhaps the Arita model of an eagle (No. 172) later copied at Meissen. There were, besides, two Japanese ducks and two white dogs 'bien faits, du Japon'.[74]

The objects which circulated amongst influential people at the French Court as a result of these diplomatic gifts helped form a taste for the Eastern arts that was still very much alive when the young Louis-Henri, Prince de Condé (1692–1740) was at the height of his power as Chief Minister, on the death of the duc d'Orleans in 1723. Condé made a financial killing out of John Law's speculations, but in politics he was less skilful or less lucky and, in 1726, he fell from grace and was exiled to his estate at Chantilly, where he studied chemistry and natural history, besides promoting the production of porcelain and *toiles peintes*, presumably a form of chintz wall-covering.

From the fact that an inventory drawn up on the death of Condé's first wife in 1720 cites few pieces of porcelain, whereas an inventory drawn up on his death, in 1740, lists nearly 2,000 pieces (of which more were Japanese than Chinese) Nicole Ballu deduces that Condé's porcelain collection must have been formed in the intervening years,[75] which would suggest that he

73. W. M. Zappey, A. L. den Blaauwen, A. W. A. van der Goes and A. C. Pronk, *Loosdrechts Porselein*, Zwolle, 1988, Nos 108, 123, 141, 144 and 163.
74. Mlle H. Belevitch-Stankevitch, *Le Goût Chinois en France au temps de Louis XIV*, Paris, 1910. See especially the Appendix with its description of the gifts, extracted from *Relation de l'Embassade du Chevalier de Chaumont à la Cour du Roi de Siam*, 1686.
75. Nicole Ballu, 'Influence de l'Extrême-Orient sur le style de Chantilly au XVIII Siècle', *Cahiers de la Céramique et des Arts du Feu*, 11, 1958, pp. 105–107.

began collecting a little later than Augustus the Strong at Dresden.

The presence of a large collection of Kakiemon wares at the Château de Chantilly was to have great importance for the Chantilly porcelain factory. We have to deduce the early history of the factory very largely from the letters patent granted in 1735 by the King of France to its first proprietor, Cicaire Cirou, which state:

Our well-beloved Ciquaire Cirou has informed us that he has for more than ten years applied himself to the manufacture of porcelain similar to that which was formerly made in Japan; that his pains and the expenses he has lavished on it have achieved so favourable a success that there is no room for doubt that his porcelain is superior to that of Saxony, which had none the less achieved a great reputation in France and in the rest of Europe; that the different works he has produced with it, and the eagerness with which foreign countries like England, Holland and Germany ask for it, tend to confirm the superiority of his porcelain over any that has so far appeared in this manner. . . we permit and grant to the said Ciquaire Cirou, his heirs and assigns, to make in the factory he has established at Chantilly fine porcelain in all colours, types, styles and sizes in imitation of the porcelain of Japan, and this, during the space of the following twenty years. . . [76]

We may excuse the claim to superiority over the Saxon factory of Meissen because the soft-paste of Chantilly, if less tough than Meissen, and certainly less like Japanese hard-paste, none the less has an attractiveness all its own. Notice, too, the emphasis in the letters patent on copying Japanese rather than Chinese porcelain, and the assumption that the Japanese porcelain of former times was superior to contemporary production. Another point of importance concerns the date when Chantilly production began. Cirou claims to have applied himself to the manufacture of porcelain

for more than ten years, which would take us back to 1725 or slightly earlier, so that Chantilly porcelain would pre-date Lemaire's escapade at Meissen. We do indeed know that from 1725 a turner call Robert Dubois and a modeller called Jacques Poisson were at Chantilly,[77] while by 6th March, 1729, the chemist Réaumur had even set his tongue on the Chantilly glaze-mixture.[78] Yet it was only in 1730 that Cirou acquired his sizeable premises off what came to be called the 'rue du Japon',[79] so it looks as though any production from 1725–30 is likely to have been small in scale and experimental in character. Condé was an amateur of chemistry and it has been suggested that before 1730 a laboratory may have been set up in his Château itself.[80]

With the possible exception of the Red Dragon pattern, whose origin is a mystery, Chantilly's Kakiemon style seems virtually independent of Meissen, being probably based on Japanese originals in Condé's collection. One feature that Chantilly often copied successfully from genuine Arita Kakiemons, and that no other factory in Europe seems to have done, is the way the green and blue pigments are made to shrink back from the black veining on leaves, as though these enamels had been repelled by some greasy substance. There is a greater degree of stylization in the Chantilly Kakiemons than is to be found in most Dutch or Meissen versions, which makes one wonder about the role of a certain Jean-Antoine Fraisse.

In 1735 Fraisse published a book of engraved designs entitled *Livre de Desseins Chinois Tirés d'Après des Originaux de Perse, de la Chine et du Japon, Dessinés et Gravés en Taille-Douce par le Sr. Fraisse, Peintre de S.A.S. Monsieur le Duc...*[81] (Fig. 8). Fraisse makes it plain in his dedication to

76. Chavagnac and Grollier, op.cit., pp. 59 and 60.
77. Chavagnac and Grollier, op.cit., pp. 70–71.
78. Nicole Duchon, *La Manufacture de Porcelaine de Mennecy Villeroy*, le Mée-sur-Seine, 1988, p. 12.
79. N. Ballu, loc.cit., p. 102.
80. F. Chapard, 'Cicaire Cirou, Premier Maître Porcellainier de la Manufacture de Chantilly', *Musée de Condé*, No. 1, 1971, p. 10; Nicole Ballu, loc.cit., p. 105.
81. There is a photocopy in the National Art Library at the Victoria and Albert Museum of the copy in the Bibliothèque Nationale; N. Ballu, loc. cit. illustrates three plates from a hand-coloured example at the Musée Condé, Chantilly, which she says is dated 1737.

FIG. 8 Engraving from *Livre de Desseins Chinois* by Jean-Antoine Fraisse, published in 1735. Bibliothèque Nationale, Paris. Compare the Chantilly jar, Fig. 9 (No. 188).

Condé that in order to execute what Condé required he had sought out in the works of the Chinese the taste that was to be imitated; and where better to study the works of China and India than in Condé's own collection at Chantilly? Having mentioned Indian textiles and 'toiles peintes', he continues: 'porcelains of China and Japan of the first ancientness, works of lacquer and varnish of all lands where this art has been carried to its highest perfection, all these marvels are found spread with profusion in this magnificent Château'. Nor had Fraisse's patron 'disdained…to spend some moments in discovering and perfecting these Arts…and one sees with admiration your works in all these categories, confused with those of China and India, so that the cleverest connoisseur cannot distinguish the one from the other.'

There seems today very little likelihood of a porcelain expert mistaking Chantilly porcelain for the authentic product of Arita, not least because the Chantilly porcelain of Cicaire Cirou's time bears an unusually sleek, opaque-white tin-glaze quite unknown in the East. The forms of Chantilly wares and figures often give the game away by their sheer inventiveness (Nos 187 and 314). Sometimes the floral patterns, the banded hedges, birds and beasts are painted in passable imitation of the Japanese prototypes but, if they are placed on the white ground with more restraint than was usual at Meissen, the resultant effect is still wholly un-Japanese. One or two motifs from the engravings of Fraisse have been recognised on Chantilly porcelain,[82] including the

82. N. Ballu, loc. cit., Pls 1, 3, 5 and 7.

51

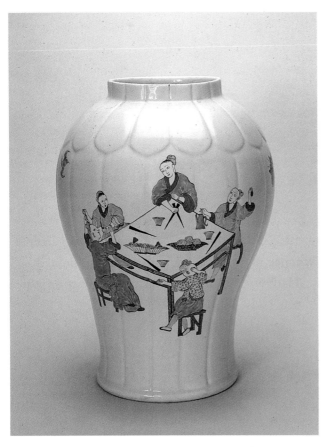

FIG. 9 Jar, porcelain enamelled with a design after J.-A. Fraisse, Chantilly, 1735–45. Private Collection. No. 188 in the exhibition.

scene of Orientals seated round a table and eating with chopsticks (Fig. 8) that appears on the magnificent Chantilly vase in this exhibition (No. 188 and Fig. 9). But we are entitled to wonder whether he may not have provided drawings of other models for the factory, as he probably also did for the factory of chintz wall-coverings.

The presence at Chantilly by 1734 of Grémy, a painter born at Delft and recorded at the Sinceny faience factory in 1747[83], has already been mentioned, but it is often on St Cloud porcelain that one is most reminded of the Delft enamellers. The Kakiemon designs that appear on St Cloud porcelain in the 1730s and 1740s seldom have the lightness or originality of those on Chantilly,

except when they break away from Japanese precedent almost completely and indulge in pure chinoiserie. It may be coincidence, but the harsh linear manner in which the more run-of-the-mill St Cloud pieces handle bamboos and banded hedges looks a little reminiscent of the so-called *Amsterdams Bont*. Was there an influence from Delft?

Only in the very earliest years of Vincennes can genuine Japanese patterns be found (No. 320), but invariably on small and unambitious pieces. We should probably be right to consider most of them as copied, along with *Holzschnittblumen* and harbour-scenes, from Meissen.[84] When the factory was taken over by the King, and even more after it was transferred to Sèvres, imitation of true oriental styles, as opposed to elegant chinoiserie, became unthinkable. By 1750 Japanese decoration on French porcelain was dead or at least dying just when, over the Channel, the English were eagerly taking it up.

JAPANESE STYLES AT THE ENGLISH PORCELAIN FACTORIES

The late 17th century vogue for Japanese porcelain had in England been led by Queen Mary, who seems to have brought the taste, and probably some of the wares themselves with her from Holland. Remnants of her collection, including hexagonal Kakiemon vases and covers, remain at Hampton Court.

Chelsea was probably the first English porcelain factory to copy Japanese patterns and a cream-jug in the Victoria and Albert looks, from its paste and glaze, as though it may date from around 1745–46 (Fig. 10).[85] Most wares from Chelsea's Triangle Period (*c.* 1745–49) seem somewhat later, either by reason of their heavy tin-glazing, as on the strawberry-leaf moulded tea-wares,[86] or

83. Paris, Grand Palais, *Faiences Francaises*, 1980, p. 270, No. 412.
84. A rare example of rather accurate copying of a Kakiemon pattern at Vincennes is shown in Svend Eriksen and Geoffrey de Bellaigue, *Sèvres Porcelain,* London, 1987, p. 212, No. 27. The decoration of this could have been copied from Meissen just as the scattered flower-heads on No. 320

could have been copied from such a Meissen piece as Masako Shono op. cit., Pl. 99.
85. V. & A., No. c. 269–1921.
86. F. Severne Mackenna, *Chelsea Porcelain, the Triangle and Raised Anchor Wares,* Leigh-on-Sea, 1948, Pl. 9, Figs 23 and 24.

FIG. 10 Cream-jug, porcelain enamelled with a Kakiemon design, Chelsea, *c.* 1745–46. Victoria and Albert Museum, London.

because they can be associated with rare underglaze-blue triangle[87] or crown and trident[88] marks which may be thought transitional to the succeeding Raised Anchor Period (*c.* 1749–52).

The great bulk of Chelsea's porcelain in Japanese styles dates from the Raised Anchor and early Red Anchor periods. From the sale catalogues of 1755 and 1756 we can identify quantities of ware made in Kakiemon or Imari taste. Sometimes such pieces are described in such terms as 'A fine octagon bowl of the rare old japan pattern and red panel',[89] but more often the word 'Japan' is taken as understood whenever we read 'old', as in the description 'Old Stork Pattern' (No. 333).[90] Imari patterns seem also comprehended in the adjective 'old', unless I am wrong in identifying the blue or gold anchor

marked Chelsea Imari dishes under the catalogue entry 'six scollop'd compotiers, *old japan'd pattern* blue and gold' (No. 345).[91] Sir Everard Fawkener, probably a part-owner of the Chelsea factory, seems to be using the word 'old' in this sense, though also probably including Chinese wares, when he writes to Sir Charles Hanbury Williams, our envoy in Dresden, on 12th August 1751 listing amongst the advantages possessed by Meissen the fact that 'there exists at Dresden the greatest collection of old china in Europe, from whence many excellent patterns are to be had'.

Hanbury Williams put his own collection, then at Holland House, at the disposal of the factory, and from the same letter we know that imitations of such Meissen porcelain as had then arrived from Dresden were made 'as well in some forms as in paintings'.[92] In this instance the Meissen porcelain copied would seem to have been in European style, but Fawkener, with the Court connections he had by virtue of his post as Secretary to the Duke of Cumberland, was well placed to gain access to such Japanese style 'patterns' as existed within range of Chelsea, whether these were from Arita or were Meissen copies. Someone, it seems, had 'Hampton Court' jars for Mr Sprimont of the Chelsea factory to copy (Nos 196 and 198); and someone seems to have possessed the very pair of Meissen vases of 'Hampton Court' form, but painted in J. G. Höroldt's orientalizing manner, that are today preserved in the Rijksmuseum at Amsterdam (Fig. 7), though in copying these the Chelsea artists preferred to alter back into their own version of Japanese style the decoration on the vases' shoulders (No. 197).

All the Chelsea Kakiemon-style vases I have seen have a thick tin-glaze suggesting a date

87. Ibid., Pl. 13, Figs 31 and 32.
88. John Austin, *Chelsea Porcelain at Williamsburg*, Williamsburg, Virginia 1977, No. 34.
89. 13th March, 1755, lot 42.
90. 22nd March, 1755, lot 62.

91. 10th April, 1756, lot 30. See the section 'Old Pattern' in J. V. G. Mallet, 'A Chelsea Talk', *Transactions of the English Ceramic Circle*, Vol. 6, I, 1965, pp. 16–19.
92. T. H. Clarke, 'Sir Charles Hanbury Williams and the Chelsea Factory', *Transactions of the English Ceramic Circle*, Vol. 9, II, 1988, pp. 110–20; Elizabeth Adams, *Chelsea Porcelain*, London, 1987, pp. 63–65.

around 1750–54, so it is rather surprising to find that the sale held in Dublin by the Chelsea factory in December 1758 included '3 sets of the most magnificent Jars and Beakers of the rare old Japan'; but then that sale was probably an attempt by the Chelsea proprietors to clear old or unwanted stock.[93] After 1758 we hear no more of Japan patterns at Chelsea.

It may be that the extent of Chelsea's direct copying from Japanese porcelain has been under-estimated: has anyone ever seen a Meissen prototype for the Chelsea carp No. 341 or of the Chelsea blue-and-white plates with ho-ō, birds No. 344? Nor, for instance, does there seem to be a Meissen version of the pattern at first very exactly copied by Chelsea on decagonal plates and with underglaze blue details (No. 329) of the pattern I believe to have been designated, in its later and less accurate form, as 'octagon soup plates of *a fine old pattern*, wheat sheaf and pheasant'.[94] If Oliver Impey is correct in thinking much of the Japanese porcelain that reached England had been traded not through the Dutch, but through the Chinese, then we need not be surprised if the Japanese pieces copied by English factories do not always match examples that would have been available to Augustus the Strong, through agents buying in Holland.

For the Bow factory we have, as already mentioned, documentary evidence that at least some Japanese originals were borrowed for copying. John Bowcock, an employee of that firm, noted in his *Memorandum Book* for 1756: 'May 28. Patterns received from Lady Cavendish: a Japan octagon cup and saucer, Lady pattern; a rib'd and scollop'd cup and saucer, image pattern; a basket bordered dysart plate; a Japan bread and butter plate'. On 29th November Bowcock repeated the descriptions adding: 'To be returned in a month, May 28th, 1756'.[95] Of these it seems possible to recognise the first; the Chelsea sale catalogues also refer to 'Old Lady pattern',[96] and at each factory a variant of the Kakiemon pattern with a lady and a birdcage in a pavilion was produced (Nos 327 and 328).

The early Bow 'New Canton' inkwells dated 1750 already show familiarity with the banded hedges of the Kakiemon style; but if 'patterns' for Japanese Kakiemon designs were still being sought out in 1756, it may be that writers on Bow have inclined, using their knowledge of the more fashion-conscious Chelsea factory, to date the cessation of Kakiemon patterns at Bow a shade too early. Thomas Craft, in the description that accompanies the bowl he so inventively decorated in an elaborate version of 'what we used to call the old Japan taste, a taste at the time much esteemed by the Duke of Argyle' (No. 339), says that he painted it around 1760; and when John Crowther, one of the Bow proprietors, had to sell up his stock in 1764, it still included 'beautiful deserts of the fine old partridge and wheatsheaf patterns'.[97]

These 'partridge' (or quail) patterns with prunus trees bearing cog-wheel-like blossom were much the most popular of the Bow Kakiemon designs and were used on ware of all manner of shapes, including the Japanese double-leaf dish. The Dresden Collections include a blue-and-white example of this shape (No. 65)[98] that may

---

93. J. V. G. Mallet, 'The Dublin Sales of 1758' in 'A Chelsea Talk', *Transactions of the English Ceramic Circle*, Vol. 6, I, 1965, pp. 23–29.
94. 31st March, 1756, lot 12. For comparison of a Japanese decagonal dish with a nearly exact Chelsea copy of the decagonal form, see J. V. G. Mallet, ibid., Pl. 27; for the octagonal soup plates, on which overglaze blue enamel has replaced the underglaze blue, see F. Severne Mackenna, *Chelsea Porcelain, the Red Anchor Wares*, Leigh-on-Sea, 1951, Pl. 3, No. 5.
95. Elizabeth Adams and David Redstone, *Bow Porcelains*, London, 1981, Appendix IV, p. 211. A taste for 'Old Japan' porcelain in the Cavendish family seems further attested by the most unusual Chinese armorial service

with a Japanese tiger and bamboo pattern in underglaze blue (No. 260) bearing the arms of Horatio Walpole, later Lord Orford, who married in 1748 Lady Rachel Cavendish, daughter of the 3rd Duke of Devonshire.
96. E.g. 9th April, 1756, lot 41.
97. William Chaffers, *Marks and Monograms on Pottery and Porcelain*, London, 1876 ed., p. 901.
98. *Blaumalerei aus Drei Jahrhunderten*, exhib. cat., Hamburg Museum für Kunst und Gewerbe, Leipzig, 1989, Pl. 16 and No. 7; M. Shono, op. cit., No. 101 for the Meissen model; E. Adams, op. cit., Fig. 47 for a Chelsea version with European flower-painting.

have fathered the Meissen copies; Meissen copies in their turn probably inspired the Chelsea copies, since at Chelsea the double-leaf seems never to be decorated in a Japanese style, suggesting that there its oriental origin was not even known. It is anyone's guess where Bow picked up the idea for its own double-leaf dish (No. 338), or for the somewhat coarsened 'partridge' pattern often used to decorate it.

Outside London it was probably harder to gain access to Japanese, or for that matter Meissen porcelain to copy, with the result that much Lund's Bristol and early Worcester porcelain is neither Japanese nor Chinese in appearance, merely oriental in its intended associations. When, say, a Worcester (No. 371) or a Cookworthy's Plymouth jug (No. 340) bears a 'partridge' pattern, we are entitled to wonder whether Bow porcelain was not the 'pattern' for it, or indeed if a Bow painter had not wandered West.

During the 1760s Worcester developed its own range of attractively simplified 'Japan patterns', the equivalents of the cheapened versions of Sèvres and Chelsea coloured-ground wares that the factory was producing in the same period. Indeed the two genres sometimes became genially confused, as when a *ho-ō* bird on a rock was framed within a panel reserved on a dark underglaze blue ground to produce the design known to modern collectors as the 'Sir Joshua Reynolds Pattern'.[99] From the Worcester factory's catalogue of the sale at Christie's in December

1769, we can try to identify such things as 'fine old Japan star pattern', 'fine old pheasant pattern', 'fine old japan fan pattern', 'fine old rich mosaic japan pattern', 'scrole japan pattern' (? No. 349) or 'fine old rich dragon pattern, blue *Céleste* borders'. The 1769 sale catalogue lists only one 'set of three elegant Jars and Covers', and these were evidently painted in the European taste; but the shape of such Worcester vases echoes, in slightly attenuated form, the 'Hampton Court' jars of earlier times and when the workmen painted oriental dragons the effects were often hallucinatory.

One could almost wish that the influence of 17th century Japanese porcelains had died on this relatively high note, but blue, red and gold patterns, derived as much from the Chinese copies of Imari as from the Japanese originals, continued to be made in the late 18th century despite the rise of a Neoclassical taste antipathetic to such frivolities. As the 19th century dawned it occurred to a number of English factories such as Bloor-Derby and Spode that, with very little expense, an appearance of great opulence could be produced by a revival of the old Imari patterns. What had reached Europe as a decoration for the palaces of kings and noblemen was cheerfully vulgarised to suit a thousand suburban tea-tables.

99. H. Rissik Marshall, *Coloured Worcester Porcelain of the First Period*, Newport, Monmouthshire, 1954, Pl. 8, No. 140. I know of no justification for associating this pattern with the first President of the Royal Academy.

Porcelain for Palaces

OLIVER IMPEY

The huge quantities of porcelain that were imported into Europe in the first half of the 17th century, mostly Chinese blue-and-white or white wares, ensured the onset of 'china-mania'; it was the coloured enamelled porcelain of Japan that stimulated the display of the results of this 'mania' in massed array in rooms in great houses all over Europe.

Daniel Defoe in the late 17th century blamed Queen Mary for introducing into England 'the custom...of furnishing houses with Chinaware... piling the China upon the tops of Cabinets, scritoires, and every Chymney Piece...[1] and this may be partly true in that she brought the taste to its full fruition in England. But it had its origins both on the continent and in England long before this time.

Such was the rapid increase in quantity of this most fashionable decorative accessory, porcelain, in the 17th century, that we can trace its progression in European houses, first out of the cabinet of curiosities onto the table and then from the table onto the walls. This reached its extreme limits in the late 17th and early 18th centuries in 'Porcelain Rooms' where the walls were dressed in massed Chinese and Japanese porcelain (Fig. 11). Early in the 18th century this perhaps excessive display of porcelain tended to be reduced, save in the hands of certain fanatical collectors such as Augustus the Strong, whose amazing collection at Dresden we will discuss later.

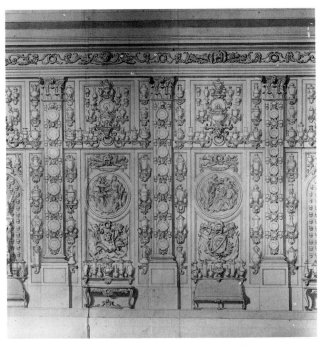

FIG. 11 Project drawing for the Elb Gallery, the Japanese Palace, Dresden. From the second series by Zacharius Longelune, 1735. Staatsarchiv, Dresden.

By the mid 18th century porcelain, still as fashionable as ever, was perhaps not so visible; the glass-fronted cabinet, the china cabinet, itself often of pseudo-oriental aspect (e.g. 'Chinese Chippendale') contained the pieces that had formerly stood on the lacquer cabinets, upon brackets on the walls or on and over the chimney piece. Conversation-piece paintings of English families show oriental porcelain in use on the tea table or displayed discreetly about the room. We have come back to the conditions visible in Dutch still-life painting of the mid 17th century

1.   Daniel Defoe, *A Tour thro' the Whole Island of Great Britain* (1724–27); ed. G. D. H. Cole and D. C. Browning, London and New York, 1962, i, p. 166.
2.   Manuscript inventory, 1629, Hatfield House.

3.   Manuscript will of Sir Walter Raleigh, 1597, Sherborne Castle.
4.   Louise Avery, 'Chinese porcelain in English Mounts', *Metropolitan Museum of Art Bulletin*, N.S.2, New York, 1944, p. 266.

where porcelain was an attractive but never dominant part of the scheme of decoration.

The great vogue for the display of porcelain in massed array in European rooms follows, then, almost precisely the rise and fall of the dominance of Japanese porcelain in the European market, from its beginnings in the 1660s to its decline in the 1740s. This can be no coincidence; it must have been these bright new Japanese coloured porcelains that gave the impetus to the use of porcelain as a dominant feature in a room rather than as the fashionable accessory it had always been.

Porcelain was, of course, functional. At Hatfield House in 1629 there was, 'in the Chamber over the Porters Lodge…XXVI China dishes to sett out a banquett'.[2] This is a great change from the treatment of porcelain as a valuable curiosity; probably also at Hatfield would have been the 'suite of Porcellane sett in silver and gylt' left by Sir Walter Raleigh in his will in 1597 to 'my Right Honorable good Frinde Sir Robert Cecill'[3]. (It has been suggested that this suite may be the famous set, sold from Burghley House in 1888, now in the Metropolitan Museum.[4])

By the mid 17th century, numbers of porcelain (Chinese, still, before 1659) were very much higher. Already by 1632 porcelain had been displayed on shelves in the Oude Hof, at Noordeinde in the Netherlands, the Residence of the Stadtholder, and the numbers of porcelain listed in the possession of his widow, Amalia von Solms were considerable.[5] When the Earl and Countess of Arundel built their Dutch banqueting room at Tart Hall in 1641, there were rarities, including porcelain, arranged on sets of shelves over the door, in the corners and on other surfaces,[6] much as was the case later for the early projects for porcelain rooms visible in the engravings of Daniel Marot.[7]

At Somerset House in 1649 the 65 pieces of 'purselaine' described in the inventory of the goods of King Charles I were probably displayed on shelves. The items immediately previous to the porcelain in the inventory lists are 'Nyne Woodden hanging Shellves turned and guilt'[8]. These may well have resembled the hanging shelves of nearer the end of the century still hanging in Drayton House.[9]

The only extant display of porcelain that dates from the middle of the 17th century is the extraordinary ceiling of a room in the Santos Palace in Lisbon. Here a specially constructed pyramidal ceiling is clad in late Ming blue-and-white plates held in place by a wooden framework. Although not documented adequately for us to be certain of the date, there is little reason to doubt that it dates from the middle of the century. There is, however, no

5.   Peter Thornton, *Seventeenth-century Interior Decoration in England, France and Holland*, New Haven and London, 1978, p. 249.

6.   Thornton, op. cit., pp. 249, 383 and note 22.

7.   See, e.g., Thornton, op. cit., Pls 71–73.

8.   Anna Somers Cocks, 'The non-functional use of ceramics in the English Country-house during the eighteenth century', *Studies in the History of Art*, 25, 1989, pp. 195–216.

9.   For an illustration of one of these, see Mark Hinton and Oliver Impey, *Kakiemon porcelain from the English Country House*, London, 1989, Fig. 2.

FIG. 12 Engraving of a 'China Closet' by Daniel Marot, from *Nouveaux livres de Partements*, published before 1702. British Museum.

information at all on what else was kept in the room or what was upon the walls.[10]

At Rosenborg Castle, then outside Copenhagen, porcelain was simply used as decoration; in King Christian IV's bedroom there were *blanc-de-Chine* figures placed over the doors, in the late 17th century, and in his study, two Arita blue-and-white bottles on the chimney piece. This was, at the time of the appearance of the first Japanese porcelain, the normal state of affairs; porcelain formed a modest display. Only the Santos Palace room is aberrant.

For the mid century period we have little information. Louis XIV had no porcelain in the Gallery at Versailles,[11] though the arrangement of his mounted hard-stone vessels on serried ranks of brackets was just that which was later to be used for many an ambitious porcelain room. It may well be that this was to be the stimulus to the

porcelain room proper; if so, then it was through the agency of the Huguenot Daniel Marot that it was to reach Holland. And it was from Holland that it spread throughout Europe. Remember that the Arundels had described their banqueting room as 'Dutch'.

Daniel Marot left France in 1684, just before the revocation of the Edict of Nantes, for Holland. He appears to have risen to favour quickly for he was almost certainly the designer of the closet at Honselaardijk, built for Queen Mary in 1686. No engraving of that closet survives, but Marot's published designs, some of which must have been done for Queen Mary after her accession to the throne of England give us some hint of its appearance (Fig. 12).[12] Furthermore,

10. Daisy Lion-Goldschmidt, 'Les porcelaines chinoises du palais de Santos', *Arts Asiatiques*, 25, 1984, pp. 6–72.
11. For the drawing of 1684, see Thornton, op. cit., Pl. 236.
12. See, e.g. Thornton, op. cit., pp. 249–50.

the Swedish architect Nicodemus Tessin in 1687 described the room's mixture of lacquer panelling, mirror-glass ceiling and massed porcelain over the chimney that well coincides with Marot's engraved work.[13]

The use of mirror-glass panels as wall-coverings did come from France and seems to have become an obligatory feature of the later porcelain rooms, which were sometimes, as at Schloss Weissenstein, Pommersfelden, in Germany, actually called a *Spiegel-Kabinett*.[14] At Het Loo, the ceiling of the former porcelain room, later converted into a library, survives, with a canted oval frame of mirror-glass.[15] Almost all, if not all, later porcelain rooms were to make much use of mirror-glass.

Queen Mary was a passionate collector of porcelain, and we shall examine her collection at Kensington House in some detail below. King William was not; he took no interest in porcelain whatsoever and after Mary's death lost no time in giving away most of her collection. But a taste for porcelain seems to have run in his family.

It is not by chance that so many *maisons de plaisance* were named after the Orange family; two of William's aunts took the fashion to Germany. Luise Henriette married Frederick Wilhelm, Elector of Brandenburg who built for her the Oranienburg Palace near Berlin, before 1663 and Albertina Agnes married William Frederick of Nassau-Dietz who built for her the Oranienstein, near Koblenz, completed in 1683.[16] A curious latecomer on the scene makes the point of the connection of the Orange name with such houses; when Catherine the Great built a pavilion

near St Petersburg, in the late 18th century, it was named the Oranienbaum.[17]

To some extent, these 'pavilions', or small palaces were descendants of the chinoiserie garden houses of France. Perhaps the most famous of these was the *Trianon de porcelaine* of 1671, in reality an ordinary European house of the period dressed up in Delft faience.[18] The craze for chinoiseries of course included the real thing. Louis XIV may have had no porcelain in the Gallery at Versailles, but he had plenty elsewhere. Much of this porcelain came to France from the extraordinary 'Embassy' sent from Siam, supposedly by the King of Siam but in reality through the agency of a Greek adventurer, Constant Phaulkon, in 1684.[19] The great number of gifts given to the Court included much Japanese lacquer[20] and porcelain,[21] some of it specially ordered.[22] Thus among the 'Agates, Cristaux, Porcelaines, Bronzes, Et Autres Curositez Qui Sont Dans Le Cabinet De Monseigneur Le Dauphin A Versailles' inventoried in 1689, were a considerable number of 'Porcelaines Données par les Siamois'.[23] That these were shown on shelves is suggested by the arrangements at Meudon, where, in 1702 the Dauphin had in the gallery 'sur le cheminée et sous les cabinets, quatre porcelaines, six autres de Siam, neuf bronzes donnez par le Roy, deux autres bronzes'.[24] The reference to Siamese porcelain should presumably be read as porcelain given by the Siamese embassy.

But this was not a porcelain room in its extreme form, not like that of the Oranienburg in its later manifestation nor that of Charlottenburg.

13. Quoted in Somers Cocks, op. cit., p. 195.
14. Gerhard Bott (ed.), *Die Grafen von Schönborn*, Germanisches Nationalmuseum, Nürnberg, 1989, Pl. 46.
15. A. M. L. E. Erkelens, 'Delfts aardewerk op Het Loo', *Nederlands Kunsthistorisch Jaarboek*, 31, 1980, pp. 263–72.
16. L. Reidemeister, 'Die Porzellankabinette der Brandenburgisch-Preuszischen Schlösser', *Jahrbuch der Preuszischen Kunstsammlungen*, Part 1, 54, 1933, pp. 262–72.
17. Giles Worsley, 'The Chinese pavilion at Oranienbaum', *Country Life*, 183, Nov. 16, 1989, pp. 68–73.
18. Hugh Honour, *Chinoiserie: the vision of Cathay*, London, 1961, p. 53.

19. The best account of this embassy is in H. Belevitch-Stankevitch, *La Chine en France au temps de Louis XIV*, Paris, 1910.
20. See, e.g., Oliver Impey, 'Japanese export lacquer of the seventeenth century', *Lacquerwork in Asia and beyond: Colloquies on Art and Archaeology in Asia*, 11, Percival David Foundation, London, 1981, pp. 124–58.
21. Perhaps the jars No. 149 in this exhibition, formerly in the collection of the Prince de Condé, were part of this gift.
22. Impey, op. cit., (note 20), p. 139.
23. To be published by F. J. B. Watson in the *Journal of the History of Collections*.
24. See Thornton, op. cit., (note 5), p. 249.

FIG. 13 Engraving of the Porcelain Room at Oranienburg, by Jean-Baptiste Broebes, published in *Vues des palais et maisons de plaisance de Sa Majesté le Roy de Prusse*, Augsburg, 1773.

It was, however, more akin to the Dutch and English forms, for as we have seen, the original idea may have been transferred from France to Holland and thence to England by Daniel Marot.

The first porcelain cabinet at Oranienburg was later dismantled (by 1690 it is referred to as 'die alte Porcellain Cammer' when it had been redecorated with gilt leather on a blue ground),[25] during the rebuilding by Luise Henriette's son Frederick I of Prussia to the designs of Christof Pitzler. It is this later room, some 9m by 12m in size, that is familiar to us in the famous engraving by Jean Baptiste Broebes of 1733 (Fig. 13).[26] Here a basically Baroque room has been literally covered in porcelain; on walls, pillars, pilasters and cornices are line upon line of plates, dishes and saucers. Seven great giltwood pyramidal *étagères*, of which at least one survives at Charlottenburg, carry tier upon tier of jars and vases.[27] Each may have borne about 100 pieces. Broebes's engraving

suggests that these were not surrounded by miniature vases and bottles as were those at Charlottenburg[28] and at Pommersfelden.[29] These *étagères* stood before walls of panels of mirror-glass, doubling the splendour of the effect. But this, too, was simply a room in fancy dress. At Charlottenburg in Berlin (Fig. 14), built in the early years of the 18th century by Frederick III for Sophie Charlotte, Johann Friedrich Eosander von Göthe created a much more full-blooded porcelain room. Not only are plates and dishes ranked on the cornices, but vases and bottles in sets stand before them and miniature bottles are suspended, like raindrops, below. From the

25. Reidemeister, op. cit., (note 16), p. 264.
26. Jean-Baptiste Broebes, *Vues des palais et maisons de plaisance de Sa Majesté le Roy de Prusse*, Augsburg, 1733.
27. One is illustrated in Arthur Lane, 'Queen Mary II's porcelain collection at Hampton Court', *Transactions of the Oriental Ceramic Society*, 25, 1949–50, pp. 21–31, Pl. 7c.
28. See the print by Eosander von Göthe in M. Merian, *Theatrum Europei* XVI and XVII, Frankfurt, 1717 and 1718.
29. Gerhard Bott (ed.), op. cit., (note 14), Pl. 46.

FIG. 14 Engraving of the Porcelain Room at Charlottenburg, Berlin, *c.* 1705, after Eosander von Göthe in M. Merian, *Theatrum Europeii XVI and XVII*, Frankfurt, 1717 and 1718. Staatliche Museen Preussischer Kulturbesitz, Kunstbibliothek, Berlin.

wainscot upwards, specially shaped swirls of giltwood bracketting hold myriads of vases that are clearly selected for size and for shape and colour, all before walls of mirror-glass. Chinoiserie figures wearing upturned basins as hats hold up great bowls, while tiers of bottles and of cups and saucers line the edges of the mirror-plates. Vases stand on pedestals in the corners, in garnitures over the chimney piece and even on the floor. It is all integral; nothing was left to chance and the whole room was specifically designed to show not just oriental porcelain, but this collection of porcelain. The rebuilding of room and collection after the war

has been a triumph of skill and persistence.

It was not only the shapes that were important, it was also the colours. Chinese and Japanese porcelain was mixed together, not indiscriminately, but very carefully, in order to achieve the desired effects of symmetry and harmony. No interest at all was taken in the origin of the various porcelains.

In the only other porcelain room (*sensu stricto*), one that has survived more or less intact, the *Spiegel-Kabinett* at Pommersfelden, the opposite was true. A high proportion of the collection in this room was Japanese Imari; those Chinese pieces present were either Chinese Imari or blue-

61

FIG. 15 *Spiegel-kabinett*, 1719, at Schlöss Weissenstein, Pommersfelden, Graf von Schönborn Kunstsammlungen.

and-white cold-painted in Europe to resemble Imari. The intention is clear; this was to be a Japanese room.

The *Spiegel-Kabinett* at Schloss Weissenstein (Fig. 15), Pommersfelden, was built for the Elector-Archbishop of Mainz and Prince-Bishop of Bamberg, Lothar Franz von Schönborn, in 1719.[30] Situated in the north-east corner of the great Baroque palace, it was adjacent to the Prince-Bishop's bedroom and study. The woodwork, of extreme sophistication and with superb inlays of ivory and exotic woods was carried out by Ferdinand Plitzner.[31] The porcelain was placed in groups on brackets ranged in tiers either side of and above large wall mirrors. The engravings of the room by Salomon Kleiner of 1728[32] show that around each group of porcelain of medium size on each bracket – three

or five pieces of up to 30-odd centimetres tall – there was an array of miniature jars and bottles. These were also arranged along the dado. Many of them are still there; most of the blue-and-white ones are Chinese, most of the coloured, Japanese. Such miniatures are also visible in Eosander von Göthe's engravings of Charlottenburg, but not, as we have observed, in Broebes's engravings of Oranienburg.

At Pommersfelden, much of the porcelain that came to the house was chosen from an earlier collection, that in another von Schönborn house, the nearby Schloss Gaibach. So the collection was mainly older than the room. Curiously, perhaps, Kakiemon is conspicuously absent, and Arita blue-and-white uncommon. This argues a purposeful accumulation by the Prince-Bishop, specifically of Imari. Given the jewel-like quality of the room and its furnishings, this may sound an odd choice – in fact it is ravishing.

Plitzner was working in a transition style between the Baroque and the Rococo; the room was light, airy, almost frivolous. It was a very different thing from the solid and heavy designs of Marot for Queen Mary. The Queen's temporary decoration of the old Water Gallery at Hampton Court was described by Defoe as 'the pleasantest little Thing within Doors that could possibly be made'.[33] It probably looked very like one of Marot's engravings, that of the 'China closett' in his *Nouveaux livres de Partements* of about 1700,[34] though this room seems rather lacking in case furniture. Defoe further remarks:

And here was also her Majesty's fine collection of *Delft* ware, which indeed was very large and fine; and here was also a vast stock of fine *China* ware, the like whereof was not to be seen in *England*; the long Gallery, as above, was fill'd with this China and every Place, where it could be placed, with Advantage.[35]

30. Sigrid Sangl, 'Hofhandwerk und Wohnkultur unter Lothar Franz und Friedrich Karl von Schönborn' in Bott (ed.), op. cit., (note 14), pp. 60–71.
31. Sangl, op, cit., Pls 45–48.
32. Salomon Kleiner, *Representation au naturel des chateaux de Weissenstein au desus de Pommersfeld, et celui de Geubach. . .*, Augsburg, 1728.
33. Defoe, op. cit., (note 1) p. 175.
34. Thornton, op. cit., (note 5) Pl. 238.
35. Defoe, op. cit., p. 175.

Defoe had already remarked rather scathingly on Queen Mary's introduction of the massing of porcelain into England. But he was only right to a limited extent. Even in vast houses such as Burghley, if one had much china, one had to have somewhere to put it, and porcelain was very much part of the decoration of great houses in England.

It is the 'Inventory of the Goods in Burghley House belonging to the Right Honble John Earl of Exeter and Ann Countesse of Exeter taken August 21st 1688' that makes Burghley quite so important, for much of the stuff listed is still in the house, and this was some months before the arrival in England of William and Mary.[36]

Porcelain is found, in this inventory, in some quantity in thirteen rooms, mostly as 'China over the Chimney' or among 'China & other things over the Chimney'. Many of the fireplaces at Burghley were in the corner of rooms. These, now altered, had shelves in pyramidal tiers, much like one at Beningborough Hall in Yorkshire. The shelves in the Green Damask Room have recently been restored. Such a corner fireplace was described by Marot as a 'cheminée a L'angloise'.[37] The inventory does not tell us in which position each piece stood (which the later one of Kensington House does[38]), but merely lists the pieces. Thus in 'My Lords Dressing Roome' there were:

2 Doggs, 2 Lyons, 2 Staggs, 2 blue & wt Birds

1 heathen Godd with many Armes

2 figures with Juggs at their backs.

Apart from the presumably *blanc-de-Chine* 'heathen Godd' and possibly the 'Lyons', these were probably all Japanese, and a blue-and-white bird No. 156 and two figures with gourds on their backs, No. 162 which presumably answer

these descriptions are exhibited here.

So Defoe was correct in that all the china was over the chimney, it was not all over the room on furniture, pedestals and shelves, as it was to be at Kensington House. This is why the Marot print of the 'China closett' is odd; there is no case furniture on which to place pots.

The 'account of what goods is now in hir Laite Maties Lodgeings of blessed Memory at Kensington March ye 24th 1696/7'[39] taken by Simon de Brienne, Keeper of His Majesty's Wardrobe gives us details of exactly which piece of porcelain stood in which position on each shelf in each room in the Queen's apartments. Colours are given, often enabling one to attribute a description to a type of porcelain. Thus 'two large eight square caudle cupps with flowers of blew red & green on them' may very well be Kakiemon bowls such as No. 128. The detail is insufficient for us to be certain. Probably similar were the 'two basons of eight square each with branches & burds on them of red, green & blew'. In all probability the 'two fine coloured flasks foure square each' were similar to No. 149, and, most famous of all, the 'coloured jar and cover of six squares' (there were several of these) was surely an eponymous 'Hampton Court' jar such as No. 151 or No. 152.

All these things were ranged about the rooms on any surfaces available. Where there were no surfaces, they were made, either as pedestals or as shelves.

In the Gallery, to take the best example, there was porcelain:

over the dressing roome door	(9 pieces)
over the false doore	(9 pieces)
over the next chimney	(19 pieces)
on the pedestalls	(7 pieces)

36. See No. 17: Manuscript inventory, lent from Burghley House.
37. See Thornton, op. cit., Pl. 74.
38. Th. H. Lunsingh Scheurleer, 'Documents on the furnishing of Kensington House', *Walpole Society*, 38, 1962, pp. 15–58.
39. Lunsingh Scheurleer, op. cit., pp. 33–50.

Over the next chimney	(19 pieces)
Upon the pedestalls	(7 pieces)
Over the doore goeing downe staires	(7 pieces)
Over the door goeing into ye closett	(7 pieces)
Under the Jappan desk	(2 pieces)
Under the cabenett next close	(3 pieces)
Under ye table next it	(1 piece)
Under the next cabbenett	(3 pieces)
Under ye next table	(1 piece)
Under ye next cabenett	(3 pieces)
Under ye next table	(1 piece)
Upon ye cabbenett next ye closett	(18 pieces)
On the cabbenett in the midle of the Gallery	(20 pieces)
on the next cabbenett	(18 pieces)

Thus there was a total of 154 pieces arranged, as one can see, in strict symmetry. The false door and the dressing room door were presumably on the same wall and each bore 9 pieces; the door going downstairs and the door of the closet were presumably both on the wall opposite and each bore 7 pieces. Each chimney had 19 pieces over it and so on.

Sometimes pieces were piled upon or fixed to each other. 'In the closett at the end of the Gallery' were 'on a pedestall in the forme of a stand'… 'one fine high large roll waggon/one large shallow bason upon ye roll waggon', and on another pedestal: 'two stands each stand made up with three jarrs & one china platt att the top'.

The rollwagon (No. 38) was probably blue-and-

white porcelain.

We can also work out the colour scheme from the detailed descriptions of each room. In the Queen's Ante-room, for instance, there were six shelves over the chimney. The list is as follows:

China in this Room
over the chimney
Topp shelfe
four large platts two of each of a sorte
one fine white platt with red & green branches
on ye second row
six platts of white & blew all of sorte
one white platt with red & green branches
on ye third row
six small platts of white & blew all of a sorte
one white platt with red & green branches
on the fourth shelfe
seven white platts all of a sorte whith branches of
several coloures
on the fifth shelfe
six platts of white & blew all of a sorte
one white platt with red & green branches
on ye bottom
one large dish of several colours
four lesser dishis

In all in this roome 38 pieces of fine china
(all the china to Albemarle 24 Nov. 1699)

If we understand that 'all of a sorte' means either matching or *en suite* and we assume that the arrangement was symmetrical, which it must most certainly have been, we find that there are even numbers of blue-and-white, or of undescribed (top and bottom shelves) which would have been placed either side of the 'white platts with red & green branches'. These latter were probably very similar to, or perhaps even *en suite* with the ones on the fourth row, which therefore would have made a coloured cross (perhaps Kakiemon?) on a blue-and-white background. We do not know what the pieces either side of the centre on either the top or bottom rows looked like, but from this point of view it does not much matter; they were point of view it does not much matter; they were certainly symmetrically arranged.[40] Not all the rooms had such careful and tidy arrangements simply because not all the pieces of porcelain were susceptible to such formality; in the old bedchamber of the Queen, the bottom shelf (of six) over the chimney had 21 pieces on it.

Notice the rubric '(all the china to Albemarle 24 Nov. 1699)'. There has long been controversy over the fate of Queen Mary's porcelain.[41] From the evidence of this inventory all the 801 pieces at Kensington House (except for the teapot stolen 'by strainge gentry') were given to the Earl of Albemarle. But this would not necessarily have been the case for any left in Hampton Court or any other Royal houses; it was specifically the porcelain at Kensington that was Albemarle's perquisite. Thus the Kakiemon-style jars now at Windsor Castle[42] may well have been part of Queen Mary's collection. It has recently been suggested[43] that some of Albemarle's pieces may have been included in the sale of the contents of de Voorst, a country house of Albemarle's in Holland, in 1744.

Queen Mary's collection was small in comparison with that of Augustus the Strong, King of Poland and Elector of Saxony, whose vast collection has largely survived neglect, wars and sales, and is today still in Dresden.[44] Augustus became Elector in 1694, but did not begin to collect oriental porcelain until about 1715, perhaps partly stimulated by a visit to Berlin, where he would have seen the Porcelain Room in the Charlottenburg, in 1706. He was an accumulator more than a discriminating collector, employing agents to buy for him in Holland and buying or otherwise acquiring whole collections

at once. Once he exchanged twelve large Chinese jars for a regiment of dragoons. By 1717 the collection was already large enough for the Elector to acquire the Dutch Palace (that was later to be rebuilt as the Japanese Palace), specifically to house his collection. By 1723 this was so full that even the cellars were fitted out to hold porcelain. The Japanese Palace (built between 1729 and 1737) had a central courtyard whose Baroque façades are upheld by fantastic caryatids that owe little to Japan but a great deal to chinoiserie. The roofs have the canted outlines, tilted upwards at the corners and at the edges that are almost a hallmark of 18th century chinoiserie and are also visible at the Palace of Pillnitz, just up the river from Dresden. The porcelain was to be displayed in a manner somewhat similar to that at Charlottenburg, but with even more eclectic mixtures, in that some of the pieces were to be the products of Augustus's Meissen porcelain factory.

The Dutch Palace porcelain rooms had been thoroughly Baroque, but the Japanese Palace rooms were more open and light. Some drawings in the Dresden *Kupferstich-Kabinett* show designs for some of the walls. Quite clearly these are from more than one hand; a drawing of alternative projects for the long wall of the Elb Gallery (the Gallery on the river side of the courtyard) is strikingly similar to the walls of Charlottenburg.[45] Tier upon tier of plates, saucers and vases stand around pyramid-like *étagères* supported by lion figures or around plaster or giltwood medallions. There is none of the sense of lightness of the Rococo, such as there is at Pommersfelden. In another drawing (Fig. 16), things are very different; brackets and pedestals hold up

40. Linda R. Shulsky, 'Queen Mary's collection of porcelain and Delft and its display at Kensington Palace based upon an analysis of the inventory taken in 1697', *Bulletin of the American Ceramic Circle*, forthcoming 1990.
41. Arthur Lane did not know of the inventory of Kensington House published by Lunsingh Scheurleer (note 38) when he published his paper on Queen Mary's collections (note 27).
42. See Hinton and Impey, op. cit., (note 9), Pls 18 and 19.

43. Linda R. Shulsky, 'Kensington and de Voorst; two porcelain collections', *Journal of the History of Collections*, 2, No. 1, forthcoming 1990.
44. See Friedrich Reichel, *Early Japanese porcelain*, London, 1981. I am much indebted to Dr Reichel for information included here.
45. Reichel, op. cit., and Jean-Louis Sponsel, *Kabinettstücke der Meissner Porzellan-Manufactur von Johann Joachim Kändler*, Leipzig, 1900, illustration between pp. 19 and 20.

FIG. 16 Project drawing for a gallery in the Japanese Palace, Dresden. From the second series by Zacharius Longelune, 1735. Staatsarchiv, Dresden.

individual pots or small groups of pots with none of the repetitious line of the former drawing. Exceptionally, several of these pots are actually identifiable; in very few other designs for a porcelain room, or even depictions of an existing porcelain room was the artist actually familiar with the porcelain that was the model for the illustrations. One can quite clearly identify, for instance, the vases with the birdcage surround and elephant-head handles (see Fig. 17); no fewer than seven were to be displayed on two panels of wall.[46] The only other artist who seemed to care about the exact depiction of specific pieces of porcelain was Eosander von Göthe, whose engravings of Charlottenburg display certain carefully depicted pieces such as the two large Kakiemon-style figures of eagles (No. 172) and a few other identifiable pieces. Unfortunately, Salomon Kleiner did not take such care in his depictions of Pommersfelden, and no individual piece is identifiable.

The second drawing mentioned above[47] was to some extent a forerunner of the Rococo porcelain rooms where porcelain was a major part of the scheme of decoration, but not completely dominant. Photographs of the *Porzellankabinett* at Schloss Montbijou[48] show that the room had niches with brackets supporting porcelain, opposite windows. This was built by Johann Michael Hoppenhaupt the Elder in 1753–54 and is distinctly Rococo in arrangement and in detail.

Inventory books of the Dresden Collection were drawn up after 1721, and each piece was engraved with a number and with a category code-mark. The classification was crude and inaccurate in the extreme, resemblance being the main criterion for any class; thus both Chinese and Japanese blue-and-white were classified together as 'Old Indian' and marked with a wavy line code mark. Coloured Imari, which alone was recognised as Japanese at Dresden, bore a cross code mark and most of the Kakiemon wares were placed under 'Krack' porcelain (*kraak*), marked with an oblong! It is these numbers that are now referred to as 'Johanneum' numbers.

The collection, as John Mallet tells us in his

46. Reichel, op. cit., Pl. on pp. 120, 121.
47. Reichel, op. cit., Pl. on pp. 120, 121.
48 L. Reidemeister, 'Die Porzellankabinette der Brandenburgisch-Preuszischen Schlösser', Part 11, *Jahrbuch der Preuszischen Kunstsammlungen*, 55, 1934, pp. 42–56, Pl. 9.

Introduction (pp. 44–48), provided the models for the Meissen factory, just as the collection of the Prince de Condé provided the models for the Chantilly factory. Perhaps Augustus planned a room that was to be panelled in interlocking pieces specially made at Meissen. Such a room was made at Capodimonte between 1757 and 1759 for the royal villa at Portici for Carlo III, King of the Two Sicilies.[49] Now back at Capodimonte, it was made of some three thousand interlocking pieces. On accession to the throne of Spain in 1759, Carlo took the best artists from the Capodimonte factory to Buen Retiro where an even bigger room was made for the Aranjuez Palace. Hugh Honour has suggested that Gian Domenico Tiepolo may have been responsible for some of the design.

We have not, except in the strange case of the Santos Palace, and in the more normal case of Het Loo, discussed the ceiling of any porcelain room. In Germany, these were often painted, and the scene depicted may include porcelain of the type exhibited in the room. Occasionally porcelain is identifiable on other ceilings, too. On the huge vault of Balthasar Neumann's Grand Staircase in the Würzburg Residenz, Giovanni Battista Tiepolo painted a representation of the four continents which is signed and dated 1753. Here one of the figures included in the group of Africa holds up a jar very similar to the landscape jar shown here as No. 93, save that Tiepolo has altered the shape of the lid. But the most relevant case for us here is one of the ceilings at Oranienburg, where, in a small oval panel, three *putti* hold up an unmistakable Kakiemon-style vase of the same pattern as No. 138. [50] This is particularly useful for dating, as the ceiling was painted by Nicolai Augustin Terwesten before 1695; this makes it certain that this type of decoration is late 17th century. Other ceilings in the room depict Chinese porcelain.

Porcelain, whether Japanese or Chinese,

FIG. 17 Vase, porcelain with applied birdcage ornament, Japan, *c.* 1700, height 52 cm. Porzellansammlung, Dresden, PO 5181.

certainly represented Asia, but there was often some confusion over the country of origin, within Asia, of any single group of porcelain. We have already seen how Augustus the Strong, who should have known better, called blue-and-white 'old Indian' and only recognised brocaded Imari as Japanese. Where did he think Kakiemon came from? The Prince de Condé seems to have thought it was Korean, or at least he called it Korean.[51] New confusion was, of course, caused by the arrival in Europe of Chinese Imari, confusion that often persists today. The word Kakiemon does not seem to have appeared in

49. See Honour, op. cit., (note 18), Pl. 3 and pp. 123–24.
50. Reidemeister, op. cit., 1933, (note 16), p. 8.
51. Quoted in Reichel, op. cit., p. 126.

Europe until the beginning of this century. But both Kakiemon and Imari were usually acknowledged as Japanese in the 18th century, both by the imitators of Japanese porcelain, the new porcelain factories that were springing up all over Europe, and by collectors.

We have referred to Augustus the Strong as a collector; in reality he was an accumulator. Only to a greater degree was he different from the owners of great houses all over Europe for whom porcelain was a fashionable decorative material suitably exotic and rare for the status of the owner of such a house. The Prince-Bishop of Würzburg may have selected his pieces for Pommersfelden very carefully, and there is some evidence that other owners did so, too. At Burghley House there is an extraordinary series of small, shaped (that is, not round) blue-and-white Japanese dishes, varying in date over at least fifty years (Nos 34 and 62) that must have been chosen. Similar dishes, which are most rare, are or were to be found in other houses, in particular in Drayton House and in Welbeck Abbey[52] but rarely elsewhere. There are a few at Twickel Castle in Holland[53] (No. 126). We do not know on what basis or from what stock these pieces were selected. We have clear evidence of continued purchases by the Exeters for Burghley after 1688. In the sale from that house held by Christie's on 7th and 8th June, 1888, of 'Old Oriental Porcelain' under the category 'Old Japan Porcelain', lot 203 was 'A Pair Of Figures Of Ducks, with coloured plumage' and the following lot was 'A Pair Of Figures Of Tigers, on pedestals painted with plants – 9 1/4 in. high'. No duck or tigers appear in the 1688 Inventory, and as we can

safely assume that Culpepper Tanner would have been able to recognise both a tiger or a duck (even if the duck were an exotic species such as a mandarin) these must have been bought after 1688. Presumably they can be identified as similar or identical to Nos 168 and 171. Incidentally, No. 164 has been identified with the lot 206 in the same category in the same sale, one of 'A Pair Of Figures Of Ladies, with coloured drapery – 12 in. high'. There is insufficient evidence to identify these with the '1 Indian Queen' in 'My Lords Anty Roome' listed in the 1688 Inventory – after all, there was only one, not a pair.[54]

A collector who is known to have been active in the 18th century, and clearly did select carefully was Margaret, second Duchess of Portland. The sale of her collection, which took place after her death in 1786, lasted twenty-eight days.[55] Most of the collection was of sea-shells – another exotic oriental import – but there was also a large quantity of 'Fine Old China'. Few pieces are well enough described for identification to be more than a reasonable guess, but many of the pieces were 'brown edge Japan', in all probability Kakiemon. We can be fairly sure of lot 412 'A pair of fine old japan ducks' (No. 171, and see above), and of lot 421 'Two fine fluted japan dishes of the lion butterfly and sprigs,[56] and a pair of brown edge ditto with wheatsheaf and flowers'.[57] Lot 2388 was 'A capital octagon brown edge partridge dish' (No. 359), '2 smaller ditto, an octagon dish – Hob in the Well' (No. 122), and '2 fine brown edge plates'. Clearly the brown edge of the Kakiemon *nigoshide* was recognised as a hallmark of quality. Not all of the Duchess's collection was sold in 1786; at a sale in 1970, a

52. See Oliver Impey, 'Collecting Oriental Porcelains in Britain in the Seventeenth and Eighteenth Centuries' in *The Burghley Porcelains*, Japan Society, New York, 1980, pp. 36–43.

53. Information kindly given me by Dr C. J. A. Jörg.

54. *pace* Soame Jenyns, *Japanese Porcelain*, London, 1965, p. 125 and Pl. 55B.

55. The sale of 'The Portland Museum' was held by Mr Skinner 'At her [the Duchess's] late Dwelling House in *Privy-Garden, Whitehall*', not at Welbeck Abbey.

56. See Hinton and Impey, op. cit., (note 9) for a dish of this pattern at Burghley House. The pattern is also that on the covered jar in this exhibition No. 188.

57. This must refer to a 'banded hedge', a relatively common motif in Kakiemon porcelain in particular. See, e.g. Nos 124, 126 and 131 in this exhibition.

58. Jenyns, op. cit., p. 7 and Pl. 8.

large quantity of Japanese blue-and-white, much of it remarkably similar to pieces at Burghley, was sold from Welbeck Abbey (No. 61).

A testament to the Duchess's passion for collecting still exists in the form of a remarkable plate at Melbury,[58] a blue-and-white plate of about 1700, possibly from the Kakiemon kiln, on the back of which is stuck a label, said to date from the 1760s, reading 'Plate bid for at a sale & obtained by Elisabeth Countess of Ilchester against the Duchess of Portland & which was carefully put away when the Duchess visited her for fear of recalling the fact'. Underneath is added in pencil in another hand '+ for £100', an addition which may well be spurious. Clearly the reputation of the Duchess as a collector was formidable.

Japanese export porcelain has been accumulated and collected, displayed and neglected, copied, sold, stolen, broken, mended and loved for three centuries and more. Prized first for its colour and then for its vigour of decoration, it was the height of fashion for some eighty years, until economic realities forced it out of the European market. So much was first Kakiemon and then Imari copied and adapted that it was not long before its oriental origin was all but forgotten. Japanese design had become so much part of the European world that it was accepted as vaguely 18th century taste (and therefore 'good' taste), with no-one bothering about its derivation. Only in the late 19th century, with the contemporary passion for accuracy, did anyone bother to enquire from whence came this lovely porcelain. As this exhibition will show, the effect of Japanese porcelain in Europe was so profound that its results are around us all the time.

I The Early European Trade with Japan

Portuguese first arrived by chance in Japan in 1543, and soon after, in 1547, they were able to set up their entrepôt at Macao (close to modern Hong Kong). From here they dominated the East Asian trade with Europe, challenged only late in the century by the Spanish operating from the Philippines. In 1549 St Francis Xavier (though himself a Spaniard) led Portuguese Jesuit missionaries from Goa via Macao to Japan. Large numbers of Christian converts, perhaps as many as a million, were made in Western Japan by them and by rival Spanish Franciscans. While increasing Portuguese influence for the time being, it proved to be their undoing when Christianity was totally banned in 1639.

The Portuguese sailed mainly to Kagoshima and Nagasaki in Kyūshū (No. 1). They introduced tobacco to Japan, and imported it as it gained instant popularity; they also introduced guns, which the Japanese soon began to make with far-reaching military effects. But the main import was always silk, for which there was an inexhaustible demand in the densely populated islands, where textiles and especially silk were crucially prestigious. The Portuguese were interested mainly in trade in precious metals, which were mined in Japan, and helped finance the lucrative spice trade in other parts of Asia.

Yet culturally it was the relatively small trade in Japanese lacquered wares which was to have the longer-lasting effects. Europeans had no equivalent to lacquer, with its durability, lightness and brilliant gloss, and particularly admired the application of gold dust and leaf (*maki-e*) and inlaying of mother-of-pearl in which the Japanese were acknowledged masters. 'Japanned' chests, escritoires, mugs and other items in European shapes were imported in large numbers, the trade being joined in the early 17th century by the English and the Dutch (Nos 2, 3 and 4), who finally gained the upper hand. Through all this period, the Europeans were in competition with the Chinese and the Japanese themselves, but were able to do business with them successfully in China and South-East Asia.

The Dutch East India Company (V.O.C.) was founded in 1602, and was allowed to act virtually as the navy and the Colonial Office of the Dutch government in Asia (Nos 5 to 7). It set up its great entrepôt, port and local headquarters in Batavia (Jakarta) on the island of Java in 1622 (No. 9). Also from 1622–62 it had a strong trade presence in Taiwan (Formosa) and from 1637 negotiated trading rights in Tongkin. With good access to silk, acute administration, and seamanship and shipbuilding skills becoming the best in Europe, the Company was able to take over much of the South-East and East Asian trade, including Japan.

As the Portuguese and Christianity fell out of favour in Japan, the Dutch, who had already seen off the British hampered by a lack of access to silk, grew in influence at their station on Hirado. Japanese government policy then played into their hands. Between the years 1633–39, a series of edicts expelled all foreign Roman Catholics, shut down the Japanese ocean-going marine, forbade Japanese to travel abroad, and totally proscribed Christianity. In 1639 the Portuguese were finally eliminated, and the policy of *sakoku* – 'the closed country' – continued until 1854. Only the Dutch and the Chinese traders were permitted on the mainland, and in 1641 these were confined to Nagasaki (Nos 10 to 14).

From 1641 to 1854, the Dutch alone of Europeans had access to Japan. As Protestants with apparently no colonial designs on Japanese territory, they were tolerated in small numbers, but were nevertheless closely guarded and watched. Their main import continued to be silk, and their main export copper, but their real interest was in a complex import/export operation with gold and silver, making skilful use of the differences of price of these commodities in various parts of Asia and Europe. They continued also to export the much-admired lacquers in quantity well into the 18th century.

From the beginning of the Japanese porcelain industry in Kyūshū around A.D. 1600, the Chinese and Japanese were exporting relatively simple products to Southern China and South-East Asia. Chinese porcelain of much higher quality was still coming into Japan, but this was stopped in the 1630s, thus giving a boost to the young Japanese industry. Thus it was that when the supply of fine Chinese porcelain to Europe (handled also by the Portuguese and Dutch successively) was interrupted in the 1650s, the Company turned to Japan for a new supply. Up to 1683, as described in the Introduction pp. 15–24, most of this was shipped directly from Nagasaki to Holland by the Company, but after that the trade fell more into the hands of private individuals; while the Chinese merchants, who had never in fact stopped shipping Japanese porcelain, began to take it in larger quantities to Canton and Macao where it could be sold to ships of other European countries – hence the direct arrival in 1704 in London (No. 16). By 1723, the Dutch Company itself had virtually stopped shipping Japanese porcelain except as lower-grade utensils and everyday wares for Batavia and for selling in South-East Asia. The Company was dissolved in 1799, and taken over by the government of the Netherlands who continued to monopolize the direct Japanese trade until 1854.

L.R.H.S.

I

The Arrival of a Portuguese Ship at Nagasaki

Folding screen, ink and colours with gold leaf on paper
Japan, late 16th–early 17th century
Height 158 cm; width 366 cm
(painted area 141 cm by 348 cm)
Victoria and Albert Museum, London, 803–1892.

This is the surviving left-hand screen of a pair. Complete sets normally have a right-hand screen showing a scene on shore, often including Jesuit missionaries and a Christian chapel. Here the visitors are seen on their ship and also loading or unloading goods, which are unfortunately not clearly identifiable. The Portuguese are distinguished in Japanese eyes by their huge noses and balloon-like pantaloons. To Western eyes, the painting is dominated by the great bands of gold cloud (filled in with squares of gold leaf) separating areas of blue representing water, but these are simply decorative conventions of the Kanō School of painters, whose lesser masters often executed these so-called *Namban* screens. They seem to have been produced in relatively large numbers before the expulsion of the missionaries and the Portuguese themselves in the period 1633–39.

LITERATURE: J. Ayers, 1983, pp. 46–47.

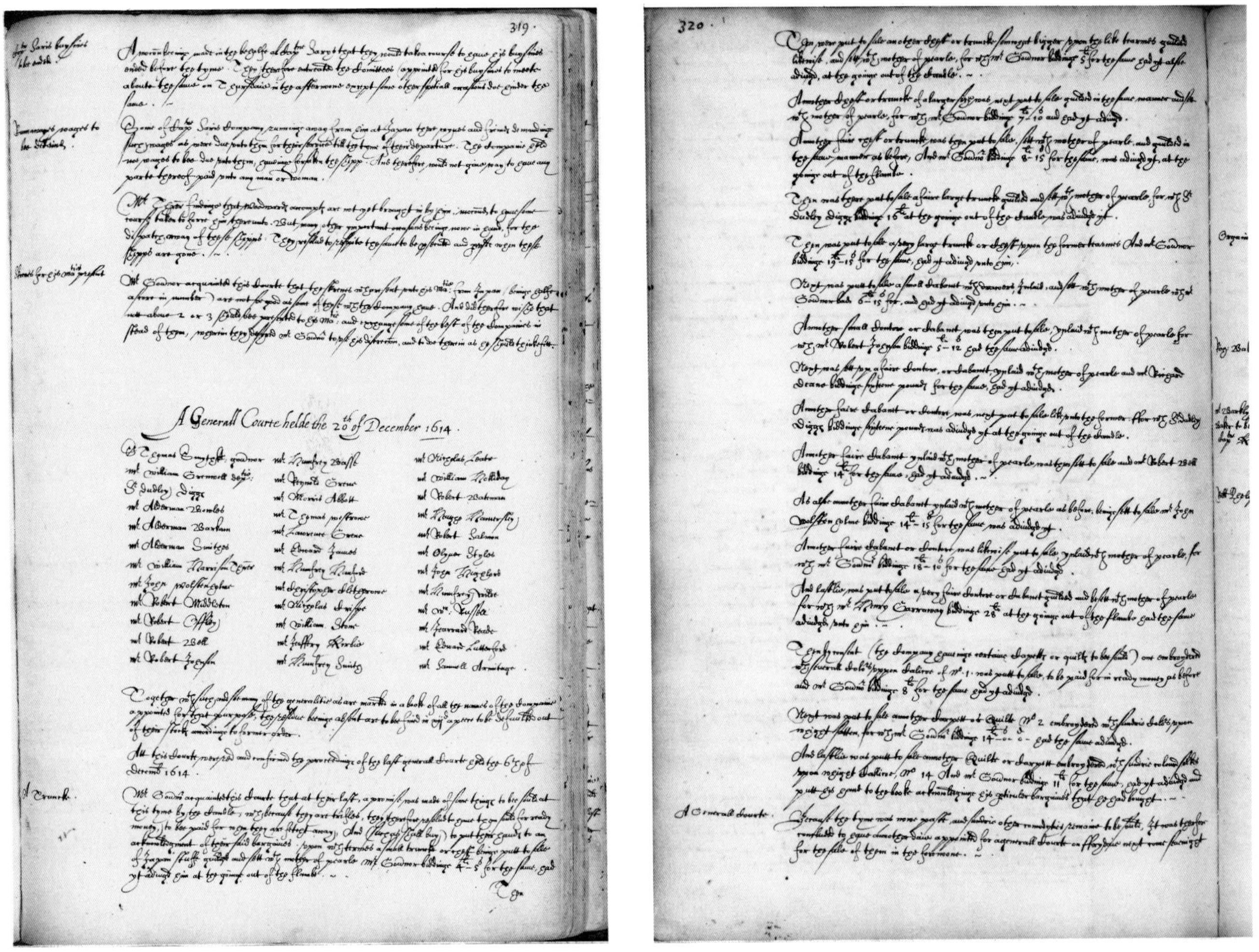
319
A Generall Courte helde the 20th of December 1614
320

2

Minutes of the Court of the Company Merchants of London, 20th December 1614

Height 46 cm; width 33 cm (closed), 68 cm (open)
India Office Library and Records, B/5.

Following the return from Japan of Captain John Saris of the English East India Company in 1614, the Minutes (p. 320 – illustrated) record various gilt lacquer 'trunks' decorated with mother-of-pearl. These are the first recorded commercial import of Japanese material into England.

3
Lacquer Cabinet of Drawers
Wood covered in black lacquer and decorated in gold
maki-e and mother-of-pearl inlay
Japan, *c.* 1620
Height 57 cm; depth 44 cm; length 85.5 cm
British Museum, JA 1977, 4–6, 1.

This is a drop-fronted cabinet, with drawers, decorated
overall with dense designs of birds, flowers, trees and
long-armed monkeys and with borders of geometric
patterns. These designs conform to the basic florid
Namban style also found on religious objects ordered
originally by the Portuguese in the late 16th century, and
continued on secular exports through them and the
Dutch from 1610 onwards. Cabinets arrived in the
Netherlands in that year, in London in 1614, and
continued to be imported throughout the century.
Frequently found in English country houses, they were
sometimes used to stand porcelain on. This piece
originally had its own legs (probably added in Europe),
but now stands on a replacement table.

4
Tankard with Cover

Wood covered in black lacquer and decorated in gold *hiramaki-e* lacquer with inlay; with silvered mother-of-pearl hinge and thumb-piece
Japan, 1610–20, with later European restorations
Height 18.5 cm
Victoria and Albert Museum, London, FE.23–1982.

With tapering sides, spreading foot, bent loop handle and stepped domed cover with ball finial. The painted designs incorporate maple, mandarin orange, Chinese bellflower, morning-glory and grapevine.

The Diary of Richard Cocks, who was head of the English factory in Japan, records that in December 1617 he presented his Dutch opposite number with '1 tankard maky work': ('*maki-e*' being the Japanese technique of gold-sprinkled lacquer decoration). This is the only surviving example of what must have been a relatively common type.

LITERATURE: N. Murakami, 1899, p. 337; J. Earle, 1983, pp. 24–27.

5
The Amsterdam Headquarters of the Dutch East India Company

Engraving
Late 17th century
Rijksprentenkabinet, Rijksmuseum, Amsterdam, 1925–609.

The importance of the V.O.C. as a semi-official administrator of the Dutch Colonial empire is embodied in the grandeur of their headquarters.

LITERATURE: F. M. Wieringa, 1982, Pl. 2.

6
The Amsterdam Dockyard of the Dutch East India Company

Engraving
1692, or shortly after
Rijksprentenkabinet, Rijksmuseum, Amsterdam, FM 2301–19A.

The scene is precisely dated to 1690, and shows a new ship under construction. Unfortunately, a fire broke out which severely damaged its stern, and because of Pentecost the fire was not brought under control in time. Continuing advances in ship design by the Dutch enabled them to keep ahead of their rivals in the Asian trade.

LITERATURE: F. M. Wieringa, 1982, p. 140.

7
Model of the *Dolfijn* on a scale of 1/44

Netherlands, c. 1778
Length 137 cm; height 115 cm; width 66 cm
National Maritime Museum, Greenwich.

This model of a Dutch East India Company merchantman of about 1778 is contemporary with the original ship. Being a cargo vessel, it was exceptionally wide in relation to its length, but still carried 18 9lb guns. Although there were continual changes in European ship design, the basic design philosophy is not substantially different from that of the vessels which carried porcelain at the height of the trade in the late 17th century. In this model, much of the rigging was replaced in 1929.

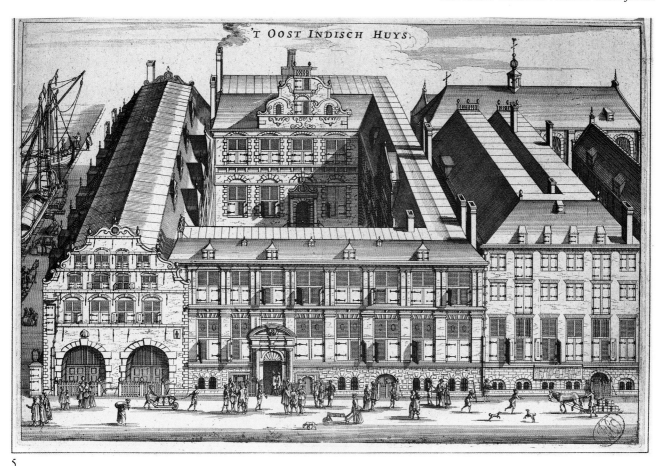

'T OOST INDISCH HUYS.

5

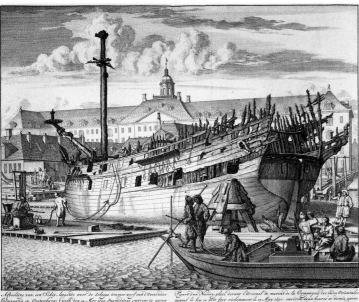

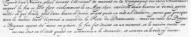

6

7

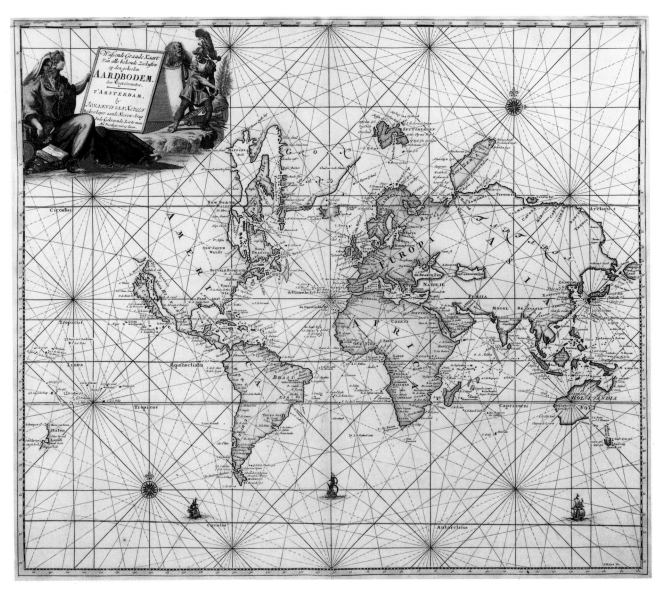

8

World Map ('*Aardbodem*')
Engraving with hand colouring, by Johannes van Keulen
Amsterdam, 1682
Height 51.5 cm; width 60 cm
British Library, Map Library, 7, TAB, 84.B.

This is from van Keulen's *Sea Atlas* of 1682. It shows
very good knowledge of the coasts from the Netherlands
round Africa to the East Indies, China, Taiwan, and
Kyūshū, but the northern parts of Japan and beyond are
not well understood.

9

Batavia from the Sea
Engraving with hand-colouring, by Johannes Vingboons
Amsterdam, *c.* 1660
Height 41.5 cm; length 92.5 cm
Algemeen Rijksarchief, The Hague, VELH 619–32.

Batavia (Jakarta) was the greatest entrepôt of the Dutch
East India Company in Asia, and was vital to their trade
with China and later Japan. In this print, the offing is
shown full of Dutch ships.

LITERATURE: Berlin, 1985, No. 5/7, p. 233.

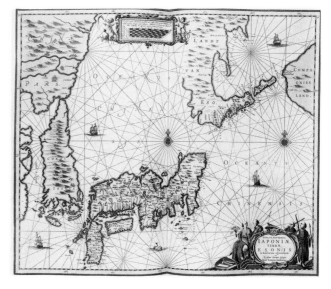

10

**Map of Japan ('*Nova et Accurata Japoniae Terrae
Esonis…*')**
Engraving, by Jan Jansson
Amsterdam, 1659
Height 45.5 cm; length 55 cm
British Library, Map Library, 9 TAB 24.

This Dutch map is from almost the exact year of the
beginning of the trade of Japanese porcelain to Europe.
Honshū, Shikoku and Kyūshū are moderately well
understood, and Nagasaki is named on the West Coast
of the latter. But the northern island of Hokkaidō seems
attached to the mainland, 'Compagnies Land' is a vast
enlargement of some small islands, and Korea is shown
almost as a peninsula.

11

Woodblock printed Map of Nagasaki

Japan, *c.* 1680
Height 30.5 cm; length 61 cm
British Library, OMPB. 75.9.25.

The small Dutch trading settlement on the artificial fan-shaped island of Deshima can be seen at centre, also the Chinese station on the outskirts of the city, at left. The harbour shows Dutch and Chinese vessels among its shipping. The map includes an inset with figures of foreigners, among them Dutch and Chinese, and a table of distances to several other countries, the furthest being Holland. The map was brought back to Europe from Nagasaki by the physician Englebert Kaempfer, who was attached to the Dutch Factory there in the years 1690–92.

LITERATURE: J. Elliot, 1987, No. 19.

13

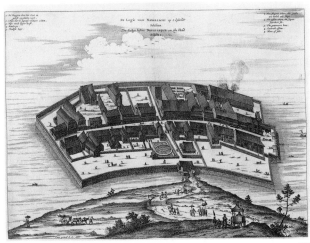

12

12

View of Deshima Island
Engraving from Arnoldus Montanus, *Atlas Japonnensis, being remarkable addresses by way of embassy from the East-India Company of the United Provinces, to the Emperor of Japan, containing a description of their . . . territories, cities, temples and fortresses, their religions, laws and customs . . . englished by J. Ogilby*, London, 1670
British Library, 457, F.12.

This is from the English edition of the Dutch original published in 1669. The engraving gives a clearer view than the Japanese map (No. 11) of the layout of the Dutch Factory, but the 'oriental' carriage and figures in the foreground are fantasy and unrelated to real Japanese life. It should be noted that the 'Emperor of Japan' in the title was in fact the Shogun, whom the Dutch mistook for the head of state.

13

Scenes of life at the Dutch Factory at Deshima
Long handscroll in ink and colours on silk
Nagasaki School, late 18th century
Height 33 cm
British Museum, JA, ADD 170.

Between 1641 and 1854, Dutch traders were the only Europeans permitted in Japan. Their activities in their Factory at Nagasaki came under constant close scrutiny by the Shoguns' officials stationed in the city, and were recorded by official painters. This very lively series is probably the work of such an artist, for others would not have had sufficient access to provide such detail.

14

15

14

Scenes of life at the Chinese Settlement at Nagasaki
Long handscroll in ink and colours on silk
Nagasaki School, late 18th century
Height 33 cm
British Museum, JA, ADD 171

This is a pair to the above. The Chinese traders were allowed more freedom, and lived on shore. From the late 17th century they played an increasingly important role in the export of Japanese porcelain to ports in China and South-East Asia. In the section of this scroll illustrated, they are seen buying blue-and-white wares from the Japanese traders decorated in the simple scrolled pattern called *karakusa*. These were not fine enough porcelains for the European market, and were made for Japanese use or export to adjacent Asian countries.

15

Andō Hiroshige (1797–1858)
The Kiyomi Temple at Okitsu
Colour woodblock print (No. 18 from a series of views along the Tōkaidō route) *c.* 1847–51
Height 23 cm; length 36 cm
British Museum, JA 1906 12–20, 833.

Under the proclamations closing the country (completed 1639), Japanese were no longer allowed to build or operate large ocean-going vessels. Because of the geography of Japan, however, coastal trade became ever more important in the smaller ships of the sort shown in this print, which would have helped transport porcelain from the port of Imari to Nagasaki. By the early 19th century, most porcelain was in fact shipped for the internal trade, and coastal vessels would often have passed Mt Fuji on their way to or from Edo.

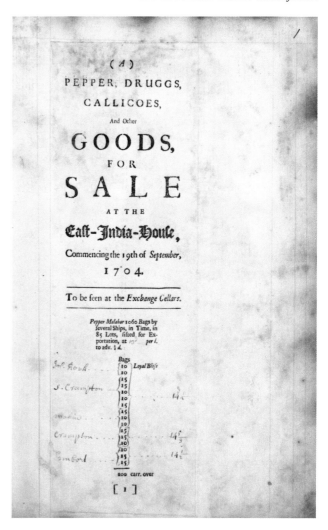

16

Sale Catalogue at East India House, London, 19th September 1704, of goods from the *Fleet* frigate
Sheet size, height 40 cm; width 25 cm
India Office Library and Records, H/11.

In the sale catalogue the section 'China and Japan-Ware' gives a surprising glimpse of the quantities of porcelain then being imported. Nearly 40,000 'Brown Tea Cups', presumably Chinese, are listed. By this period, the Chinese porcelain industry had revived, and was beginning to take back the European market, whilst what Japanese porcelain did still arrive mainly came via Chinese ports. Things specifically described as Japanese on these pages include nests of covered bowls with dishes, 'scollop' sugar bowls with dishes, flasks with stoppers, barbers' basins, beakers and 'garden pots'.

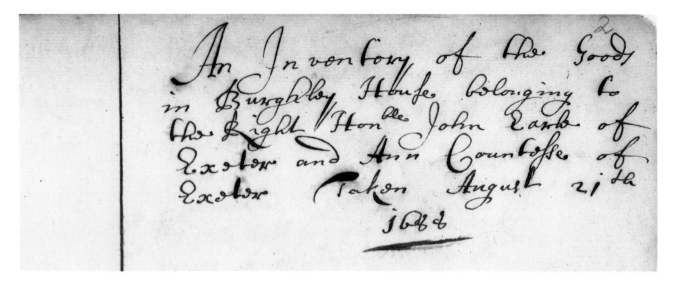

17
Burghley House Inventory of 1688
The Inventory was at a late date bound in a book
Height 31 cm; width 21 cm; depth 2 cm
The Burghley House Collection, Stamford, Lincolnshire.

The 1688 Inventory was drawn up by Culpepper
Tanner, personal secretary to the 5th Earl of Devonshire.
It is the earliest known inventory describing Japanese and
blanc-de-Chine porcelains, which were apparently
acquired by Tanner in Europe; and provides important
evidence for the dating of porcelains that can be
identified in it – some of which appear in this exhibition.
Illustrated here are the title and a relevant extract. See
the Introduction by Oliver Impey, pp. 63 and 68.

LITERATURE: G. Lang, 1983, Introduction and jacket
where papers from the Inventory are illustrated.

II *Shoki-Imari*: The Early Porcelain of Arita

The term '*shoki-Imari*' covers those porcelains made at Arita before the beginning of the export trade in the mid 17th century. The earliest Arita porcelains were, as we have seen, made in Karatsu kilns. These early pieces were mostly blue-and-white, though celadon (No. 19) and iron-brown (No. 27) as well as combinations of the colours began very soon; these blue-and-white pieces, mostly bowls and dishes, were decorated in a style that reflects their Karatsu, and hence, ultimately, their Korean origin. To that extent the style can justifiably be called, as it is in Japan, 'Korean', but only to that extent.

The early patterns were landscapes (No. 20), often very perfunctory, or flowers and grasses, to be followed by geometric patterns often of striking individuality (Nos 25 and 26). Much of the blue-and-white was closely akin to the Chinese Tianqi porcelain (called in Japan *ko-sometsuke*, or old blue-and-white; No. 24) and there is some argument as to whether the Japanese *shoki-Imari* copied Tianqi styles or whether the Chinese competed with existing Japanese styles for the domestic market in Japan. Whichever of these possibilities is true, and it is logical to assume it to be the latter, the Chinese and Japanese porcelains, competing for the same market, influenced each other.

Most pieces of *shoki-Imari* were of modest size, due in part to inadequacies of the kiln furniture available, being mostly plates, bowls, cups and bottles, though other shapes are not uncommon. A few kilns could make larger pieces (No. 28). Some kilns specialized in certain types: Hirose, for instance, made bottles decorated in underglaze red (No. 22), Yamagoya made unique shapes in iron-brown (No. 27) and in celadon. On the whole, however, most things were made at most kilns, though there is some grouping of kilns either by location or by similarity of products, and, of course, there is a clear evolution of styles.

Before the beginnings of the trade to Europe, there had been some limited export of Arita porcelain to South-East Asia. Much of this was in the form of large celadon dishes (No. 29), which seem to have been much in demand as substitutes for the Zhejiang celadons they so closely resemble. Many of these celadons were made at a kiln called Maruo, and it seems more than probable that Maruo and one or two other kilns were exporting enamelled wares to the same market in the late 1640s, the earliest Japanese overglaze wares. Towards the middle of the century, *shoki-Imari* wares joined the ranks of those ceramics deemed suitable for use in the tea ceremony, and pieces such as *mizusashi* ('water jars') and incense burners were made specifically for tea ceremony use. Dishes (No. 23) and plates were also made for use in the *kaiseki* meal that accompanied a formal tea ceremony. Much more commonly, ordinary things, more or less for every-day use, were in the generally accepted tea taste.

In the great reorganisation of the Arita kilns at the time of the first large Dutch orders, some kilns ceased production, others amalgamated and others made export and non-export wares concurrently.

O. R. I.

18
Twelve sherds of Arita porcelain and Karatsu stoneware
Japan, *c.* 1620–50
Ashmolean Museum, Oxford.

These sherds were collected from kiln sites at Arita and represent different styles in the work of a number of factories. A stack of dishes of Karatsu-type stoneware fused to a porcelain dish, and so fired with it in the same kiln, makes the point that this form of pottery manufacture was common at Arita before the introduction of porcelain-making.

19
Celadon-glazed Jar
Japan, *c.* 1620–30
Height 15 cm
Ashmolean Museum, Oxford, 1987.34, Story Fund.

An oviform jar with faceted sides and straight neck, covered in a dark, uneven celadon glaze; the interior mainly with a colourless glaze.

20
Blue-and-white Plate
Japan, *c.* 1630
Diameter 19.2 cm
Mark: *Da Ming* in Chinese characters.
Private Collection.

A flat plate with outward-curving rim. Painted in the centre is a river landscape with a temple and mountain peaks, surrounded by a floral-scroll border. The back is boldly decorated with trailing plants.

19

20

21

Blue-and-white Saké Bottle

Japan, *c.* 1640–50
Height 15 cm
Ashmolean Museum, Oxford, 1989.11, Story Fund.

A bottle with tapering, fluted sides and small flared neck
with gold lacquer repair. Each facet is painted with a
column of seven *fuku* ('good luck') characters and round
the shoulder is a fretted border.

Sherds of bottles of this type have been found at
Tenjinmori kiln.

22

Underglaze red Oil Bottle

Japan, *c.* 1620–40
Height 13 cm
Private Collection.

A squat globular bottle with narrow neck (repaired) and
slightly flared rim. It is painted in underglaze red with
two circumferential bands and roughly-drawn grasses.

Sherds of these bottles have been found at Hirose kiln.
The underglaze red of Arita was never very successful
and was not much used; occasionally it occurs with
underglaze blue.

23
Blue-and-white Peach-shaped Dish

Japan, *c.* 1650
Width 30 cm
Ashmolean Museum, Oxford, 1987·10, gift of Mr
Motosuke Imaizumi.

A peach-shaped dish with slightly fluted vertical sides,
turned-out rim and small foot. Boldly painted in the
centre are two sages and an outsize bird in a tree; round
the well is a chrysanthemum-scroll border and on the
rim a formal pattern. On the outside are leafy sprays.

24
Small blue-and-white Dish

Japan, *c.* 1630−40
Width max. 16.5 cm
Mark: commendation mark within a square.
Private Collection.

A small dish shaped as the presentation paper for a bunch
of chrysanthemum. The paper is folded twice, with one
fold decorated with a landscape and the other with a
geometric pattern and several *mon*. The flowers are
moulded and left white and overlap the edge, where
their petals are touched with iron-brown; two insects
are painted in blue. The back is decorated with three
leafy sprays.

24

25

25

Small blue-and-white Plate

Japan, *c.* 1640
Diameter 15 cm
Private Collection.

A small plate with flat petalled rim decorated with florets reserved on a blue ground. In the centre is a formalised lotus flower with a geometric pattern at its heart.

Sherds of this pattern have been found at Tenjinmori kiln site.

26

Blue-and-white Dish

Japan, *c.* 1650–60
Diameter 20.5 cm
Private Collection.

A dish with shallow, curving sides and a brown-glazed rim. The centre is divided in two by a zig-zag line, one half being painted with a geometrical diaper pattern overlaid with half-chrysanthemums and the other with two interlocking circles in pale and dark blue, all within a cash-pattern border. On the back are simple sprigs.

27

Bowl decorated in blue and brown

Japan, *c.* 1630
Diameter 15 cm
Ashmolean Museum, Oxford, 1986·7, Story Fund.

A shallow conical bowl with a wavy rim and high foot. It is covered with a speckled, rather matt brown glaze both outside and inside, where an asymmetrically-placed reserve panel contains an abstract plant pattern painted in blue.

Sherds of identical pieces have been found at Yamagoya kiln site.

28

Large blue-and-white Dish

Japan, *c.* 1650
Diameter 35 cm
Ashmolean Museum, Oxford, 1985·33, Story Fund.

A plain saucer dish, painted asymmetrically across its surface with a bold, rush-like plant and with clouds. On the back are perfunctory leaves.

Sherds of dishes of this type have been found at Maruo kiln site.

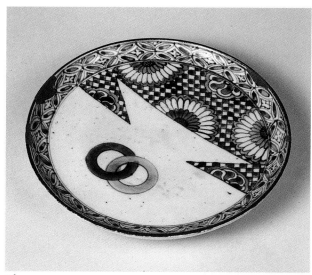

26

27

28

29
Large celadon Dish
Japan, *c.* 1650
Diameter 47 cm
Private Collection.

A heavily-potted celadon-glazed dish with flat spreading
rim. It is decorated in the centre with an incised design
of peonies framed by a ring of elongated key-fret
segments. Round the rim is a border of plant sprays.
There is an unglazed ring burnt brown within the foot.

Probably from Maruo kiln.

III Blue-and-white

When the Dutch turned to Japan for the supply of porcelain to be traded in South-East Asia and in Europe, they did so for reasons of choice; they could obtain coloured porcelain and they could order the shapes and decoration they wanted. Naturally enough a great part of what they ordered was to be as a substitute for the porcelain that they had, up until then, been obtaining from China. This had mostly been blue-and-white and had been in the two styles current then, the Wanli style (*kraak porselein* in Europe, *fuyo-de* in Japan) or the Transitional style. The *kraak* style had a central motif surrounded by a segmented border on dishes (No. 31); and three cartouches enclosed by borders on jars (No. 54); the Transitional style was characterised, in the Japanese version, by strange elongated human figures and 'bottle-brush' trees (Nos 37 and 38). It is noticeable that Wanli patterns are most commonly found on plates and dishes and relatively rarely appear on closed shapes, while Transitional styles predominate on closed shapes such as mugs, jugs and bottles, themselves frequently of European form.

A rapid development of these styles in Japan produced the curious hybrids and extensions of the styles, often boldly and excitingly painted, that are a feature of the early blue-and-white export wares and, indeed, of the coloured wares too. Sometimes a wholly Japanese pattern would appear within a segmented border, sometimes a standard Wanli pattern would appear in a *karakusa* ('octopus tendril') scrolling pattern or similar border. Finally the decoration might show no direct Chinese ancestry at all; this was because of the continuation of the *shoki-Imari* tradition into the early phases of the export wares, parallel with the Chinese influences.

Most of the shapes of export blue-and-white were utilitarian shapes ordered from Holland or from the other factories of the V.O.C. throughout Asia. Shapes and patterns therefore would reflect local demand and local tastes; it is possible to recognise, sometimes, pieces made for India by the Mogul flavour of their patterning and, of course, the ubiquitous *kendi* shape (No. 91) is an Islamic one. What is surprising is how often such pieces turn up in the wrong context; there are many *kendi* in Europe. Many of the actual shapes seem to have been taken from wooden models, which had presumably been painted by Delft pottery painters, rather than from either Chinese or European original ceramics.

Japanese blue-and-white of the export period can be seen, in this exhibition, to have varied from the bold or crude (No. 42) to the highly sophisticated (No. 62). In all its forms it seems remarkably distinct from any contemporary Chinese porcelain. The decoration tends to be strong (No. 47) rather than careful, the designs striking and asymmetrical (No. 60) rather than illustrative or repetitive.

Shades of blue could be made by overpainting underglaze blue on underglaze blue (No. 126), or reserve patterns made by resist techniques (No. 61), both methods of decoration being much used for borders in particular. The brown edge, found on both coloured and blue-and-white Kakiemon, was used at other kilns, too, and designs were likewise used at more than one kiln, suggesting either competition or collaboration. A Kakiemon style in blue-and-white is recognised from its similarity to the enamelled wares and from the evidence of kiln site material (No. 133); but at the kiln site are also found many pieces of blue-and-white that would not usually be recognised as Kakiemon.

Sometimes European painted or printed originals were used, more or less adapted, as the basis for designs; among the most common is the so-called 'Deshima Island' pattern, not Deshima at all but a Dutch landscape probably adapted from a number of prints (No. 67). A series of small shaped dishes and small cups imitate Delft tin-glazed wares associated with the painter Frederik van Frytom; these have European scenes, and use a particular way of depicting clouds by a series of outline loops (No. 69). Most famous of all, perhaps is 'the lady with the parasol' after drawings by Cornelis Pronk sent to Japan in 1736 (No. 70). Pronk was commissioned to produce several designs; while these were duly copied in China, only 'the lady with the parasol' was copied in Japan, in colours as well as in blue-and-white. This may give some indication of the decline of the Dutch involvement in the Japanese porcelain trade, which was to peter out in the late 1740s, defeated by the technical and commercial superiority of Jingdezhen.

O. R. I.

30
Drug Jar
Japan, mid 17th century
Height 26.5 cm
Private Collection.

A jar of Western *albarello* drug-jar shape with everted lip and spreading foot. Painted on one side are a horned satyr's head, floral scrolls and swags and a shell surrounding an empty scroll; presumably designed to name the contents of the jar.

Jars for the apothecary's shop in Batavia are listed in the purchases of the V. O. C. in Arita in 1652; possibly they were of the *albarello* shape. Sherds of *albarello* that imitate Dutch models have been found at Sarugawa and Shimoshirakawa kiln sites. This type has not been found, nor is the European model precisely known.

LITERATURE: O. Impey, 1985, pp. 267–73 and Pl. 105; O. Impey, 1989, Pl. 3.

31
Dish
Japan, 1660–80
Diameter 40.7 cm
Private Collection.

A dish with broad flat rim. Painted in the centre is a deer between two clumps of lotus with chrysanthemum and other plants, a butterfly above and a ground half striped and half patterned below, the broad border containing four panels with flower sprays and four alternately with precious emblems among scrollwork, separated by ornamental tassels.

This dish presents a simplified version of the type of design found on the *kraak porselein* dishes that were exported in such numbers to the West from China earlier in the century. The Dutch had turned to the Japanese kilns when this trade collapsed, following the fall of the Ming dynasty in 1644. It is intriguing to see the liberties taken with these now out-of-date designs.

LITERATURE: Fraeylemaborg, 1977, No. 249.

32

Large Dish

Japan, 1660–80

Diameter 39.5 cm

Ashmolean Museum, Oxford,

1976.59.

A large dish with wide spreading rim. Painted in the centre is the monogram VOC (for *Vereenigde Oostindische Compagnie*) surrounded by two phoenixes, fruiting peach and camellia; the rim is divided into six panels alternately with bamboo and peony.

It is always assumed that dishes with the VOC monogram, or with subsidiary monograms such as NVOC, were for Company use; nowhere is this documented. Sherds bearing the monogram have been found at three kiln sites in Arita.

33

Large Dish

Japan, 1660–80

Diameter 34.3 cm

Mark: VOC monogram within a circle

British Museum, JA 1961, 12–12, 5.

A deep saucer-shaped dish painted in a purplish underglaze blue with fruiting branches of pomegranate and 'Buddha's hand' or finger citron and with a small monogram, VOC (for *Vereenigde Oostindische Compagnie*) in the centre. On the reverse are three peach sprays. The VOC monogram is repeated on the base.

LITERATURE: London, Royal Academy of Arts, 1981, No. 211.

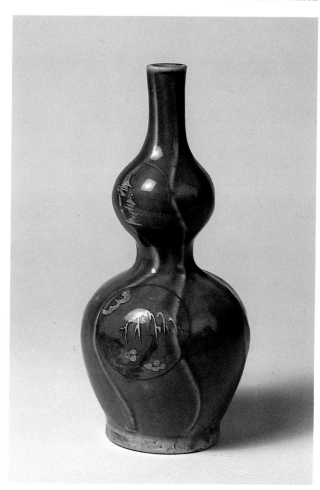

34
Small Dish
Japan, 1660–80
Diameter 10.8 cm
The Burghley House Collection, Stamford,
Lincolnshire.

A *mukozuke* or food dish of irregular scalloped form
resembling a peony flower, and decorated in shallow
relief with chrysanthemum flowers floating on a stream
in white reserved on a swastika-diaper ground washed
with blue.

Small dishes shaped in a variety of unusual and ingenious
forms were very popular in Japan for use in connection
with the tea ceremony and related functions and a number
of these evidently reached Europe (see also Nos 61 and 62).
Dishes identical to this have been found at the
Cho-kichi-dani kiln site. See K. Ohashi, 1989, pp. 7–42,
Pl. 66–16 and O. Impey, 1989, Pls 5 and 6 where it is
demonstrated that such pieces were found fused in kiln
accidents to Wanli-style dishes of the early period.

LITERATURE: G. Lang, 1983, No. 12; New York, Japan
Society, 1986, No. 33.

35
Blue-glazed Double Gourd Bottle
Japan, 1660–70
Height 18.7 cm
British Museum, JA FRANKS 1240+.

A small dark blue-glazed bottle with five spiral ribs
running down its sides. It is decorated in red enamel,
silver and gilt with five medallions showing river scenes,
willows and a pagoda.

The silver pigment is tarnished black. Zacharias Wagenaer,
who was Principal in Japan for the Dutch East India
Company, wrote in his report of 10th December, 1659:

…I had contracted with a certain person for about 200
pieces after my own invention, to be made curiously, on
a blue ground with small silver tendrilwork…But seeing
later that all corners and shops were filled with them and
that they were now as common as grass I have taken less
of them…(T. Volker, 1954, p. 136).

Could this be the origin of the Chinese 'powder blue' of
the Kangxi period?

36
Blue-glazed Jug with Silver-gilt Mount
Japan, 1660–70
Height 15.5 cm
Groninger Museum, Groningen, 1981·1031.

A pear-shaped jug with slender neck spreading to a cup-shaped mouth with pinched spout, and a high loop handle. It is covered in a dark blue glaze overpainted in gilt with floral motifs and rocks.

The rim is mounted in contemporary silver-gilt to accommodate a small lid with leaf-moulding border and bud finial which is attached to the handle by a fitment with shell thumb-piece.

Blue-glazed wares (Nos 35 and 36) figured among the earliest Japanese porcelains shipped to Europe.

LITERATURE: C. J. A. Jörg, 1984, No. 58.

37
Jar
Japan, 1660–80
Height 24.5 cm
Private Collection.

An oviform jar with short neck. Round the sides in somewhat purplish-grey blue is a roughly-painted landscape in Chinese 'Transitional' style broken on either side by towering crags, with two sketchy seated figures and one standing among rocks and brush-like pines, a palm and another taller tree, with areas of mist left white; round the neck is a dentate border.

As on much blue-and-white ware belonging to this group, the painting is a fairly crude travesty of the more accomplished Chinese style. Compare the Dutch delftware jar (No. 271) which has this distinctive shape and the same subjects of decoration, also the bowl (No. 272) with date 1665.

38
'Rollwagon' Vase
Japan, 1660–80
Height 28.5 cm
The Burghley House Collection, Stamford, Lincolnshire.

A tall cylindrical vase with constricted neck and open mouth. It is painted in greyish blue in a style derived from Chinese Transitional porcelain, with two scenes of robed figures sitting or standing in a rock-strewn landscape among pine trees, bamboo and clouds. The neck is decorated with lappets and spearheads.

The so-called 'rollwagon' shape deriving from the same Chinese source as the design is relatively rare in Japanese blue-and-white.

LITERATURE: G. Lang, 1983, No. 50; New York, Japan Society, 1986, No. 48 (a pair).

39
Ewer
Japan, 1660–80
Height 25.5 cm
Mark: a flower spray.
Ashmolean Museum, Oxford, 1978.700, Reitlinger Gift.

An ovoid-bodied vessel with cylindrical neck encircled by a rib and with loop handle, which is pierced to hold a mount forming a cover. It is painted with figures in a landscape in Chinese Transitional style, and with bands of formal ornament round the shoulder, neck and foot. The form itself derives ultimately from German stoneware, while some of the decorative borders are surely borrowed from Dutch delftware: cf. D. F. Lunsingh Scheurleer, 1971, Afb. 85, 86, and pp. 21–24 and 51 where the range of similar shapes is investigated.

LITERATURE: Oxford, Ashmolean Museum, 1981, No. 241.

40

Apothecary Flask with Inscription
Japan, 1670–90
Height 25.5 cm
Private Collection.

A swelling, globular bottle with tall tapering neck and thickened mouth rim with a corresponding rib set just below it. It is painted round the body with a band of plant sprays set among which is a three-lobed panel with the inscription D^r: VAND^r:HOF., and with a band of spearheads round the neck.

The 'gallipot' shape is probably not as early as is usually suggested. Nowhere in the early records is any bottle-shape qualified; the word used is that for bottle, only.

For a discussion of the use of initials, possibly of persons connected with the V. O. C., on this and other shapes, see C. J. A. Jörg, 1989, pp. 396–407, where this bottle is illustrated as Pl. 3. The name 'Dr [Pastor?] van der Hof' is the only full name yet recorded.

LITERATURE: Fraeylemaborg, 1977, No. 256.

41

Jug with Armorial
Japan, 1670–90
Height 21.3 cm
British Museum, JA 1963, 4–22, 1.

A baluster jug with narrow waisted neck and tall cylindrical mouth section with a pinched spout. The simple curved handle terminates in a scroll below; the foot is an inverted pan shape. The face is painted with an unidentified coat of arms and helm surmounted by a crest of a bird with spread wings. The neck and foot are banded in plain blue and the mouth is painted on each side with a flower spray within borders of flowers and stiff leaves; on the foot and handle are scrolling foliage. The handle is pierced for a metal mount.

The shape is based on a German stoneware original. Other examples are known bearing various arms.

42
Large Silver-mounted Tankard
Japan, 1670–90, the mount Netherlandish
Height 27.8 cm (to top of thumb-piece)
Marks: on the silver: S, crowned E, star above keystone.
British Museum, JA 1952, 11–13, 1.

A tankard with oviform body and broad slightly tapering
neck and loop handle. It is painted with a small goose, a
butterfly and a moth among flowering branches and with
blue dashes along the handle. The silver lid has a shell
thumb-piece and is engraved with a laurel wreath tied by
a ribbon; below is a silver foot.

LITERATURE: S. Jenyns, 1965, Pl. 16B; D. F. Lunsingh
Scheurleer, 1980, Abb. 417.

43
Large Bottle
Japan, 1660–80
Height 44.5 cm
Ashmolean Museum, Oxford, 1978.727, Reitlinger Gift.

A pear-shaped bottle with tall neck and cupped mouth,
decorated on the body with peony and chrysanthemum
sprays growing from rocks and with bands of lappets
and stiff-leaf ornament on the neck and shoulder.

Bottles of this sort have a long history in East Asia. They
were clearly popular in the Near-Eastern markets
supplied by the Dutch and no doubt to some extent also
in Europe, but they were never widely copied by
potteries there.

LITERATURE: Oxford, Ashmolean Museum, 1981, No. 249.

44
Large Bowl
Japan, 1660–70
Diameter 46 cm
Private Collection.

A bowl with wide everted rim, painted with flowering
plants in the centre and round the well with a bold
decoration of bamboo among rocks; on the rim are five
shaped cartouches of flowers set in a diapered ground.
Round the outside is a well-painted landscape with
houses, pavilions and fishing-boats, and a border of
formal leaves above.

Sherds of very similar bowls have been found at Cho-
kichi-dani kiln. The large scale of the decoration on the
inner walls of this bowl is unusual and relates to that on
bottles such as No. 43. Quite possibly this is one of the
'wash basins' mentioned in the Dutch archives of 1660
(T. Volker, 1954, p. 139).

45
Large Dish
Japan, 1680–1700
Diameter 55 cm
Private Collection.

A dish with broad flat rim, painted in the centre with a
pheasant descending and another perched on a rock
among peonies, and with a pair of phoenixes flying
among camellia and pomegranates in the border. The
back is plain.

A logical extension of the *kraak* style, with strong central
element and wide border, neither of which, however,
resemble *kraak* motifs. The Japanese word for phoenix is
ho-ō, certainly the origin of the hoho bird of Rococo fame.

46
Large Dish
Japan, 1680–1700
Diameter 55 cm
Groninger Museum, Groningen,
1982–5.

A plate with broad spreading rim.
Painted in the centre is a double-
gourd shaped urn with scrolling
handles containing a variety of
flowers, and in the broad surround
are two scrolling leafy branches
springing from a single source, both
above and below, with smaller
scrollwork filling the ground.

With its near-symmetrical design,
this dish has an almost heraldic
appearance designed for the
Western market. It is repeated in an
Imari-style version, No. 230 below.

47
Covered Bowl
Japan, 1680–1700
Diameter 32 cm
Private Collection.

A deep, rounded bowl with a low
domed cover and flattened knob. Both
bowl and cover are painted in broad
bands with a finely executed design of
large exotic birds with crests and long
tails among pine and bamboo.

48
Beaker Vase
Japan, 1680–1700
Height 44 cm
Sherborne Castle Estates.

A cylindrical vase with a flaring mouth and sides spreading towards the inset foot. It is decorated with a mountainous landscape with a large pine tree beside houses, bridges and a waterfall, and with a petal border.

The beaker form comes from Chinese Transitional ware but the angled cut-in of the sides above the foot became an Arita hallmark, and was adopted, for example, in Meissen vases such as No. 186. The decoration, derived somewhat remotely from Kano school painting, is found on several other shapes, suggesting a single workshop.

49
Beaker Vase
Japan, 1680–1700
Height 49.8 cm
Private Collection.

A broad cylindrical vase with flaring mouth and sides spreading towards the inset foot; at mid-point they are encircled by two ribs framing a decorative band interrupting the main design. The vase is painted in a purplish blue with on one side a tall aged pine tree among clouds and on the other a prunus growing by rocks and bamboo, with a *karakusa* scroll border below; the central band repeats formalized blooms and leaves.

Painted round the sides are sprays of pine, prunus and bamboo: the *shochikubai* or 'Three Friends of Winter', and on the lid, in brocade style are plum blossom on one half and a 'sunburst' motif on the other, the wavy radiating arms alternately plain blue and decorated with basket-weave diaper.

The filigree work comprises bands above and below linked on either side by leafy straps.

The mounts are possibly South-East Asian or Indian work. See G. Lang, 1983, No. 97, who comments that the boxes are included in the 'Devonshire Schedule' of 1690 under: 'Lesser China garnifht with Silver Guilt': 'A pair of Boxes of three pieces Each painted in colours garnifht with philigrin Top Bottoms Hinges and Clasps'. Also New York, Japan Society, 1986, No. 70. Quite possibly boxes of this shape would have been called, in the Dutch archives, *sioubacken*: a transliteration of the Japanese *jubako*, meaning a tiered box.

50
Bottle Vase
Japan, 1670–90
Height 28 cm
Ashmolean Museum, Oxford, 1978.727, Reitlinger Gift.

A slender pear-shaped bottle with tall neck and thickened mouth rim. It is decorated round the body with a continuous trail of seaweed and shells, and with three concentric lines below.

LITERATURE: Oxford, Ashmolean Museum, 1981, No. 251; V. Woldbye and B. van Meyenburg, 1983, Pl. 140.

51
Box with Silver-gilt Filigree Mounts
Japan, 1660–80
Height 4.6 cm; diameter 6.4 cm
The Burghley House Collection, Stamford, Lincolnshire.

A small three-tiered cylindrical box with flat lid, the sections bound together in finely wrought silver-gilt filigree. The porcelain is decorated in underglaze blue, red enamel, gilt and a silver enamel (now oxidized).

52
Bottle Vase
Japan, 1660–80
Height 25.2 cm
Private Collection.

A broad cylindrical bottle with rounded shoulder above an indented band and tubular neck with spreading mouth. In the broad band round the sides is painted a laughing *shishi* lion leaping on to a flowering branch, one of two which straggle outwards from an overhanging rock. Round the shoulder is a floral-scroll band above the indented band, which is in plain blue, and on the neck, a spearhead border.

51

52

53
Dutch Spirit Chest holding Nine Porcelain Flasks

Japan, 1670–1690
Height 16.5 cm; width 25.5 cm; depth 26 cm
Rijksmuseum, Amsterdam, NG 444.

The square wooden chest with hinged lid has a Dutch
East Indies chased silver lock-plate and was perhaps made
there. It is designed to hold nine square bottles with
coved shoulder and silver-mounted neck and cap. They
are painted on each side with a growing plant, with a
karakusa scroll round the shoulder, and on the base with
a large VOC monogram: the insignia of the Dutch East
India Company.

This travelling chest illustrates well a Dutch captain's
requirement, made originally with bottles of glass or
metal, which inspired one of the most common of
Japanese export porcelain forms.

LITERATURE: D. F. Lunsingh Scheurleer, 1980, Abb. 420.

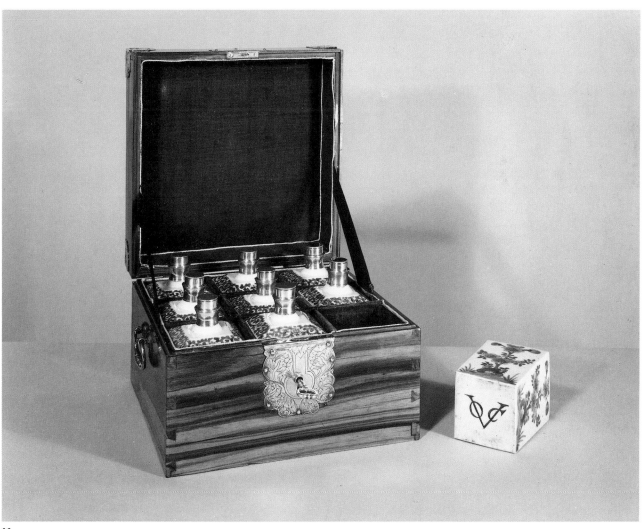

53

54
Large Covered Jar
Japan, 1660–80
Height 48 cm
Private Collection, on loan to the
Fitzwilliam Museum, Cambridge.

A large ovoid jar, with a domed lid,
painted with three shield-shaped
panels of flowering shrubs and rocks
divided by formal floral scrolls; there
are borders of plaited pattern and
lappets on the shoulder and neck. The
lid is similarly decorated and has a
chrysanthemum-flower knob.

The break-up of the decoration into
three cartouches divided by patterns
derives from the *kraak* style. See also
No. 55.

55
Cylindrical Jar
Japan, 1670–90
Height 30.5 cm
The Burghley House Collection,
Stamford, Lincolnshire.

With slightly tapered sides, sloping
shoulder and short neck. Four vertical
panels round the sides are painted
alternately with a peony in a vase and
with chrysanthemum sprays; the
panels are separated by formal designs.
Round the shoulder is a collar of
chrysanthemum petals and round the
neck a band of stiff leaves.

LITERATURE: G. Lang, 1983, No. 53;
New York, Japan Society, 1986,
No. 46.

55

56
Square Flask and Cover
Japan, 1670–90
Height 29 cm
Private Collection.

A tall, straight-sided flask with rounded shoulder and
short round neck, the stopper having a button knob.
Painted on alternate sides are landscapes with shrubs and
small figures, in one case holding a fan and in the other
carrying two buckets, with a rose in a vase and a
chrysanthemum plant on the others. There are leafy
scrolls on the shoulder, neck, and lid.

Like the 'ship's bottles' (see No. 53), square flasks such as
this were based on Western models primarily in glass,
and the larger ones were used to store liquids, such as
gin. The range of such flasks is discussed by D. F.
Lunsingh Scheurleer, 1971, Pls 165–70, pp. 38–39.

LITERATURE: H. A. Daendels, 1981, Pl. 73.

57
Pair of Beaker Vases
Japan, late 17th century
Heights 21.2 cm
Private Collection.

A pair of narrow beaker vases with waisted centres, each
roughly painted in underglaze blue with a sketchy
flowering tree and with clouds.

58
Pair of Cylindrical Vases with Lids
Japan, late 17th century
Heights 14.3 cm
Private Collection.

The cylindrical vases are roughly painted in underglaze blue with Chinese bell-flower, the lids with prunus.

59
Large Bowl
Japan, *c.* 1700
Diameter 52 cm
Private Collection.

A bowl with a narrow everted rim and small foot, decorated in a painterly style round the outside with egrets among waterplants. Inside, round the rim is a *karakusa* pattern in shades of blue and in the centre, a slight design of fruiting pomegranates.

The size of this bowl, as well as the originality and fluency of the decoration, is exceptional.

60

Covered Ewer with European Silver-gilt Mounts
Japan, 1680–1700
Height 17 cm
Private Collection.

A straight-sided square vessel with short, square neck, the handle and spout also square, the lid having a strap handle. On either side are finely-painted floral patterns resembling textile designs with half flower-heads superimposed also in silhouette, and scattered florets, and beside the spout, bamboo. Formal scrolls decorate the flat shoulder and there are fans and florets on the lid. On both handle and spout are chased silver-gilt fittings of the period with loops, a chain from which will once have secured the lid.

Not strictly a European shape, but perfectly adaptable to European usage, this kettle is a good example of the finer-quality porcelain shipped to Europe.

LITERATURE: London, Royal Academy of Arts, 1981, No. 218.

61

Dish in the form of a Stone-basket
Japan, 1680–1700
Length 15.9 cm
Private Collection.

Moulded as a stone-basket with wavy sides and rim outlined in brown glaze. Inside, two similar baskets in blue, with a criss-cross of scratched white lines, are lapped by foam on a ground of regularly-drawn waves.

Bamboo baskets full of stones, used in Japan as breakwaters, were more commonly depicted in painting than on porcelain. Formerly in the collection of Margaret, 2nd Duchess of Portland.

62

Small Dish

Japan, 1680–1700

Length 13.5 cm; width 9.8 cm

The Burghley House Collection, Stamford, Lincolnshire.

An oval dish with moulded chrysanthemum-petal sides interrupted by two double-lobed panels. The petals and the flat centre are outlined and shaded in blue; in one panel is painted a pine tree and in the other, a flowering prunus. On the underside are floral scrolls and on the high foot, a *nuyi*-head border.

LITERATURE: G. Lang, 1983, No. 17; New York, Japan Society, 1986, No. 28.

63

Small Box in the form of an Aubergine

Japan, *c.* 1700

Length 7.8 cm

The Burghley House Collection, Stamford, Lincolnshire.

The box and its cover are together moulded in the form of an aubergine with its leafy sheath. The top is painted with an artemisia leaf and a fly-whisk among ribbons of chrysanthemum sprays. The inside is plain.

LITERATURE: G. Lang, 1983, No. 28; New York, Japan Society, 1986, No. 66 (two boxes).

64

Dish

Japan, *c.* 1700

Diameter 21 cm

Mark: commendation mark *fuku* ('happiness') in a square within a ring.

Private Collection.

A saucer dish with a wavy rim edged with brown glaze. Inside, the sides are moulded with a pattern of turbulent waves lapping a mill-wheel and stone-baskets, under a broad band of blue, and in the centre is a peony spray.

65
Leaf-shaped Dish
Japan, late 17th century
Length 32 cm
Mark: of the Dresden Porcelain
Collection: N:473, wavy line and
square seal mark.
Porzellansammlung, Dresden, PO 636.

Moulded in the form of two overlapping leaves, with
the partly serrated rim of the dish picked out in brown
glaze. One leaf is white and is painted with a banana
plant growing by a hollow rock; the other shows
sections of pine-branches reserved in a sea of formalized
waves, which are flooded with blue overall.

The dish was acquired for the collection in Holland by
Count Vitzthurn in 1723. Copies of the form were
popular in Europe, notably at Meissen and later, in
England, at Bow and other factories (see No. 338). A
coloured Meissen version is not uncommon, see the
example in Schloss Lustheim illustrated by M. Shono,
1973, Pl. 101.

LITERATURE: F. Reichel, 1981, Pl. 12; who illustrates also
a Meissen copy of the form of 1725–30, decorated in
blue enamel: Pl. 93; and Tokyo, 1989, Nos 15 and 16–17
where this dish and two others are reproduced.

66
Teapot and Lid
Japan, c. 1690
Height 8.7 cm
British Museum, JA 1953, 11–20, 2.

A teapot of lobed hexagonal form with angular curving
handle and hexagonal spout. It is painted on either side
with a bird perched among flowering branches and with
a lappet border above. On the lid are painted flowering
branches surrounding the chrysanthemum-bud knob.
Scrolling foliage decorates the handle and spout.

The introduction of the teapot, along with tea, into Europe was hastened by the importation of Chinese examples in Yixing red stoneware or *blanc-de-Chine* porcelain from the first half of the 17th century, while Jingdezhen blue-and-white porcelain teapots were specifically ordered by the Dutch Company from 1639 onwards. Earlier than this Japanese piece is probably the enamelled teapot from the Fitzwilliam Museum (No. 98).

67
Dish

Japan, late 17th – early 18th century
Diameter 19 cm
Ashmolean Museum, Oxford, 1978.742.

A saucer dish with low, lobed sides and turned-out rim with raised edge glazed brown. Across its face is painted a Dutch landscape scene with three figures in the middle ground, one with an animal on a lead, and beyond, a hill with a watch tower, the roofs of a village and the tall sails of ships. In the sky are cumulus clouds and some islands which add an oriental perspective to the composition.

A variety of blue-and-white plates and other wares, both Japanese and Chinese are known bearing this subject, which has been popularly known as 'Deshima Island': cf. S. Jenyns, 1965, Pl. 19A. However, it is recognisably a Dutch scene and was copied, if not from engravings, then from a Delft plate decorated in the style associated with the painter Frederik van Frytom (*c.* 1632–1702). Another version which follows its original rather closely, incorporating a church with a tall spire, is in the Kastel Sypesteyn, Loosdrecht: see D. Howard and J. Ayers, 1978, p. 73 and Pls 32 to B, where the subject is discussed in relation to a Chinese example. Also C. J. A. Jörg, 1984, p. 110, who remarks that in the Netherlands it is traditionally called 'View of Scheveningen'. Recently Hetty Terwie, 1989, pp. 494–501 has argued that it does not derive from a single print, but from a synthesis of several sources. A Meissen bowl in Japanese style which makes use of the design is No. 301.

68
Octagonal Bowl

Japan, early 18th century
Diameter 20.2 cm
Mark: six-character reign mark of the Ming Emperor Chenghua (1465–87) in blue.
The Burghley House Collection, Stamford, Lincolnshire.

67

68

The bowl is painted with a continuous scene outside showing a busy waterway with European and other trading vessels, a fortified wall on the far shore beneath towering hills and a bank of clouds above; a border of leaves and florets appears below. Inside in an octagonal medallion is a similar scene within a leafy frame and below the rim are two registers of lappets and large maple leaves.

The European origin of these scenes has not yet been identified. A similar piece was in the collection of Margaret, 2nd Duchess of Portland.

LITERATURE: G. Lang, 1983, No. 45; New York, Japan House, 1986, No. 64.

69

Small Dish
Japan, late 17th – early 18th century
Diameter 12.6 cm
Mark: a nonsensical reign mark.
The Burghley House Collection, Stamford, Lincolnshire.

A small leaf-shaped dish with irregularly-lobed sides and
everted rim bordered in blue. It is painted with figures
on a quay, a man in a rowing boat and various sailing
vessels, and distant islands.

Various dishes of this type showing different Dutch
scenes are known. As Gordon Lang remarks (1983,
pp. 11–15, Pl. 35 *et seq.*), they are copied from Delft
originals painted in the 'van Frytom' style: cf. A. Vecht,
1968, Pl. 40 for an example of the latter dated 1684.

It is a curiosity that the Japanese dishes were in turn
copied in England at the Bow factory from *c.* 1752. A
pickle dish identical to No. 69 is reproduced by B.
Watney, 1973, Pl. 10A; and the quayside design was used
there on other wares.

LITERATURE: New York, Japan Society, 1986, No. 62.

69

70

Plate
Japan, *c.* 1740
Diameter 27 cm
Private Collection.

A deep plate with flat rim. In the centre is the well-
known design of a lady under a parasol held by an
attendant, gesturing towards some wading birds standing
by a clump of reeds. An inner border of flower sprays
and rosettes is surrounded by a rim border with four
cartouches framed in scrollwork showing birds
alternating with four smaller panels with human figures,
all set in a honeycomb ground. Painted on the back are
flying insects.

The decoration follows one of several designs
commissioned by the Dutch East India Company from
the Amsterdam artist Cornelis Pronk (1691–1759) during
the years 1734–37. What he produced were 'chinoiseries'
drawn apparently from his acquaintance with oriental
porcelains or lacquerwork. Drawings were sent in 1736
from Batavia both to China, where porcelains were
ordered in three differing styles, namely blue-and-white,

70

enamelled, and 'coloured and gold' – to be interpreted
as 'Chinese Imari' – and to Japan, where blue-and-
white and enamelled versions were made. The subject is
exhaustively studied by C. J. A. Jörg, 1980, who
reproduces original watercolour designs in Pls 3A and 5
and a range of porcelains on which they appear.
Officially, the order from Japan was abandoned in 1740
on economic grounds, but it seems likely that it was
continued by private traders.

In Europe, the decoration was taken up by Dutch
enamellers on oriental porcelain or Delft wares and later,
at various porcelain factories.

71
Pair of Vases in the form of Cycad Trees,
mounted in Ormolu
Japan, late 17th – early 18th century
Heights 33.6 cm
Her Majesty the Queen.

The vases are modelled as short stumpy trees with scaly
trunks which are covered with brown glaze and
terminate above in a spreading mouth with wavy rim,
painted in blue to resemble leaves; two smaller bulb-like
shoots lower down also with blue-painted orifices are
perhaps intended for flowers. The vases are supported on
ormolu cups of leaves attached to short leafy branches.

72

Spirit Keg in the form of a
Dutchman astride a Barrel
Japan, mid 18th century
Height 36 cm
British Museum, JA 1927, 11–4, 1.

The figure is seated astride a barrel with
a goblet in his right hand and raising an
upturned flask in his left; on his head
(which is detachable and forms the
cover) he wears a feathered hat. His
white coat has blue cuffs, lapels, buttons
and pockets and he is wearing breeches,
stockings and blue shoes. The keg is
painted at each end with scrolling
foliage and has an aperture for a metal
tap. The Baroque rectangular base is
modelled with scrolls and painted also
with flowers, above a border of stiff
leaves.

This subject was popular over a lengthy
period in European ceramics of the 18th
century: cf. for example the Delft
version in the Musées Royaux d'Art et
d'Histoire, Brussels which is dated 1757
(Tokyo, 1982, No. 50); and see D.F.
Lunsingh Scheurleer, in *Mededelingenblad*,
58, p. 71. Sherds of the figure were
excavated in 1988 in the spoil heaps of
the Aka-e-machi, the Enamellers'
Quarter in Arita.

LITERATURE: S. Jenyns, 1965, Pl. 13A, p. 57.

IV Early Enamelled Ware

It seems clear that the Japanese were using overglaze enamel in Arita before the time of the export trade. This appears to have been dark in colour, not unlike the so-called Kutani palette based on dark green, and was fired onto ordinary *shoki-Imari* pieces. Enamel was already being used in Kyoto on low-fired wares, but this was of much brighter and more translucent colouring. The first written record of enamelled ware from Arita occurs in the tea diary of the priest Horin (the *Kakumeiki*) which records, in 1652, the gift of an Imari *nishiki-de* bowl.

The earliest Arita porcelains of export type to bear enamels are similar neither to the enamelled *shoki-Imari* wares nor to the Kyoto wares. Nor do they closely resemble Chinese overglaze-decorated wares; most particularly is this noticeable in the Japanese use of overglaze cobalt blue, which was not in use in China until considerably later. On the other hand, many of the earliest Arita coloured wares did not use yellow, which was used in Ming China and had been used on *shoki-Imari*.

The earliest enamelled export wares are probably, then, the coarse coloured imitations of Wanli *kraak* patterns (No. 82); these patterns can be seen to change, as the colours improve in clarity and translucency, as time goes on (No. 85). The types that do not immediately use yellow have better quality colours (No. 81) and it is tempting, even at this early stage to differentiate the enamelled wares into two streams, those that will lead to the Imari wares (including here many of the types formerly called Kutani (Nos 75, 76,

77 and 78) and, on the other hand, those that will lead to the Kakiemon and the Kakiemon-like wares (Nos 83 and 84).

We have no knowledge of kiln procedure related to enamelling in Japan at this date; were enamellers attached to certain kilns, or were they independent? Were they all together in the Aka-e-machi as they probably were fifty years later? Clearly, judging from the variations in the palettes of colours used, as opposed to individual colours, there must have been groups of enamellers or workshops who used certain available colours, in apparently different combinations. Several groups have been recognised, the most obvious being those enamellers that worked in a predominantly blue-and-yellow palette. As there are only two shapes found enamelled thus, jars in at least two sizes (see the Porcelain Room pp. 136–37, No. 7) and narrow-necked bottles and as the scene depicted seems nearly always to include a verandah and a rolled-up blind, it seems likely that this was a specialist workshop. The shapes on which they worked, however, are also found enamelled in other palettes and so it would seem logical to assume that they bought, or were allotted, wares in the white from some kiln with which they did not necessarily have a direct connection. In other cases, certain palettes only occur on certain shapes which never bear other palettes of enamels, though they may occur in underglaze blue only. Thus the square gin-bottle shape (No. 149), often with a wide neck, and the squat form of the so-called 'Hampton Court' hexagonal jars No. 151 appear to be the only shapes that bear a Kakiemon-like palette that includes overglaze brown. Here a direct connection between kiln and enamellers is to be assumed.

Nor can we see a direct connection at this early, settling-down stage between the decorators in underglaze blue and the decorators in enamel. While early enamelled pieces often have underglaze blue, this is confined to circumferential lines at neck, shoulder or foot (No. 84) or, at most, to some minor decorative scheme that gives no indication of kinship with the enamel decoration. Only later are there spaces left in the underglaze blue painting to be filled, for the second firing, with specific enamel designs.

This type that we shall call the 'blue-and-yellow' group (mentioned above) fits neither into the Kakiemon nor into the Imari and clearly belongs in an earlier, ancestral phase. Nor do the basically green, red and yellow palettes (Nos 73 and 74) fit into either category. It is better to call these 'Early Enamelled ware' and to include with them some other palettes not exhibited here as unavailable or irrelevant to the European connection as well as others (Nos 77 and 78) which seem to lead towards the vast and heterogenous variety of porcelain that we still classify merely as Imari (though we make some attempt here to differentiate sub-styles (see pp. 31–33 and 204–205), and yet others that we could call 'proto-Kakiemon' (Nos 83 and 84), leading to the Kakiemon and to its competitors. This classification assumes a parallel importance of all these groups which may or may not be justified.

O. R. I.

73

74

73
Jar
Japan, 1660–70
Height 30 cm
British Museum, JA 1970, 2–2, 1.

A swelling oviform jar with short neck, painted in green, red and yellow enamels outlined in black. In large shaped panels on either side are flowering plants, rocks and clouds, with blossoms in green on a sea of red waves between; a leafy scroll band encircles the shoulder and a red key-fret border, the neck.

The rounded outline of this jar and of No. 74 is characteristic of the early period.

LITERATURE: T. Nagatake, S. Hayashiya, 1978, Col. Pl. 19.

74
Jar and Cover
Japan, ? 1660–70
Height 31 cm
British Museum, JA 1950,10–24, 1 & A.

An oviform jar with short waisted neck and domed cover with small knob. Painted round the sides in green, red, yellow and blue enamels mainly outlined in black are stems of various flowers and two grasshoppers, with irregular green-and-black borders above and below. Sketchy green (?) clouds encircle the neck and there is green enamel inside the neck and on the base. On the cover are flower sprays.

LITERATURE: S. Jenyns, 1965, Pl. 80A.

75
Bottle
Japan, 1660–80
Height 41 cm
Ashmolean Museum, Oxford, 1978.689, Reitlinger Gift.

A pear-shaped bottle with long tapering neck. It is decorated in red, green, yellow and aubergine enamels with three large, lobed panels each with a sage in a landscape and with six small roundels containing flowers or emblems, all reserved on a ground of red scrollwork, with shield-shaped cartouches below the mouthrim.

The use of iron-red patterns as background to either

75

cartouches as here, borders (No. 76), or overpainting (No. 78), is a feature of one of the 'proto-Imari' groups.

LITERATURE: S. Jenyns, 1965, Pl. 85B and p. 151; O. C. S. exhibition catalogue, 1956, No. 55; T. Nagatake, 1959, p. 256, Fig. 21; Y. Imaizumi, 1974, Pl. 71; Oxford, Ashmolean Museum, 1981, No. 215; London, Royal Academy of Arts, 1981, No. 213.

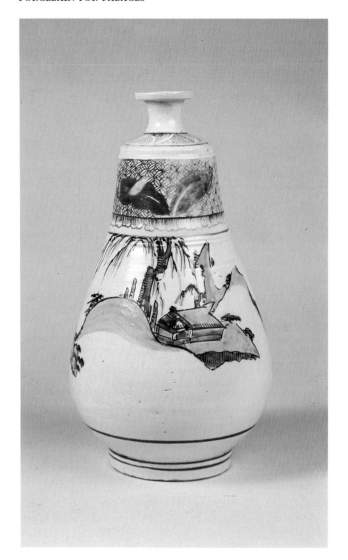

76
Bottle
Japan, *c.* 1660
Height 26.3 cm
British Museum, JA, 1960, 2–16, 1.

A bottle in Japanese tea-whisk form with pear-shaped body, tapered shoulder and small waisted neck. Painted round the sides in yellow, aubergine and green enamels, outlined in black, is a scene with a house by a willow in the mountains with peaks rising from the white mist. Above is a band with red leaves on a diapered ground and on the shoulder, a wave design in red.

This shape sometimes bears designs related to that on No. 78, or geometric designs in green and red.

77
Bottle
Japan, 1660–80
Height 42.5 cm
Victoria and Albert Museum, London, C. 70–1953.

A swelling pear-shaped bottle with tapering neck and spreading rim, painted in red, green, aubergine-purple, yellow and blue enamels with black outlines. Round the body in a broad zone are entwined branches of chrysanthemum and other flowering plants, with a solid band below and border of stiff leaves above in red alone.

The shape is closely allied to a standard shape of blue-and-white bottles, e.g. No. 43.

LITERATURE: S. Jenyns, 1965, Pl. 87A; J. Ayers, 1980, Fig. 252.

78
Bottle
Japan, 1660–80
Height 24.5 cm
Private Collection.

A slender pear-shaped bottle with tapering neck and
spreading rim enamelled in red, green, turquoise and
yellow. The decoration is predominantly red with leaves
and flower-heads in silhouette against a striated ground,
with a turquoise dot border below. There are cursory
panels and a cash-pattern border round the neck and
several red bands round the body.

This stylized decorative scheme also occurs on tea-whisk
shaped bottles (No. 76) and on the mugs of German
stoneware shape.

79
Circular Box and Cover
Japan, 1660–70
Diameter 22.6 cm
British Museum, JA 1947, 14–17, 1.

A shallow, flat-topped circular box and cover with
rounded sides above and below. The decoration is
enamelled in red, gold and a now blackish silver. The
top is a circular panel with a bird perched by a flowering
plant growing by rocks, and in six smaller medallions
round the sides are a sampan, prunus, pine, bamboo,
figures in a landscape and a thatched building in a
mountainous landscape, with tree branches and blooms
between, all on a red scrollwork ground. The decoration
is repeated on the lower part.

The use of a silver pigment has already been noted on
No. 35.

80

Tankard, comprising a Jar with Dutch Silver-gilt Mounts and Chinese *famille verte* Lid

Japan, 1660–80, the lid and mounts *c*. 1680–1700
Height 14 cm
Ashmolean Museum, Oxford, 1978.533, Reitlinger Gift.

The jar is enamelled in red, green, yellow and blue with a dense design of birds among flowers and foliage set between key-fret, cell-diaper and spearhead borders, with encircling lines in underglaze blue. The original lid is replaced by one in early Chinese *famille verte* porcelain which like the foot is fitted in silver-gilt, with a falcon thumb-piece on the butler-grip and a caryatid handle.

The shape and decoration can be found paralleled in blue-and-white. The replacement of missing lids, either with an oriental lid not too far removed in colouring or with one made to order in European faience, was not uncommon. Such can be found in the Dresden Collection No. 138, and in the exhibition, No. 181.

A similar small jar complete with cover is in the same collection: cf. Oxford, Ashmolean Museum, 1981, No. 214.

LITERATURE: D. F. Lunsingh Scheurleer, 1980, Abb. 464.

81

Bottle

Japan, 1660–70
Height 23.1 cm
Ashmolean Museum, Oxford, 1985.52, Jeffery Story and Walter Cook Bequest.

A slender pear-shaped bottle with tall neck. It is painted with horizontal lines in underglaze blue and with four vertical panels of growing lotus and formalized flowers, with a band of spiky leaves round the neck.

82
Dish
Japan, 1660–70
Diameter 32.4 cm
Mark: a square seal, *fuku* ('happiness') in red.
Ashmolean Museum, Oxford, 1978.680, Reitlinger Gift.

A dish with broad spreading rim, decorated in blue, green, red, yellow and black enamels with designs derived from late Ming *kraak porselein*. Geese are shown flying or perching by a pond in a central octagonal medallion surrounded by eight principal panels containing alternately flowers and emblems. On the back are three flower sprays.

The enamels are harsh and densely applied to the thick and crudely-made body.

LITERATURE: Oxford, Ashmolean Museum, 1981, No. 154.

83
Bowl
Japan, *c.* 1660
Diameter 11 cm
Private Collection.

A small bowl with vertical sides, formerly with a lid, decorated in enamel colours of red, green and blue only with black outlines. Three formal flower-heads are incorporated in a leafy scroll band between red lines above and below.

The enamel palette of this and No. 84 seem to be very early essays in the line that leads to the Kakiemon.

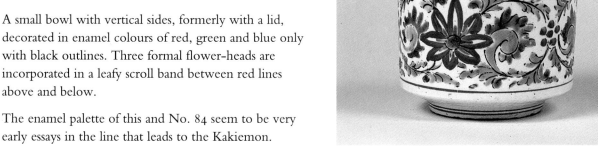

84
Small Jar
Japan, *c.* 1660
Height 9.5 cm
Ashmolean Museum, Oxford, 1978.653, Reitlinger Gift.

A small jar with flat shoulder and short wide neck, the rim unglazed to take a cover. It is decorated in blue, red and green enamels with two sprays of pomegranate and peony, flanked by hatched borders on the neck and shoulder in underglaze blue.

The use of underglaze blue for a patterned border reflects *shoki-Imari* styles.

LITERATURE: Oxford, Ashmolean Museum, 1981, No. 152.

85
Large Dish
Japan, 1660–80
Diameter 41.5 cm
British Museum, JA 1959, 7–24, 1.

A shallow dish with broad spreading rim, painted in underglaze blue and enamels after the style of late Ming *kraak porselein*. In the centre, painted in green, red, blue and yellow with outlines in black, is a tripod vessel containing flowering and fruiting plants on a squared pavement flanked by balustrades. In the surround are eight main panels outlined in blue enamel and holding alternately flowering plants or 'precious objects', with narrow panels of tassels on a scale-blue ground between. On the reverse is a floral scroll.

LITERATURE: Tokyo National Museum, 1987, No. 59.

86

Large Jar
Japan, 1660–80
Height 52 cm
British Museum, JA 1956, 2–5, 1.

A slender ovoid jar with narrowing shoulder and brief
neck, painted in green, red, yellow and blue enamels
with outlines in black. In three large, shield-shaped
panels round the sides various birds are perched among
flowering plants growing by rocks and from watcr, with
formal floral scrolls as a surround. A band round the

shoulder displays three flower sprays in cartouches on a
green-and-yellow cell-diaper ground, with this pattern
again in red above. A band of scrolling red foliage with
yellow blooms encircles the foot.

Described by Jenyns (see below, p. 150) as 'a magnificent
wreck', this large jar can be compared in type to the
blue-and-white jar No. 54, though the decoration here is
entirely in subdued polychrome.

LITERATURE: S. Jenyns, 1968, Pl. 50A and B.

87

Tankard with Silver-gilt Rim

Japan, 1660–80
Height 15 cm
The Burghley House Collection, Stamford, Lincolnshire.

A tankard of European form with globular body and cylindrical neck. Round the body are four lobed panels alternately with dragons or chrysanthemum sprays in shallow moulded relief on an unglazed 'fish-roe' ground and in four upright panels above are sea-birds in relief flying above waves; these 'biscuit' areas are dressed with a pinkish-brown wash of iron-oxide. The designs are painted in Kakiemon colours of red, turquoise, blue and black. The glazed handle is painted with a foliage scroll and pierced for a metal mount. The mouthrim is encased in a silver-gilt band, added in Europe.

Under the heading 'The Drawing Rooms…China over the Chimney', the 1688 Inventory cites '2 painted relev'd brown Juggs with handle Guilt rimms'.

The clear colours of the enamels represent a more advanced stage in the development of the Kakiemon palette than is shown in Nos 83, 84 and 158. It seems likely that the 'brown Juggs', along with 88, 90, 91, 92, 93, 94 and 95 were decorated by the Kakiemon enamellers before the actual Kakiemon kiln began operation.

LITERATURE: G. Lang, 1983, No. 83; New York, Japan Society, 1986, No. 98 (a pair).

88

Jar and Cover

Japan, *c.* 1670
Height 27.7 cm
Ashmolean Museum, Oxford, 1976.52,
Christie Miller Gift.

An oviform jar boldly decorated in red, green, blue and yellow enamels with a large flowering chrysanthemum growing by rocks with butterflies and insects; and a band of stylised petals round the neck. The lid is similarly decorated, with a blue knob.

This style must surely be ancestral to the Kakiemon.

LITERATURE: H. Nishida, 1977, Pls 15 and 16.

89
Two Goblets

Japan, 1670–90
Heights 13.5 cm
The Burghley House Collection, Stamford, Lincolnshire.

Goblets of European form, with straight-sided cup on a
tall narrow stem with spreading foot, and ribbed with
double rings at mid-point. They are enamelled in a
palette of red, blue, turquoise and gilt with three clumps
of flowers on the bowl and three sprays on the foot;
inside is a chrysanthemum roundel.

The shape was no doubt copied from similar
Netherlandish glass.

LITERATURE: G. Lang, 1983, No. 85; New York, Japan
Society, 1986, No. 107.

90
Dish

Japan, 1670–80
Diameter 32.8 cm
Ashmolean Museum, Oxford, 1978.682, Reitlinger Gift.

A dish with broad, spreading rim decorated in blue, red,
dark green, yellow and black enamels. The central
design, which derives ultimately from Chinese *kraak
porselein* of the late Ming, is of peonies in a vase on a
terrace, and round the rim are two wide-spreading
prunus trees growing from rocks.

The border design is markedly similar and clearly
ancestral to that of the blue-and-white plate No. 133.
Blue-and-white sherds have been found at the Kakiemon
kiln site.

LITERATURE: Oxford, Ashmolean Museum, 1981, No. 156.

91
Kendi 'drinking-vessel'
Japan, 1660–80
Height 19.7 cm
Ashmolean Museum, Oxford, 1978.641, Reitlinger Gift.

A globular vessel with faceted tubular neck and splayed mouth with petalled lip; a squared mammiform spout projects from the body and on either side is a modelled representation of Hotei, the God of Contentment. The decoration is in the Kakiemon palette with no use of yellow, the lines of the moulding picked out in blue and red and the ground between decorated with scrollwork, fan shapes and cash patterns.

The *kendi,* or gorgelet, is an Islamic form of water-pouring vessel popular in South-East Asia. The Ashmolean Museum has another *kendi* from the same mould and employing the same palette.

LITERATURE: Oxford, 1981, No. 172; a smaller one is illustrated and the type discussed by S. Jenyns, 1965, Pl. 53B, p. 61.

92

92
Bowl
Japan, *c.* 1680
Diameter 32.6 cm
Ashmolean Museum, Oxford, 1978.683, Reitlinger Gift.

A large bowl painted in the Kakiemon enamel palette.
Inside in the centre is a medallion of a dragon chasing a
fiery pearl and round the sides are two groups of banded
hedge, rocks and flowering branches, with a bounding
tiger in between. On the outside are two spreading
sprays of peony.

Several motifs that were to become standard in
enamelled wares from the Kakiemon kiln are here used
in conjunction.

LITERATURE: Oxford, Ashmolean Museum, 1981,
No. 160.

93
Large Covered Jar
Japan, 1660–80
Height 46 cm
Victoria and Albert Museum, London, FE.24–1985.

A large oviform jar with slightly lobed sides and short
neck, topped by a domed cover with a *shishi* lion
forming the knob. It is decorated in Kakiemon-style
enamels of green, yellow, red, blue, purple and black
with a bold landscape that encompasses the sides, the
foreground with trees, rocks, fishing-nets etc. being
separated by belts of white mist from the higher levels
beyond, where two pavilions are perched by a cliff.
Underglaze blue lines mark the main band and simple
shoulder and neck borders. The lid has a similar
style of decoration.

On the great ceiling over the staircase of the Würzburg
Residenz, painted by Giovanni Battista Tiepolo and
dated 1753, some figures representing Asia hold a large
jar which resembles this, save only that the painter has
given the jar a rounded (Chinese-style) lid.

LITERATURE: T. Nagatake, S. Hayashiya, 1978, Col.
Pl. 25. For the companion jar from the Reitlinger
collection see Oxford, Ashmolean Museum, 1981,
No. 155 and Col. Pl. III.

93

Alternative view overleaf

94
Bowl
Japan, 1670–90
Diameter 28 cm
Mark: a seal, *fuku* ('happiness'), in red.
Victoria and Albert Museum, London C. 104–1914.

A five-lobed bowl with foliated rim lined in brown. It is
painted in the full Kakiemon palette with a flowering
prunus tree and a camellia round the outside growing by
rocks; spread round the inside is a similar prunus design,
more extended and with fantastic rocks, with a phoenix
with long red tail feathers among clouds, and a medallion
of leafy green scrollwork on a yellow ground in the centre.

The strong colours and full decoration in a bold style
mark this bowl out from among its contemporaries.

LITERATURE: S. Jenyns, 1965, Pl. 37B; cf. also T.
Nagatake, 1968, pp. 9 and 37 for a similar bowl.

95
Wine Pot and Cover

Japan, Arita, *c.* 1680
Height with lid 10 cm
Ashmolean Museum, Oxford,
1978.639, Reitlinger Gift.

A small wine pot and cover moulded
and incised in the form of a lotus bud
and painted in the Kakiemon enamel
palette. The 'petals' of the body are
outlined in red and decorated with
flowering plants growing by rocks;
flower and plant scroll motifs decorate
the handle and spout.

It has been suggested that this shape may
be referred to, in the 1697 inventory of
the Kensington Palace collection of
Queen Mary II, as 'artichoke pots'.
See L. R. Shulsky, forthcoming, 1990.

LITERATURE: Oxford, Ashmolean
Museum, 1981, No. 169.

96
Bucket-shaped Vase

Japan, late 17th century
Height 22.8 cm
Ashmolean Museum, Oxford,
1978.672, Reitlinger Gift.

In the form of a Japanese bucket of
tall, square, tapering section with a
sunken top and flat yoke handle
joining flanges that rise from the rim.
It is painted round the four sides in
enamels with a blue bird perching on
one branch of a spreading camellia
tree and another in flight. A scroll
pattern decorates the handle, which is
partly restored in gold lacquer. The
handles have been built up in too tall
a repair.

This is one of a group of pieces
decorated in the Kakiemon palette
that are more than usually delicate
and restrained.

LITERATURE: Oxford, Ashmolean
Museum, 1981, No. 197.

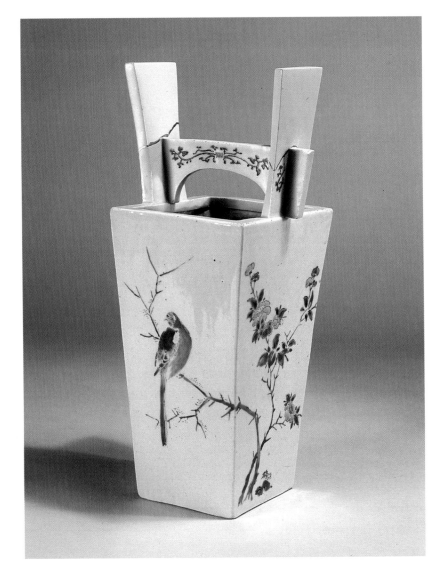

97
Dish
Japan, 1660–80
Diameter 27cm
Private Collection.

A shallow dish with narrow, curving rim, painted mainly in two shades of green, blue and yellow enamels. A pair of crested birds stand among luxuriant plants and rocks in the centre with a long-tailed bird swooping towards them; round the rim, a section of which is restored, are a variety of flowering plants growing among rocks.

The body is unusually white and may well represent an early attempt at the white *nigoshide* body. This is curious, for the enamels are not at all close to the Kakiemon.

98
Teapot with Gilt-metal Mount and Chain
Japan, 1660–80
Height 12.5 cm
Private Collection, on loan to the Fitzwilliam Museum, Cambridge, J. 118 & A.

A small teapot enamelled in blue, green, red and yellow with panels of a phoenix flying above tree peonies on either side separated by *karakusa* scrolls, a dentate border on the shoulder and floral spray on the handle and spout. A *karakusa* scroll is repeated on the lid. Metal mounts are fitted to the foot, rim and tip of the spout where a safety chain connects with the lid.

The palette used here, as on No. 97, must represent work of an early enamelling workshop away from the main line. There may well have been many such workshops in the third quarter of the 17th century.

V Porcelain for Display

THE USE OF MOUNTS ON PORCELAIN

In the time of the earlier imports of Japanese porcelain during the latter half of the 17th century, and especially in Holland where the major imports were arriving, the equipping of pieces with silver mounts was a common practice. These mounts were designed mainly to provide covers to jugs, ewers or flasks (Nos 36 and 42) or to protect lids from being lost or broken (Nos 60, 98, 101, 103, 110 and 202). Sometimes, a jar might be adapted to serve as a mug by adding a silver handle (No. 80); or a simple band might be fitted to a fragile rim (No. 87).

A steady increase in the numbers of porcelains accumulating in collections forced fresh consideration of how they were to be accommodated. For some, the obvious answer was to put them out on display. Supply had gone well beyond what was required for mere everyday use, indeed the pieces were often now chosen or ordered in the East precisely for their novelty of shape or style, or for their decorative value. In earlier times, the rarity of oriental porcelains had often led to their being mounted in gold or silver and such pieces received no more than occasional use. Now, however, mounting the porcelains became not so much a means of marking their rarity as of heightening their decorative impact, as they were placed prominently on view in some allotted area within the house or palace.

A more inventive and imaginative trend became evident in the 18th century when to begin with, as in the past, a handsome bowl or jar would often be graced with rim, foot and handles of finely-chased silver, now following the classic Louis XIV style. From this soon grew the idea of furnishing entire dinner tables with centre-pieces, tureens, candlesticks and other ambitious items in what became a rich extravagance of Baroque display. Certain of these, such as small tureens (No. 104), condiment sets (No. 241) and the occasional sauceboat were obtainable, copied in porcelain perhaps from silver models; but to produce those that could not be ordered the pieces were sometimes now piled one upon another and where necessary ruthlessly truncated, with specially-made silver elements added to bind them together into the desired shapes. Strikingly ingenious examples of this practice are the table services of gold and silver brought together by Charles-Alexandre de Lorraine, Governor of the Low Countries from 1744–80, much of which were subsequently transferred to the imperial capital in Vienna. Among the many items still there today is the remarkable Weld family *surtout de table*, an assemblage of tureens and condiment sets in Imari ware all balanced around a central stem, which in its original state had been made by a London silversmith; as well as other unusual pieces which have been lent for this exhibition (Nos 245 to 248).

In general, porcelains of this kind continued to serve a useful as well as ornamental purpose and such mounting was not infrequent right down to the 19th century: witness the Imari jar, a combination of fountain and pot-pourri, which has been lent from Windsor by gracious permission of Her Majesty the Queen (No. 250).

Different again was the tradition of mounting which grew up in France in the time of the *Régence* and which was developed more especially during the reign of Louis XV; in this, the porcelains were often made objects of decoration pure and simple – dressed in, and at times even largely concealed by, mounts of elaborately-worked ormolu that were in themselves notable works of art. In such a role the exotic designs and vibrant colours of the porcelains, with their 'chinoiserie' connotations, became part of the prevailing decorative style.

Outstanding examples of such mounting are the pair of square Kakiemon flasks from the Louvre in Paris, No. 149; the large clock lent by the Residenz in Munich, No. 147, which is supported on the back of a Japanese elephant; and the two-branched Rococo candelabrum from the same palace, No. 146, which hides among its leafy scrolls a grinning porcelain lion, or *shishi*. Or one might cite equally the brilliant pair of square Imari flasks with their painted *shishi*, peony and waterfalls set off by a black ground, set in Rococo mounts in the height of Louis XV taste, which are again lent by Her Majesty the Queen (No. 249). Such pieces were intended to be viewed and admired in the most lavish princely surroundings of their day.

THE PORCELAIN ROOM

Prior to this, various solutions to the problem of housing one's porcelains to advantage had been sought out and espoused by the more enthusiastic collectors. By the mid 17th century it was already customary in some houses to display these and other rarities on top of furniture (No. 99), or on shelves systematically arranged in particular rooms for the purpose. Paintings of Dutch interiors often show the porcelains so disposed in an ordinary domestic setting, and later in the century, in the larger houses, the matter was more seriously addressed. As Oliver Impey points out in his Introduction (p. 56), the drawings made by designers such as Daniel Marot for Dutch clients, and his possible later work for Mary II and William in England at Kensington and Hampton Court, reveal a keen application to the problem, with much shelving and brackets designed to fill overmantels, wall areas and spaces above doors, and specially-constructed, free-standing *étagères* on which the porcelains could be arranged in diminishing tiers. Much use was also made of the newly-popular mirror-glass.

This fashion reached its height at the turn of the century when Elector Frederick William of Brandenburg and his wife Sophie-Charlotte instituted at Schloss Charlottenburg, their palace at Berlin, a *porzellanzimmer* complete with mirrors, the main walls of which were entirely lined with oriental porcelains. It was among the first of many such rooms built in the following decades.

In this exhibition an attempt has been made to recreate the spirit of such a porcelain room of about 1700, using only Japanese porcelains in the display. The wares shown here are blue-and-white, Kakiemon, and those enamelled in the various styles we call 'Imari'.

J. G. A.

135

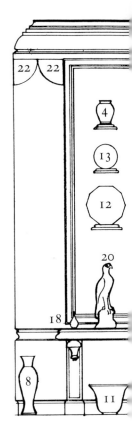

The Porcelain Room

ARITA BLUE-AND-WHITE

1　Dish, 1690–1710, diameter 31 cm

2　Dish, 1690–1710, diameter 31 cm

3　*Jardinière*, 1690–1710, diameter 37 cm

KAKIEMON

4　Two Jars, 1670–90, heights 20.5 cm and 21.3 cm

5　Covered Jar, 1670–90, height 27.1 cm. British Museum, Franks 478 (No. 155)

6　Teapot, 1680–1710, height 15.5 cm. British Museum, 1959, 7–16, 1

IMARI

7　Two Bottles, 1670–90, heights 22.5 cm and 22.6 cm

8　Two Vases, 1700–20, heights 46.7 cm. Victoria and Albert Museum, London

9　Four Covered Cups and Saucers, *c.* 1700, heights 11.5 cm. Groninger Museum, Groningen, N. 17

10　Four Covered Cups and Saucers, *c.* 1700, heights 11.5 cm. Groninger Museum, Groningen, 1936–19

11　*Jardinière*, 1690–1710, diameter 37 cm. The Burghley House Collection, Stamford, Lincolnshire

12　Two Decagonal and Four Octagonal Dishes with Pierced Sides, 1700–20, widths 32.9 cm and 25 cm. Her Majesty the Queen

13　Six Plates with Foliate Rims, 1700–20, diameters 21.5 cm. Her Majesty the Queen

14　Six Cups and Saucers, 1700–20, heights 5 cm; diameters 11.3 cm. Her Majesty the Queen

15　Dish, 1660–80, diameter 30.5 cm

16　Dish, 1660–80, diameter 30.5 cm

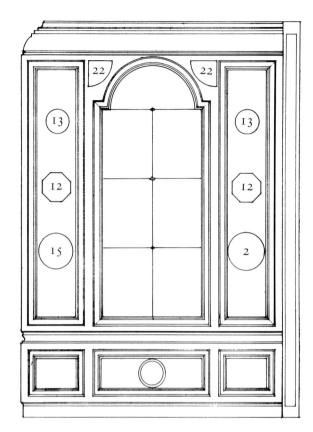

17 Large Jar and Cover, 1680–1700, height 68 cm

18 Pair of Bottles, 1670–90, heights 14 cm. Private Collection, on loan to the Fitzwilliam Museum, Cambridge

19 Pair of Bottles, 1670–90, heights 22 cm

20 Pair of Eagles, one having a gilt metal crown, c.1680–1710, heights 55 cm and 56 cm. Grimsthorpe and Drummond Castle Trust (No. 172)

21 Barber's Bowl, 1680–1700, diameter 27.8 cm

CHINESE IMARI

22 Twelve Fan-shaped Dishes, 1710–25, lengths 11.8 cm. The Burghley House Collection, Stamford, Lincolnshire

The items unidentified are lent from private collections.

99
Lacquer Cabinet with
Carved Wood Stand

Japan, *c.* 1680, the stand
probably English, 1680–90
Height 160 cm; depth 50 cm;
width 90 cm
Drayton House.

A Japanese export lacquer cabinet
raised on a European giltwood stand.
The cabinet has two doors hinged to
reveal numerous small drawers, with
carrying handles at the sides, and is
raised on its own low pedestal. The
front is decorated with a pavilion in a
landscape and with birds flying
overhead, all in shades of gold lacquer
on a black ground. The contemporary
European giltwood stand with a deep
frieze of carved, pierced scrollwork
and leafy branches, raised on squared
inverted baluster legs, ending in pad
feet and joined by a scrolled stretcher
on which are placed nine circular
stands for porcelain.

Japanese lacquer cabinets and their
Chinese and European (japanned)
imitations had been fashionable as
exotic and useful furniture for half a
century and more before they were
found additionally useful as places on
which to display porcelain. Made
with no support beyond the low
pedestal and sometimes lacking even
that, they had to be raised on some
form of stand in Europe. Their
original use in the time of Louis XIV
is betrayed by the use of giltwood
imitating the silver furniture of the
grandest palaces of the time. When
the shapes of these cabinets were no
longer fashionable, in the 18th
century, they were ruthlessly dis-
membered and the lacquer panels used
for inlays into other pieces of furniture
just as were panels of *pietra dura*.

The display of porcelain on these
cabinets is discussed on p. 56. For a
detailed discussion of the export lacquer
of Japan see Oliver Impey, 1981,
pp. 124–58.

VI Kakiemon

From among the Japanese export porcelains a Kakiemon style is generally recognised, and today cataloguers unhesitatingly attribute some enamelled wares to the Kakiemon. Usually such wares tend to be finely potted dishes, bowls, jars, figures or other shapes made of a fine white porcelain body and covered in a remarkably colourless 'white' glaze. Over this glaze is a sparse, painterly decoration in fine translucent overglaze enamels, without the use of underglaze blue. This sounds all very well, but when one comes to examine the style in general it is immediately apparent that there can be no hard and fast division between a 'Kakiemon' style and an 'Imari' style, nor is either 'style' coherent.

The legends in Japan, conflicting and doubtful though they are, generally state that a certain Sakaida Kakiemon learned the secrets of enamelling from a Chinese potter in Nagasaki and, after some difficulties, succeeded in making enamelled porcelain at a kiln in Nangawara in South-Western Arita, some time around the middle of the 17th century. These legends should not be taken at face value; those documents that are 17th century that have been used in this context are ambiguous to say the least. Other documents are later or in some cases downright forgeries.

Be that as it may, enamelling was done in Arita around mid century, though not at first in the style that we call Kakiemon. No kiln made a recognisably Kakiemon porcelain body until the 1670s or late 1680s when production began at the kiln that we now call the Kakiemon kiln, on the north-east side of the Nangawara valley. Clearly, then, the enamels used for the Kakiemon wares had an ancestry in the Early Enamelled wares,

used by enamellers who were not potters, nor tied to one kiln by contract or custom. It could be that the founders of the 'Kakiemon' kiln in Nangawara were the enamellers of the so-called Kakiemon palette before they were potters. If we are not to discard the hearsay evidence totally, then it may be logical to postulate that these potters were ancestral, possibly literally, to the Sakaida Kakiemon of today.

Sherds from the kiln site answer many of our questions while posing many others. Difficult to understand, for instance, is the lack of sherds of tall shapes or closed shapes; almost all sherds from the kiln site are plates or bowls. As enamels were fired onto the already fired, glazed body in a second, low temperature firing in a muffle kiln, enamelled sherds are not found at kiln sites; so how do we know that the kiln we are discussing was the producer of the Kakiemon plates and bowls? The evidence for this is provided by the existence in Europe of enamelled pieces in shapes, some with moulded decoration, that are identical to those found at the site. Many of these are now part of early collections such as that formed at Dresden. Evidence is also provided by the great quantity of sherds of the white-bodied, colourless-glazed plates and bowls found at the Nangawara site, the body called *nigoshide* ('milky-white'), in Japan. Admittedly sherds of this body are also found at other Arita kiln sites, notably Otaru, but nowhere in such quantity. It seems reasonable to assume that these latter kilns were imitators of the Kakiemon, competing for the same market.

The kiln site also offers evidence of variety; variety in types of wares, aimed at different levels of the market and of styles of decoration. The milky white body never carries underglaze blue but underglaze blue is a commonplace, in fact occuring on the great majority of pieces found at the site. This, of course, is to be expected; the Kakiemon kiln was a factory producing porcelains at different price levels and at different degrees of sophistication. Some of these wares were to be in underglaze blue only; others had some underglaze blue that left spaces for enamelling more or less to the choice of the enameller; yet others had underglaze blue that dictated to the enameller what had to be painted. In addition, the Kakiemon kiln made much fine celadon.

The styles of decoration were equally varied. Most of the enamelled *nigoshide* dishes are in a recognisable pictorial style, though the well-known 'Hob-in-the-well' pattern (No. 122) is somewhat aberrant. In general, it would be fair to say that the *nigoshide* pieces were the finest products of the kiln, and arguably the finest products of Arita. Some pieces, however, are patterned rather than pictorial, while the blue-and-white wares offer an even wider variety. Some do adhere to the pictorial style, while others bear formal patterns or startlingly asymmetrical decoration, often of inanimate objects.

The ancestry of the enamels is traceable in the Early Enamelled ware, as a proto-Kakiemon leading into a recognisable Kakiemon style that must be earlier than the kiln itself and that was working in parallel with other styles that are only marginally different. It is difficult to see the large jars with the figures under umbrellas, within formal borders (No. 138), as proto-Kakiemon, even though the enamels are virtually identical, while it is equally difficult to see why, if the Kakiemon had the use of overglaze brown, they should only have used it on two shapes, the (sic) 'Hampton Court' jars and the square jars derived from Dutch glass gin-bottles. Clearly these must all have been the work of other groups of enamellers, contemporary with and rivals to the enamellers of the pre-Kakiemon wares. Dating of the evolution of the palette is helped by the pieces in dated European collections; thus the Burghley House elephants No. 160, that look later than the tortoise No. 158 and the boys with 'juggs' No. 162, are certainly as early as 1688; as the

colours are very similar to the more commonplace pieces, then that helps us to date the latter.

And just as the enamels had a lineage before the commencement of the Nangawara kiln, so did the special body used at the kiln, the *nigoshide* body. This, in all probability, is made of the same basic ingredients as the other bodies and glazes of Arita, nearly all stone from Izumiyama and glaze-stone plus ash, but much better levigated to remove iron and to increase the ratio of alumina to silica. A few pieces of a body close to the *nigoshide*, but bearing early enamels are known (No. 97) which testify to an ancestry of the *nigoshide* at some kiln in Arita as yet unidentified. No sherds have been found, so we are not able to judge whether or not these were made at the Kakiemon kiln; on the whole it seems unlikely, as these rare pieces look too early. Evidence of sherds from the kiln site makes it clear that the Kakiemon kiln began production later than some of the other kilns involved in the export trade, probably in the late 1670s or 1680s. With the ascendancy of the Chinese in the international porcelain market in the 1730s, production must have dropped sharply, as it did at all the kilns of Arita; it did not, however, cease. In all probability there was a small production of recognisably Kakiemon porcelain throughout the 18th century, which would account for the anomalous pieces found, sometimes, today.

The use of the term Kakiemon is useful, identifying as it does a general style and a general palette of enamels (where present), provided that it is realised that pieces thus identified were not all produced at one kiln, nor enamelled at one workshop, that the pictorial style may be varied and that underglaze blue is more commonly found than not. Nor can firm divisions be drawn between these wares and some of the wares that are normally called Imari.

O. R. I.

100
Ewer
Japan, 1670–90
Height 20.5 cm
British Museum, JA FRANKS 1036.

With oviform body, cylindrical neck and cup-shaped
mouth with pinched spout and high loop handle pierced
for a metal lid mount. It is painted in a Kakiemon palette
of red, green, yellow and blue enamels with drawing in
black. In shaped panels on either side are two boys with
a fan and a parasol standing by a flowering peony
growing by rocks. Formal floral motifs appear between
them and on the neck and handle; double red lines ring
the lip, shoulder and base and frame the panel designs.

The decoration in the cartouches of this jug is
reminiscent of that on the large jar No. 138.

101
Ewer, with European Gilt-metal Lids, Chain and
Base
Japan, 1680–1700
Height 20 cm
Private Collection.

A slender pear-shaped ewer with tall, expanding neck,
high loop handle and bent, rising spout. It is painted in
Kakiemon colours with bamboo and prunus growing by
rocks, a floral motif on the neck and floral scrolls on the
handle and spout. The gilt-metal mounts were added at a
later date.

Only open shapes were made at the Kakiemon kiln, the
evidence of the spoil heaps informs us. Some others,
such as ewers like this one, jars (No. 120) and bottles
(Nos 113 and 119) appear to bear the same enamels. It
would seem likely that the enamellers at the Kakiemon
kiln also worked on other shapes from other kilns. In
many cases (No. 111) these appear to have been selected
for their whiteness of body.

102

Cup and Saucer

Japan, *c.* 1680–1700

Cup, height 4.2 cm; Saucer, diameter 10.8 cm

Ashmolean Museum, Oxford, 1978.594, Reitlinger Gift.

A small cup with slightly everted lip and saucer with a foliated rim. They are painted with red lotus blooms linked with formal scrolls and leaves on the outside of the cup and inside the saucer and are otherwise plain.

LITERATURE: Oxford, Ashmolean Museum, 1981, No. 164.

103

Teapot, with European Silver-gilt Mounts

Japan, *c.* 1680–1700

Length 11.2 cm

Victoria and Albert Museum, London, C.413 & A–1909 , J. H. Fitzhenry Gift.

A small, lobed oval teapot with matching lid having a flower-bud knob and attached by silver-gilt chains to mounts on the handle and spout. It is painted in Kakiemon-style enamels with prunus trees growing by rocks and cloud scrolls round the sides and lid, with *ruyi* and dentate borders on the neck and shoulder and foliage scrolls on the handle and spout.

A rather exact copy of this teapot was made at the Bow factory about 1753, see A. Gabszewicz and G. Freeman, 1982, No. 51, Pl. III.

LITERATURE: D. F. Lunsingh Scheurleer, 1980, Abb. 493.

104

Incense Burner (*koro*)

Japan, *c.* 1700

Height 11.3 cm

Private Collection.

A tripod bowl with two square handles and an everted, foliated rim; the slightly domed lid has a persimmon knob and three perforations in the shape of a flower, a fan and a double gourd. It is painted in a Kakiemon palette of red, green, blue and gilt with on either side a chrysanthemum flower-head and bud in a leafy scroll and on the lid, an all-over design of flowering pomegranate. The rim has a lappet border in alternating colours.

An identical vessel in the Porzellansammlung, Dresden is recorded as having been acquired in October, 1723 'from the merchant Konspruck': see F. Reichel, 1980, Pl. 32. The Meissen factory produced versions with Kakiemon figure designs about 1725-30: see No. 305.

105
Covered Box

Japan, *c.* 1700
Height 12 cm
Ashmolean Museum, Oxford, 1978.535, Reitlinger Gift.

A circular box with a pierced lid, shaped like a cake-box slung in a wicker frame, which may have been used for keeping crickets. It is painted in blue, green and red enamels and gilt with the upper sides divided into minute panels by stripes of black, and with sprays of hanging wistaria on the lid and round the lower sides.

LITERATURE: O. C. S. exhibition catalogue, 1956, No.182.

106
Cup and Saucer

Japan, 1680–1700
Cup, height 4.2 cm; Saucer, diameter 10.8 cm
Ashmolean Museum, Oxford, 1978.592, Reitlinger Gift.

A small cup with plain sides and saucer with foliated rim. They are painted with chrysanthemum sprays inside the saucer and on the outside of the cup, which are otherwise undecorated.

LITERATURE: Oxford, Ashmolean Museum, 1981, No. 163.

107
Dish

Japan, early 18th century
Diameter 19.9 cm
Ashmolean Museum, Oxford, 1978.634, Reitlinger Gift.

A saucer dish painted in the Kakiemon style with a lakeside scene in the centre mainly in underglaze blue, and a broad border of peony, prunus and pomegranate growing by rocks in red, green and yellow enamels. The outside is plain.

Sherds of very similar dishes have been found at the Kakiemon kiln site.

LITERATURE: Oxford, Ashmolean Museum, 1981, No. 194.

108

Covered Inkstand and Sander

Japan, *c.* 1700
Heights 5.8 cm; Inkstand, length 9.7 cm;
Sander, length 9.4 cm
Groninger Museum, Groningen,
NAP 4 A & B.

The inkstand is a square box with circular
aperture on top and a shallow overfitting
cover with small knob, having four holes
pierced in the corners. The sander is
oblong, with holes on top. Both are
painted *en suite* in Kakiemon-style enamels
with a pine growing by a rock alternating
with *karakusa* scrolls.

Designed for the Western market and
no doubt based on Delft originals. The
sander is illustrated by S. Jenyns, 1965,
Pl. 65A (ii).

109

Blue-and-white Box and Cover

Japan, 1690–1710
Width 19 cm
Private Collection.

A slab-built hexagonal box on moulded
bun feet, formerly with two side handles,
the domed cover having a strap handle. It
is painted round the sides and on top with
chrysanthemum and other plants growing
by rocks.

Formerly in the collection of Margaret,
Duchess of Portland. The Meissen coloured
version of this shape, lacking side handles
and on similar bun feet is illustrated by
M. Shono, 1973, Pl. 66.

110

Teapot and Lid, with European Gilt-metal Mounts

Japan, 1680–1700, the mounts
contemporary and probably Dutch
Height 14 cm
Ashmolean Museum, Oxford, 1978.658,
Reitlinger Gift.

An eight-lobed melon-shaped teapot, the
plain knob of the lid fitted with a gilt-metal
finial and secured by a chain to mounts on
the handle and spout. In panels and bands
outlined in underglaze blue and painted in
Kakiemon enamels are eight different
flowering plants round the sides, a floral
scroll on the shoulder and a flower spray
round the lid.

For a Chinese copy of this style of teapot
made for the European market, see No. 252.

111

Vase

Japan, late 17th century
Height 22.2 cm
Ashmolean Museum, Oxford, 1978.538,
Reitlinger Gift.

A square bottle vase with long neck. It is
decorated in the Kakiemon palette of
enamels and gilt, with stylised sprays of
prunus and daisy repeated on alternate
sides. On the neck are panels of scrollwork
and a formal floral design in red and gold.

In origin a saké flask, this shape was very
popular at the Meissen factory near
Dresden about 1725–35 (where it was
made in Böttger stoneware) and often
appears with purely Western-style
decoration. The exhibition includes an
early Meissen version with blue-and-white
chinoiserie landscapes (No. 290). A direct
copy of No. 111 in the Porzellansammlung
at Dresden, complete with stopper, is
illustrated by F. Reichel, 1981, Pl. 91.

LITERATURE: Oxford, Ashmolean Museum,
1981, No. 180.

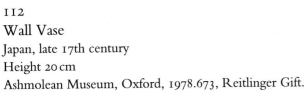

112
Wall Vase
Japan, late 17th century
Height 20 cm
Ashmolean Museum, Oxford, 1978.673, Reitlinger Gift.

A vase shaped like a quadrangular hour-glass with a
moulded ropework band at the waist and two notched
ring handles and a flat, inverted rim. It is pierced on one
side at the top for suspension. Painted round the sides in
the Kakiemon enamel palette are a prunus bough with
perching bird and a smaller one with a bird on the wing.

LITERATURE: Oxford, Ashmolean Museum, 1981,
No. 168; S. Jenyns, 1965, Pl. 65A illustrates another vase
of this unusual type in Lord Ilchester's Collection.

113
Square Flask
Japan, c. 1680
Height 14.5 cm
Ashmolean Museum, Oxford, 1978.668, Reitlinger Gift.

A straight-sided square bottle with cambered shoulder
and small waisted tubular mouth. It is decorated in the
Kakiemon palette with a different flowering plant on
each side. Scrolled bands in red, blue and green cover
the shoulder.

A European glass or metal form: compare the blue-and-
white examples (No. 53) and the accompanying note.
The decoration of the sides is in the restrained style of
No. 96, though the shoulder is strongly coloured.

LITERATURE: Oxford, Ashmolean Museum, 1981, No. 170.

114
Two Small Dishes
Japan, *c.* 1700
Diameters 9.5 cm
Private Collection.

Small square saucer dishes with rounded corners and a deep triple scallop in each side; with circular foot. They are painted with a prunus tree, bamboo and a rock; the outside is plain.

115
Bowl
Japan, *c.* 1700
Diameter 25 cm
Ashmolean Museum, Oxford, 1978.539, Reitlinger Gift.

A bowl with fluted sides and scalloped brown-glazed rim. It is enamelled in the Kakiemon style with on the inside, three large peony sprays in red and gold with green curling leaves and outside, three sprays of clematis, yellow being used instead of gold.

Other sizes of bowls of this shape and highly distinctive style of decoration are known.

LITERATURE: Oxford, Ashmolean Museum, 1981, No. 182.

115

116

117

116
Bowl
Japan, 1690–1710
Diameter 23.5 cm
Victoria and Albert Museum, London, C.293-1910.

A bowl with five lobes each sub-divided, the rim petalled and edged in brown glaze. It is painted in a Kakiemon palette of blue, green, yellow and brown enamels with inside, a pomegranate tree bearing flowers and fruit by a rock with groups of rushes and on the outside, a flowering peony and another floral spray.

Five-lobed shapes were among the more inventive designs in Japanese porcelain to enter the European repertoire. Several variations exist of this beautiful bowl form, for instance, one from the Reitlinger collection in which the subdivided lobes point outwards (Oxford, Ashmolean Museum, 1981, No. 183); or the plain five-lobed bowl in the former de la Mare collection (S. Jenyns, 1956, Pl. 61A, see also T. Nagatake and S. Hayashiya, 1978, Col. Pls 38 and 39), a close copy of which, made at the Meissen factory, is No. 184 in the exhibition.

LITERATURE: J. Ayers, 1980, Pl. 81; London, Royal Academy of Arts, 1981, No. 219.

117
Covered Bowl
Japan, 1690–1710
Diameter 22 cm
British Museum, JA 1952, 12–22, 1.

A shallow bowl, the domed cover with everted rim and a strap handle lightly moulded with a floral medallion. The top is painted in Kakiemon-style enamels with a bearded man in a conical hat with a staff, a crouching *shishi* and a flowering peony growing by blue rocks in between; round the outside are three sprays and numerous sprigs of flowers. The rims of the bowl and cover are unglazed.

The strap-handled bowl shape was not greatly favoured in Europe. The rather strange combination of Chinese figures and a winged *shishi* is however found on the cover of the French, St Cloud tureen (No. 312). Other examples of this shape have the body moulded with a wave pattern.

118
Beaker
Japan, 1690–1710
Height 8 cm
Ashmolean Museum, Oxford, 1978.551, Reitlinger Gift.

A small, flat-bottomed beaker with straight spreading sides and everted, five-lobed rim. Painted outside in Kakiemon-style enamels is a flowering chrysanthemum and on the inside are three posies in blue.

Beakers of similar shape, one in a different pattern of Kakiemon enamels, from Burghley House, and another in blue-and-white, formerly at Welbeck Abbey are illustrated by M. Hinton and O. Impey, 1989, Pls 10 and 42.

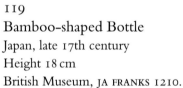

119
Bamboo-shaped Bottle
Japan, late 17th century
Height 18 cm
British Museum, JA FRANKS 1210.

The bottle is modelled as a section of bamboo with two small branches in relief having a rounded shoulder with petal fluting and a small tubular mouth. It is painted in turquoise, blue and red enamels outlined in black with a chrysanthemum growing by rocks with cloud scrolls above; on the shoulder are five florets.

120
Jar and Cover
Japan, 1690–1700
Height 26 cm
The Burghley House Collection, Stamford, Lincolnshire.

An oviform jar with angled shoulder, short neck and thickened footring, with a domed cover. It is painted in underglaze blue and Kakiemon-style enamels comprising red, deep turquoise blue, yellow and black with a bold design of chrysanthemum round the sides in all stages of development from bud to full bloom; the design is repeated on the cover and the shoulder is decorated in underglaze blue with three bands of petals.

Rather like a later and advanced version of No. 84, the blue-and-white decoration of this jar leaves the choice of enamel decoration entirely to the enameller.

LITERATURE: G. Lang, 1983, No. 82; New York, Japan Society, 1986, No. 74.

121
Dish
Japan, 1680–1700
Diameter 21.2 cm
Ashmolean Museum, Oxford, 1985.34, Jeffery Story and
Walter Cook Bequest.

A plain shallow saucer painted in blue, turquoise, and red
enamels and gilt and partly drawn in black. A long-tailed
phoenix is depicted flying by a tall flowering peony
growing by a triple banded hedge.

This is the earliest of a series of plates or dishes of
standard patterns made of the milky-white (*nigoshide*)
body at the Kakiemon kiln; it may be considered as a
descendant of No. 97. In the slightly later examples,
some of which are shown here (Nos 122, 123, 124, 125
and 127), the painting is more consistent than in this
pattern where there is considerable individual variation,
in particular in the depiction and placing of the birds.
Formerly at Drayton House. For a Meissen version of
the design see R. Rückert, 1966, Fig. 286, Pl. 74.

122

Octagonal Dish

Japan, *c.* 1700

Diameter 20.4 cm

Ashmolean Museum, Oxford, 1978.573, Reitlinger Gift.

A dish with panelled sides and a flat rim with upturned brown edge. It is decorated in the Kakiemon palette of enamels (but with no yellow) with a dramatic scene involving two figures and a large jar under a tree, and with an elaborate floral border round the rim.

One of the most imitated of all subjects on Kakiemon ware, the scene illustrated here became known in 18th century England as the 'Hob-in-the-Well' pattern. It was copied first at Meissen around 1730 (see No. 192) and subsequently at Chelsea (see No. 193). The story concerns the celebrated Chinese statesman and historian of the Song dynasty, Sima Guang, who as a child is reputed to have been very quick-witted when a friend was drowning in a large pottery jar. He picked up several small rocks and casting them at the jar smashed it, thus allowing the water to escape and his friend to survive. This story was very popular in late 17th century Japan, where Sima Guang was known as Shiba Onkō. Kakiemon patterns depicting events, or humans are uncommon, though see also No. 117.

LITERATURE: Oxford, Ashmolean Museum, 1981, No. 185. See also S. Jenyns, 1956, pp. 125 and 157 for his comments.

123
Decagonal Dish

Japan, end of the 17th century
Diameter 24 cm
Ashmolean Museum, Oxford, 1978.548,
Reitlinger Gift.

A saucer dish with an everted, petalled
rim with brown-glazed edge. It is painted
in the Kakiemon palette including some
black and gold with a curled dragon in the
centre and a broad surrounding band in
which appear a 'flaming tortoise' or
minogame, two cranes and the 'Three
Friends', pine, prunus and bamboo. The
outside is plain.

A Meissen copy of this dish of *c.* 1723-25
which bears the Dresden Palace
Collection mark is reproduced by
R. Rückert, 1966, No. 291, while a
Chelsea bowl with the design is No. 330
below. A model of the *minogame* tortoise
with rider is No. 158. The coiled dragon
in the centre of the dish is also a
characteristic Kakiemon motif:
see No. 92.

124
Decagonal Dish

Japan, *c.* 1700
Diameter 19.3 cm
Private Collection.

With panelled sides and a flat rim with
upturned brown edge. It is painted in the
Kakiemon palette with a *shishi* lion in
blue with yellow spots and red mane and
tail standing beside a tall peony growing
by a trellis and banded hedge. In the rim
border are geometric fret patterns and
florets; the outside is plain.

For models of the *shishi* in similar, almost
characteristic blue and yellow colouring,
see No. 146. This pattern also occurs in
blue-and-white without the use of
enamels.

LITERATURE: Oxford, Ashmolean
Museum, 1981, No. 187; Victoria, B.C.,
Art Gallery, 1983, No. 7.

125
Small Dish
Japan, *c.* 1700
Diameter 11.4 cm
Ashmolean Museum, Oxford 1978.565,
Reitlinger Gift.

A small saucer dish with everted, brown-edged rim. It is painted on one side with an iron-red dragon coiled round a blue bamboo by a flowering prunus and on the other with a snarling tiger; a double circle in the centre of the dish bisects both animals.

Dragon and tiger, perhaps representing Heaven and Earth, are found in several patterns of Kakiemon dishes. See No. 126, a blue-and-white example where the dragon emerges from clouds; here the dragon is supported by, or coiled around a bamboo. This pattern can be found in underglaze blue, complete with double circle.

126
Blue-and-white Dish
Japan, *c.* 1690–1710
Diameter 31.4 cm
The Stichting Twickel, Delden, The
Netherlands, JK 38.

A saucer dish moulded in ten pointed lobes with a petalled rim edged in brown. It is painted in underglaze blue with a striding tiger beneath a prunus and near a banded hedge and bamboo, looking up at a grinning dragon whose head and tail are emerging from the clouds.

This superbly painted dish has many of the finest Kakiemon features, but is not made of the *nigoshide* body, which appears never to have been used for any pieces that bear underglaze blue. See also Nos 132, 133 and 134 also 129 and 130 where blue is used with enamels.

127

Teabowl and Saucer

Japan, *c. 1700*

Bowl, diameter 7 cm; Saucer 12.5 cm

The Burghley House Collection, Stamford, Lincolnshire.

A straight-sided octagonal teabowl and matching saucer, painted in red, turquoise, blue, black and gilding with the so-called 'Old Lady' pattern. A lady in court dress listens enraptured to a nightingale which is perched on a cage set on a veranda beneath an awning. Inside the teabowl is a five-pointed floret. The rims are edged in iron-brown.

For the Chelsea version of this pattern see No. 328 and for Bow, see No. 327.

Literature: G. Lang, 1983, No. 59; New York, Japan Society, 1986, No. 110.

128

Small Octagonal Bowl

Japan, 1690–1710

Diameter 10.5 cm

The Burghley House Collection, Stamford, Lincolnshire.

A deep, straight-sided bowl on a round foot and with flat spreading rim turned up at the edge, which is lined in brown. The eight sides are painted in red, turquoise, blue and black enamels and gilt with sprays of chrysanthemum, prunus, peony and iris each twice repeated. Round the rim is a floral border and inside on the bottom is a prunus-blossom.

Sherds of this shape, in many sizes, have been found at the Kakiemon kiln site. These bowls are made of the *nigoshide* body; compare with the blue-and-white example No. 131, which is not.

Literature: G. Lang, 1983, No. 70.

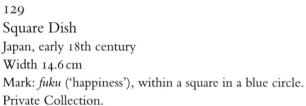

129
Square Dish
Japan, early 18th century
Width 14.6 cm
Mark: *fuku* ('happiness'), within a square in a blue circle.
Private Collection.

A saucer dish with indented corners and slightly lobed,
brown-edged rim; the footring is circular. It is painted in
underglaze blue, red, green and yellow enamels and gilt
with a cockerel and hen in the centre and round the
border, with two dragons on facing sides among clouds,
and formal lotus sprays between. Round the outside are
four scrolling designs.

Chinese copies of this shape and pattern are known, see
S. Jenyns, 1965, Pl. 79. A Meissen copy in the Dresden
Collection is illustrated by M. Shono, 1973, Pl. 64.
For a Bow version, in which the border design has the
dragons to the side instead of above and below, see
A. Gabszewicz and G. Freeman, 1982, No. 56, p. 47.

LITERATURE: Victoria, B.C., Art Gallery, 1983, No. 8.

130
Decagonal Dish
Japan, first quarter of the 18th century
Diameter 19 cm
Mark: *fuku* ('happiness'), on the base.
Ashmolean Museum, Oxford, 1978.633, Reitlinger Gift.

A ten-sided saucer dish with narrow everted rim and
upturned brown edge. It is painted in underglaze blue
and in red, green and yellow enamels and gilt with a
golden pheasant perched in a prunus tree growing by a
triple banded hedge and another pheasant swooping
nearby; a formal floral scroll in red and gold borders the
rim and a meander scroll runs round the outside.

'Brown edge' dishes in the combination of underglaze
blue and Kakiemon enamels are not common. This
pattern is the best known and may be one of the
inspirations of the so-called 'Joshua Reynolds' pattern of
Chelsea and Worcester: cf. Nos 329 and 348.

131

Blue-and-white Octagonal Bowl

Japan, 1690–1710
Diameter 10.5 cm
Mark: *fuku* ('happiness'), in a circle.
Private Collection.

A deep, straight-sided bowl on a round foot with an everted rim with petalled edge lined in brown. The eight panels are painted in underglaze blue with four repeated flowers: iris, peony, prunus and chrysanthemum.

Inside in the centre is a bird with trailing feathers and round the rim, a border with two ranks of petals.

A Kakiemon shape (see No. 128), very unusual in blue-and-white.

132

Blue-and-white Bowl

Japan, 1690–1710
Diameter 22 cm
Mark: *fuku* ('happiness'), in a square.
Private Collection.

A bowl with slightly fluted mouldings on the inside and an everted, petalled rim edged with brown. It is painted in underglaze blue with tree peonies, pomegranates and rocks round the outside and inside in the centre, a double circle with four flower sprays round the sides.

The painting on this bowl fully equals that on the best quality enamelled pieces but the body is the ordinary Kakiemon body, not *nigoshide*, and the glaze has the typical blue tinge of all other Arita glazes. A bowl of this type was registered in the Dresden Porcelain Collection in 1721, see F. Reichel, 1981, Pl. 9.

133
Blue-and-white Dish
Japan, *c.* 1700
Diameter 31.1 cm
Mark: cursive *fuku* ('happiness') in a double square.
Private Collection.

A large dish with rounded sides and a petalled brown-edged rim. Painted in the centre are two sages standing on a rocky crag under a pine tree viewing a waterfall, and round the border, two tigers among bamboo and prunus and other plants. Round the outside is a meander scroll.

Formerly in the collection of Margaret, Duchess of Portland. Sherds of this pattern have been found at the Kakiemon kiln site.

134
Blue-and-white Dish
Japan, Arita, early 18th century
Diameter 31.5 cm
Mark: *fuku* ('happiness') in a square.
Ashmolean Museum, Oxford, 1978.716, Reitlinger Gift.

A large dish with fluted sides and slightly everted ten-petalled rim with brown edge. It is drawn and painted in soft washes of underglaze blue with a man and his boy with a parasol looking across a river at a lady holding a fan and her attendant, with growing pine, prunus and bamboo and two birds; in the foreground a fisherman draws in his net. Round the outside is a meander scroll.

From the collection of the Duke of Portland, Welbeck Abbey. For a Loosdrecht/Amstel porcelain, and a Delft faience copy of this pattern see C. J. A. Jörg, 1984, Pls 157 and 120.

LITERATURE: Oxford, Ashmolean Museum, 1981, No. 272.

135
Beaker Vase
Japan, 1670–90
Height 47 cm
Sherborne Castle Estates.

A tall, trumpet-mouthed cylindrical beaker with low, inset foot. It is painted in a Kakiemon palette of blue, turquoise, red and yellow enamels with a tall pine, prunus and bamboo growing beside rocks and a small cloud scroll above.

A similar beaker in the Dresden Collection is illustrated by F. Reichel, 1981, Pl. 19. A Meissen version of the large beaker form is No. 299 in the exhibition. The AR-marked Meissen vase No. 186, is inspired by a later, Imari type of beaker.

LITERATURE: M. Hinton and O. Impey, 1989, Pl. 25.

136
Double Gourd Vase
Japan, 1670–90
Height 40 cm
Private Collection.

A double gourd vase with tubular neck and flaring mouth, painted in Kakiemon enamels of blue, green, red and yellow with on the lower bulb a pair of birds sitting on a rock beside tree peonies and on the upper bulb, a formal festoon of peonies and budding foliage. Round the waist is a key-fret border in red.

This Japanese form of the shape which occurs also in blue-and-white was copied in Europe, e.g. in Dutch delftware (No. 180). A striking Meissen adaptation of it, somewhat smaller in size and decorated in a pseudo-Chinese style, is the AR-marked vase in the Ernst Schneider Collection reproduced by R. Rückert, 1966, No. 342 and Taf. XII.

137

Beaker Vase
Japan, 1670–90
Height 47 cm
Her Majesty the Queen.

A tall, trumpet-mouthed cylindrical
beaker with low, inset foot, painted
in a Kakiemon palette of turquoise,
blue, red, yellow and black with
pomegranate and prunus growing by
rocks and a tall bamboo by a banded
hedge. A key-fret border in red rings
the foot.

One of a pair at Hampton Court
Palace. On this, see the important
study by Arthur Lane, 'Queen Mary
II's porcelain collection at Hampton
Court', *T.O.C.S.*, 25, 1949–50, pp.
21–31. Through her experience of
collecting in Holland prior to
William III's accession in 1689, Mary
came to lead the fashion for porcelain
as room decoration in England. Lane
did not argue that the collection
there now incorporates the collection
inventoried at Kensington Palace
after the Queen's death in 1694 –
which has since been shown to be
improbable; but apart from one or two
recent insertions it remains typical of
her time today. No. 151 in this
exhibition is also lent from the Palace.

LITERATURE: E. Dillon, 1910, No. 64,
p. 24; S. Jenyns, *T.O.C.S.*, 1937–38,
Pl. 7.

138

Large Covered Jar
Japan, 1670–90
Height 55 cm
Mark: on the Delft cover, PAK
monogram of the 'Greek A' factory,
1701–22.
Porzellansammlung, Dresden, PO 948.

A massive tall oviform jar with short
neck and thickened foot; the flanged,
domed cover is a Dutch delft

137

replacement. It is painted in a Kakiemon palette of green, red, blue, yellow, greyish-purple and black with three decorative panels round the sides framed by dense blue scrollwork with red peony blooms. In these, two figures with a parasol and a fan stand on either side of a gnarled prunus by rocks and a tall bamboo on which perches a large bird. Round the neck are various flower sprays and the cover repeats the main design without the figures.

It is perhaps of interest that this truly palatial jar does not have Augustus the Strong's inventory mark (see F. Reichel, 1981, Pl. 18, p. 148). A ceiling painting at Oranienburg near Berlin, the palace of the Elector of Brandenburg in the late 17th century, showed cherubs holding up such a vase (L. Reidemeister, 1934, Pl. 8, p. 272). This was allegedly destroyed during the war; S. Jenyns (1965) says that the vase used as a model is probably one today in Charlottenburg Palace. Others exist in English collections, e.g. at Blenheim Palace (H. Nishida, 1974, Pl. 5); at Woburn Abbey (Washington, National Gallery of Art, 1985, No. 131); and in the Victoria and Albert Museum (J. Ayers, 1980, Fig. 260). S. Jenyns, 1965, Pl. 57B, pp. 129 and 72, illustrates one from the former de la Mare Collection that is now in Japan, and he speculates that the figure style implies European influence. Conversely, it is quite plausible that these jars will have contributed to the chinoiserie theme of 'La Dame au Parasol' which echoes through European art of the following centuries. The same decoration occurs on trumpet vases (e.g. at Woburn Abbey) and on covered bowls (e.g. in the Louvre). This distinctive style of decoration sets this series apart from the Kakiemon.

139
Square Bottle, mounted as a Pot-pourri or Pastille-burner
Japan, 1670–90
Height 13.5 cm
Her Majesty the Queen.

A square bottle similar to No. 111, reduced and mounted in gilt metal to make a small covered pot. It is painted in Kakiemon-style enamels round the sides with a woman holding a flower by a banded hedge and looking back at a tiger cavorting by a flowering tree and a bamboo. The bottle is fitted with a square base and four leaf-scroll ormolu feet and is cut twice below the neck to create the cover. Both parts have metal rims and the cover is similarly mounted and hinged, and topped with a square porcelain knob, perhaps the original; holes are bored in its four sides and fitted with rings, to emit fragrance.

The adaptation of broken pieces demonstrates the high esteem in which this porcelain was held.

139

140

River Boat, mounted as an [?] Incense Burner

Japan, late 17th century, the gilt-metal
mounts mid 18th century
Height 18.4 cm; length 22.8 cm
Her Majesty the Queen.

A porcelain model boat painted with
swirling waves round its sides in
underglaze blue and gilt and a red key-
fret band above, set in a gilt-metal base
moulded with waves and fish. Over the
forward well area is added a porcelain
plaque, raised on pierced metal sides,
with a finial in the form of a snarling *shishi* lion on a flowering branch painted in
green, red and purple enamels and

forming a handle; towards the stern is
added a low cut-out porcelain 'platform'
with miniature models of a boy playing
with a dog, a bottle and a cup and stand
in Kakiemon colouring. There are holes
by which to suspend the boat fore and aft.

An ingenious adaptation of disparate
elements to create a somewhat whimsical
'japonaiserie', which may nevertheless
have served a practical function on
festive occasions.

For a companion fish with the same mounting and a spigot see R. J. Charleston and J. Ayers, 1971, No. 100, p. 298 where it is discussed by the last-named. No other carp of this model are known although Imari-style fish such as Nos 178 and 179, also sometimes decoratively mounted in ormolu, are not uncommon. F. Reichel, 1981, Pl. 81 illustrates such a vase in the Dresden Porzellansammlung in the form of a golden carp, decorated mainly in red and gold.

LITERATURE: D. F. Lunsingh Scheurleer, 1980, Abb. 502 A & B.

142
Tripod Candlestick, with Gilt-metal Spike
Japan, 1670–90
Height 31 cm (without spike)
British Museum, JA, FRANKS 1696.
In the form of a stem of bamboo on a base moulded with three monster-heads whose protruding, curling tongues are the feet. It is painted in Kakiemon-style enamels mainly with blue for the heads and with pine, prunus

141
Fish, mounted in European Ormolu as a *Fontaine à Parfum*
Japan, late 17th century, the mounts perhaps French, mid 18th century
Height 33 cm
Musées Royaux d'Art et d'Histoire, Brussels.

A hollow model of a carp with flat, unglazed underside and designed to hang on the wall, mounted upright on its tail in ormolu of the Louis XV style. It is decorated in Kakiemon enamels with the scales and tail finely painted in red and blue, dorsal and frontal fins in red and the eye in black and yellow. On an ormolu mound base rich with vegetation it is supported by a leafy bocage concealing the back and joining a hinged cap fitted to the cut-down mouth. Below the fin is a hole for a spigot.

142

and cloud scrolls round the stem, Buddhist emblems on the sides and *karakusa* scrolls along the feet.

A candlestick of identical form in the Tanakamaru Collection complete with flower-like top, and decorated rather in Imari-style colouring, was excavated from the grave of a man who died in 1711: cf. T. Nagatake, 1968, p. 36. Tripod candlesticks with animal feet are seen in the *blanc-de-Chine* porcelain of Dehua, see P. J. Donnelly, 1969, Pl. 57B, p. 123, although the 'candlesticks' shipped by the Dutch Company from Formosa to Batavia on 28th October 1646 (T. Volker, 1954, p. 54) were probably of an earlier pattern. Bronze versions with three feet, rarely seen in England, were probably made in both China and Japan.

143
Large Dish
Japan, late 17th – early 18th century
Diameter 55 cm
Private Collection.

A large dish with broad spreading rim. It is painted in underglaze blue and in green, red, yellow and purple enamels with a vase of flowers on a two-wheeled barrow attached to tasselled ropes in the centre surrounded by a pattern of interlinked key-fret and florets. Round the rim are eight variously-coloured horses standing or prancing among hillocks, plants and insects.

Smaller versions of dishes of this pattern were formerly in Drayton House.

144
Large blue-and-white Jar
Japan, 1670–80
Height 47 cm
Private Collection.

An oviform jar with short neck, formerly with a lid, painted in purplish underglaze blue and slightly misfired. Round the sides is a finely-composed design of birds among prunus trees and chrysanthemum growing by rocks, with a broad *karakusa* knobbed scroll round the high shoulder and meander-scroll border on the neck.

145

Covered Jar

Japan, late 17th century

Height 35.5 cm

Ashmolean Museum, Oxford, 1985.49, Jeffery Story and Walter Cook Bequest.

An ovoid jar with fluted sides and similar chrysanthemum-petal fluting extending from the shoulder to the neck, the domed cover similarly treated and with a chrysanthemum-bud knob. It is painted in Kakiemon enamels with subjects scattered over the surface: a boy in turquoise jacket and yellow trousers on a paved floor, a ribbon, a spotted blue *shishi* lion, a peacock, grasshoppers and other insects, a bird, flower sprays and a pine branch.

The Chantilly vase (No. 188) is a replica of the form; the scattered decoration is recalled in the Meissen beaker vase (No. 299). Dishes bearing the same motifs in similar randomly-scattered array are not uncommon: see, e.g. the example at Burghley House illustrated by M. Hinton and O. Impey, 1989, Pl. 12, where it is pointed out that this is referred to as the 'lion, butterfly and sprig' pattern in the sale catalogue (1786) of the collection of Margaret, Duchess of Portland.

146

***Shishi* Lion, mounted in Ormolu as a Candelabrum**

Japan, 1670–90, the mounts probably French, *c.* 1750

Height 34 cm

Residenzmuseum, Munich, K.V. C 238.

The lion, which sits on a rectangular plinth is set in an ormolu base with chased border and is half concealed among the curving, leafy branches of the two-armed candelabrum, the arms of which terminate in flower-like candle-holders. Its head is turned to the right with grinning jaws and its left paw plays with an embroidered ball. The body is spotted in blue and yellow enamels and the beetling eyebrows, mane and bushy tail are in blue, with the embroidered ball, floral scrolls on the plinth and other details in red, green and yellow.

One of a pair in the Residenz; unmounted examples of the model are in various collections, e.g. those at Drayton House illustrated by M. Hinton and O. Impey, 1989, Pl. 24. For some reason *shishi* are usually coloured predominantly in yellow and blue; compare the example on the dish, No. 124.

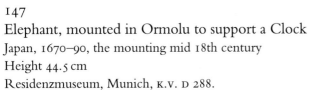

147

Elephant, mounted in Ormolu to support a Clock
Japan, 1670–90, the mounting mid 18th century
Height 44.5 cm
Residenzmuseum, Munich, K.V. D 288.

Standing with head turned to the left and trunk raised to
trumpet, its tail resting on its flank. The model is left
white apart from the Kakiemon-style enamel decoration
of the saddle-cloth with blue scrollwork and tasselled red
cinch, also the red mouth and tongue, yellow tusks and
black drawing of the eyes, etc. It is set on a modelled
ormolu base representing marshy ground with plants,
snakes and lizards and from this rises behind a tree-trunk
supporting the clock case, an adapted cylinder of
porcelain enamelled with Kakiemon flowers, topped by a
small bird in similar colouring set among ormolu foliage.
The clock face is inscribed 'E^NNE LENOIR A PARIS';
and is upheld by two long-tailed ormolu monkeys who
sit on the elephant's back.

The same elephant model is at Burghley House (No. 160).
Another such clock in the Residenz incorporating a
seated Kakiemon elephant is illustrated by O. Impey,
1977, Fig. 91. Etienne Lenoir is well-known as a Master
Clockmaker in Paris (1717–after 1778).

148

Square Flask, with Gilt-metal Top
Japan, 1670–90
Height 27.5 cm
Fitzwilliam Museum, Cambridge, C.30.1973, given by
Sir Harry and Lady Garner.

With straight sides, the rounded shoulder shaped by their
arched tops, the short neck replaced in gilt metal. It is
painted in Kakiemon-style enamels with on each face
two birds and a tree - in one case two cranes with a pine,
and in the others variously with prunus, bamboo and
another flowering shrub, also plants and a rock. On each
side of the shoulder is a flying bird in blue between the
formal sprays with red blooms which mark the four corners.

Like other square bottles (Nos 53, 113 etc.) the form
derives from that of a Dutch liquid container, probably
for spirits. In the 18th century however the finely-
enamelled pieces were richly mounted for display – e.g.
the pair lent from the Louvre, Paris (No. 149), and the
example in the possession of H. M. the Queen illustrated
in M. Hinton and O. Impey, 1989, Pl. 19.
    The use of brown enamel found, apparently, only on
this shape and on the so-called Hampton Court vases
(Nos 151 and 152) sets these apart from the Kakiemon.

149

Pair of Covered Square Flasks, mounted in Ormolu

Japan, 1670–90; the mounts French, 1725–35
Heights approx. 39 cm
Musée du Louvre, Paris, OA 5491.

Of the same general description as No. 148 but with the original necks and with covers. They are decorated with similar Kakiemon-style designs and round the neck is a repeated 'precious jewel' emblem. Each is set on a reeded square ormolu base with applied scrollwork and swags on the sides and a pendant with flower finial, the whole supported by four slender, scrolled feet. Each is topped also by its knobbed porcelain cover set in reeded mounts with leafy scrollwork.

From the collection of the Prince de Condé; in 1807 they were at the palace of St Cloud. The ormolu work is particularly fine. Published by D. F. Lunsingh Scheurleer, 1980, Abb. 485, where a pair of 'Hampton Court' hexagonal Kakiemon jars in the Louvre apparently mounted *en suite* with these appear on Abb. 484. Another pair of these square flasks in mounts of the same style are displayed in the State Rooms at Windsor Castle; they are believed to have been at the Brighton Pavilion in the time of George IV. The same author illustrates on Abb. 526 one from yet another pair in the collection of Her Majesty the Queen at Buckingham Palace which were elaborately mounted by Vulliamy about 1810.

150
Pair of Bowls, with Ormolu Mounts in Regency style

Japan, early 18th century, the mounts probably English, *c.* 1810
Heights 22.2 cm; diameters 24.6 cm
Ashmolean Museum, Oxford, 1978.664 A & B,
Reitlinger Gift.

The bowls are decagonal with everted rim and flanged, brown-edged lip, the foot being circular. They are painted in the Kakiemon palette with, inside, a central rosette and across the outlined, panelled sides a flowering plant and a phoenix medallion each twice repeated, with a scroll of ribbons and tassels on the rim; on the outside are two pairs of horses among clumps of flowering plants.

The round foot mount is supported by three winged lion-heads with single clawed feet attached to a Y-shaped base, and has a pineapple pendant.

The unusual and charming painting of horses resembles that on the Kakiemon-style dish, No. 143.

LITERATURE: Oxford, Ashmolean Museum, 1981, No. 188; D. F. Lunsingh Scheurleer, 1980, No. 492.

151
Hexagonal Jar and Cover

Japan, 1670–90
Height 31 cm
Her Majesty the Queen.

With tapering sides, steep shoulder, short hexagonal neck and matching domed cover with button knob. It is painted in Kakiemon style in red, green, blue, yellow, brown and black enamels. Three main panels with leafy frames each spanning two sides show two cranes, one swooping and the other standing by a pine tree and camellia growing by rocks; two plump birds, one flying and the other perching on a slender bamboo; and a woman in a blue coat with a fan by a flowering prunus, holding a spray. Round the shoulder is a leafy scroll band with three red-and-yellow fan-tailed birds at the corners and on the neck, a red key-fret border; the cover design matches the shoulder.

One of a pair at Hampton Court Palace, where another design is also represented; hence the shape has become popularly known as a 'Hampton Court' jar. A significant feature is that the second jar shows the designs in reverse, thus presenting a 'matched pair': possibly the earliest occurrence of this Western scheme in oriental porcelain. Another pair at Windsor Castle, mounted in 18th century ormolu, are illustrated by M. Hinton and O. Impey, 1989, Pl. 18. See note under No. 137.

M. Shono, 1973, Pl. 58 illustrates the Meissen copy of this pattern, in the Dresden Collection.

LITERATURE: A. Lane, 1949–50, Pl. 10F, p. 31; E. Dillon, 1910, No. 73, p. 27.

152
Pair of Hexagonal Covered Jars, mounted in Ormolu as [?] Pot-pourris
Japan, 1670–90, the mounts probably French, *c.* 1810
Heights 50.5 cm
Her Majesty the Queen.

Of the same form as No. 151 and again decorated in Kakiemon enamels. The single sides show pine, prunus and bamboo trees alternating with a green tendril-scroll design with single gilt bloom on a red ground. The same designs appear in counterpoint on the shoulder and cover; a floral scroll decorates the neck.

The mounting is elaborate, and the jar rises on six leaf-and-claw supports over a tall, spreading hexagonal stand of pseudo-Chinese openwork design incorporating 'endless knot' type roundels and vertical ribs ending in squared scroll feet. Above, the lid is raised on an openwork gallery, with ridges down the shoulder and projecting eave-like scrolls joined to it by crossed chains. The porcelain knob is replaced by a pagoda-type finial.

These jars were formerly at Brighton Pavilion. They were possibly brought to London about 1848 when Queen Victoria decided that the building should be emptied: see G. de Bellaigue, 'Chinoiserie at Buckingham Palace', *Apollo*, May, 1975, pp. 380–91.

153
Hexagonal Jar and Cover
Japan, 1670–90
Height 38 cm
Private Collection.

With tall, tapering sides, steep shoulder and hexagonal neck, and matching cover with knob in form of a bud, painted in a combination of underglaze blue and blue, red, yellow and turquoise enamels with some drawing in black. On each side are similar sprays of iris in different colours; round the shoulder is a band of blue-and-white *karakusa* scrollwork with red peony blooms, a design repeated in blue enamel on the cover; and round the neck is a key-fret band.

The combination of underglaze blue *karakusa* and the finely-drawn decoration in a strange palette of enamels makes this beautiful jar almost unique.

154
Blue-and-white Hexagonal Jar and Cover
Japan, 1660–80
Height 37.2 cm
Victoria and Albert Museum, London, C.38 & A–1962.

With tapering sides, sloping shoulder, hexagonal neck
and matching domed cover with button knob. It is
painted in underglaze blue with on alternate sides,
designs of chrysanthemum growing by rocks and a rose
standing in a double gourd vase. Round the shoulder and
lid are bands of *karakusa* scroll with peony heads and on
the neck is a key-fret pattern.

A blue-and-white version of the so-called 'Hampton
Court' jar form. The stylised designs on this vase invite
comparison with No. 55. An identical jar was acquired
for the Dresden Palace Collection from Count Flemming
in 1723 (F. Reichel, 1981, Pl. 6).

155
Hexagonal Jar and Cover
Japan, 1670–90
Height 31 cm
British Museum, JA FRANKS 478.

Of the same form as No. 151 and and painted in
Kakiemon enamels. Round the sides are two alternating
designs of flower sprays and on the shoulder, three
quatrefoil floral panels superimposed on a green tendril-
scroll ground with blue blooms on a red ground – a
design repeated on the cover – with a border of triangles
below. A key-fret band runs round the neck.

LITERATURE: Tokyo National Museum, 1987, No. 56.

VII Figures

Arita figures, whether blue-and-white, enamelled in Imari palettes or in Kakiemon style are well known in Europe and were influential, in the 17th and 18th centuries, on European ceramics. Free-standing models were exported to Europe from Japan even as early as 1659, when Wagenaer states that he has collected some assorted dolls and three pairs of figures of cranes for future shipment to Holland. Among porcelain shipped to Holland in the *Nieuwenhoven,* in 1665 , were among other things '310 small statuettes,... 295 statuettes on tortoises [and] 346 tortoises ...'. It is perfectly reasonable to suggest that the tortoise from Burghley House, shown here as No.158, may be from that shipment.

During the second half of the 17th century and the first thirty-odd years of the 18th, models, either free-standing or as knobs on large jars or on covered bowls were shipped in quantity. Shapes include many varieties of models of humans and several mythical figures and gods. (Hotei, for instance, the god of good fortune and fun, was among the ancestors of the *pagod* of European porcelain.) Animal figures include both real beasts such as dogs, horses and tigers and the mythical *shishi* and dragons; birds such as eagles, duck, parrots and chickens; fish, shells and flowers. Sometimes humans are found with animals: Benkei riding the giant carp, or the 'statuettes on tortoises' of 1665. Some of these figures are copied from European originals, rather than the other way round; see, for instance, the horse No. 176, clearly derived from a known Delft original.

There is an interesting cross-reference to the trade in export lacquer here; in 1662 the principal at Deshima was instructed by Batavia 'to fill the chests of drawers with small lacquered boxes, porcelain figures and other curiosities'. Volker had some difficulty with the word *poppegoet* that I have translated as 'figures'; we are now more aware than he could have been of the extent of the trade in figures.

Some of the figures are in celadon and iron brown (No. 157) and others in blue-and-white (Nos 156 and 72), but by far the greater proportion are enamelled, either in the Kakiemon palette or in varieties of the Imari palettes, usually with underglaze blue. Occasionally the same model can be found either in the one or in the other palette; for instance a figure such as the Kakiemon *bijin*, a beautiful woman (No. 165, a well-known type) that was enamelled in Imari colours was sold in London a few years ago. Much more usually, any model is found in one palette only. This implies that the making of the figure and the enamelling are somehow linked, and yet sherds of large figures are virtually never found at kiln sites. So where were they made?

Recent excavations on the site of the Aka-e-machi, the 'enamellers' quarter' in central Arita produced sherds not only of many figures (*inter alia*) but also of the moulds for the casting of figures. It may be, then, that the figures were cast at the Aka-e-machi and biscuit-fired in the muffle kiln before being sent to a *noborigama* to be high fired. If it is true that all enamelling was done in the Aka-e-machi, with the sole exception of the Kakiemon enamelling, a somewhat dubious proposition, then perhaps the Kakiemon kiln retained its models to be enamelled in its own muffle kiln after high firing; other kilns returned their models to the Aka-e-machi for enamelling.

Figures are listed among the exports from Japan in 1710 and 1711, in the *Toban Kamotsu Cho* (see the table p. 22). It is precisely because figures are easily identifiable in early records that they are so useful to the ceramic historian for dating purposes. In the 1688 Inventory of Burghley House, to take the most famous example, one can clearly recognise the '2 large Ellephants, the '2 China boyes Wrestling' and the '2 figures with Juggs att their backs' (Nos 160, 162 and 163). Such dates provide the evidence of their existence in Europe at this date; their arrival may well be, and indeed, in some cases certainly was considerably earlier.
O. R. I.

156
Blue-and-white Figure of a Hawk
Japan, late 17th century
Height 18 cm
The Burghley House Collection, Stamford, Lincolnshire.

The bird is perched on a hollow rock, its small beak open. Its modelled wings and tail feathers and head are detailed in blue, the breast is white and the talons and rock are washed in iron-brown.

As recounted by G. Lang, 1983, No.54, the 1688 Inventory at Burghley records under 'My Lords Dressing Rooms'...'China over ye Chimney...2 blue & wt Birds'. See also New York, Japan House, 1986, No. 51. The appearance of a similar white hawk on a brown rock in Staffordshire salt-glazed stoneware of the mid 18th century is worth noting: compare No. 342.

157
Two Buddhist *Rakan*
Japan, second half of the 17th century
Heights 19 cm and 20.5 cm
The National Trust: Erddig.

The figures are hollow-moulded and are seated in a relaxed pose with one leg raised and the other folded across, their emaciated bodies realistically modelled. Both are bald and bearded and one, who holds a stick or cudgel, opens his mouth to speak; the other's hands rest on his knee. The loose robes are coloured by a light celadon glaze and the stick, hair and eyes with brown glaze; the barely-glazed flesh areas have fired a thin pinkish-brown. The right foot of each is lacking.

The *Rakan* (sanscrit *Arhat* or 'Worthy Ones', Chinese: *Lohan*) were sometimes disciples of Buddha and sometimes rather legendary persons. They became a cult, first in China and then in Japan, where groups of eighteen, fifty-two or more *Lohan* were formed and venerated for their ascetic piety and supernatural gifts. These celadon-glazed figures survive in several older collections and they may be among the earliest models to have reached Europe.

158
Figure on a Tortoise
Japan, 1660–70
Length 18.5 cm
The Burghley House Collection, Stamford, Lincolnshire.

An Immortal riding on the back of a large 'flaming tortoise'. The creature has a strange bird-like head and five-toed feet and its shell is moulded with honeycomb pattern; below this are wing-like projections. The model is enamelled in turquoise, red, blue, yellow and black.

In oriental mythology, the tortoise is a symbol of longevity. The fringe of waterweed often found growing from the shell of the red-eared terrapin was considered a mark of age. As it was often rendered in overglaze red (No. 123) this was called, in Europe, the 'flaming tortoise'.

The documents of the V.O.C. (T. Volker, 1954, p. 152) mention that in 1665 the *Nieuwenhoven* was sent to Holland from Batavia bearing 19,229 pieces of porcelain from a cargo brought from Japan in the *Amerongen*. Among these were several figures, including '295 small statuettes on tortoises'.

LITERATURE: G. Lang, 1983, No. 93; New York, Japan Society, 1986, No. 88.

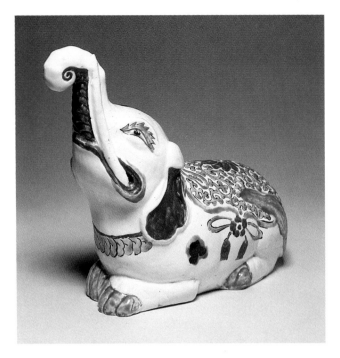

159
Seated Elephant
Japan, 1670–90
Length 24 cm
Private Collection, on loan to the Fitzwilliam Museum,
Cambridge, J.19.

The elephant is crouching with its head raised and trunk
curled. Its white body is painted in Kakiemon-style
enamels with a saddle-cloth decorated with a red lotus
among *karakusa* scrollwork and with pendent tassels; a
green and yellow chain hangs round its neck and the tail
and feet are in blue.

Although the elephant is of great importance in Buddhist
iconography it was extinct in both China and Japan from
an early date, and its depiction in art is often inaccurate.
Like some other models the Japanese porcelain elephants
may have been made in response to a foreign demand
for things curious and it is possible they were based on
models imported from South-East Asia or India; the few
elephants found in Chinese *blanc-de-Chine* porcelain
could hardly have inspired them. Some lacquered wood
basins with ewers in elephant form, possibly decorated if
not made in Japan, which probably entered the Danish
Royal Collections in the 17th century, suggest that a
trade in such objects existed. See Copenhagen,
Nationalmuseet, 1980, pp. 232–33.

160
Elephant
Japan, *c.* 1670–87
Height 28.5 cm
The Burghley House Collection, Stamford,
Lincolnshire.

An elephant modelled standing four-square with head
turned to the right and trunk raised as if to trumpet.
It wears a rectangular brocade saddle-cloth painted in a
Kakiemon palette of blue, red, yellow and black with
peonies amid *karakusa* scrolls and tied with a tasselled
cinch in red.

One of a 'pair' at Burghley, this model appears in the
1688 Inventory there located in 'My Lords Bedd
Chamr...' under '...2 large Ellephants' (G. Lang, 1983,
No. 92). A similar elephant forms part of the clock lent
to this exhibition from the Munich Residenz, (No. 147).
Another is in the Dresden Porzellansammlung: see F.
Reichel, 1981, Pl. 83.

LITERATURE: New York, Japan Society, 1986, No. 93;
M. Hinton and O. Impey, 1989, No. 6.

161
Black Elephant
Japan, 1670–90
Length 39.7 cm; height 32.7 cm
Victoria and Albert Museum, London, FE.134–1978.

Standing with trunk curled, the body enamelled mainly
in black and finely caparisoned. A brilliantly-patterned
saddle-cloth painted in Kakiemon colours is held in
place by a decorated harness that girds the body and over
the head is a patterned yellow hood; the broken tusks are
also in yellow.

This black elephant is apparently unique; an enamelled
white version of the model, however is in the British
Muscum, scc S. Jcnyns, 1965, Pl. 62A.

162
Youth seated on a Drum
Japan, 1670–85
Height 14 cm
The Burghley House Collection, Stamford,
Lincolnshire.

Seated in casual fashion on a drum, with both hands
holding tasselled cords attached to a double gourd bottle
slung over his shoulder. The model is decorated in a
Kakiemon palette which includes turquoise, blue, red
and black enamels.

Listed in the 1688 Inventory at Burghley within 'My
Lords Dressing Roome'…'China over ye Chimney…
2 figures with Juggs att their backs'. The model probably
represents the popular Chinese Immortal Li Tieguai.
Another pair in the Museo Duca di Martina, Naples is
illustrated in Naples, 1984, Pl. 1.3.

LITERATURE: G. Lang, 1983, No. 95; New York, Japan
Society, 1986, No. 89.

163
Two Wrestlers
Japan, 1670–85
Heights 30.7 cm
The Burghley House Collection, Stamford, Lincolnshire.

A group of two wrestlers stripped to grapple one another
in combat. They wear a simple loin-cloth which is
painted in red enamel, one having scattered florets and
foliate scrolls in blue and yellow; the hair, eyes and
eyebrows are in black enamel and the lips are picked out
in red.

The 1688 Burghley Inventory includes under the
heading 'The Wardrobe or Clock Chamber', '2 China
boyes Wrestling'.
    The group is described by G. Lang, 1983, No. 96 who
comments in his Introduction that they '…at first sight
seem to show two sumo wrestlers. In fact they represent
citizens perhaps from Arita wearing their simple
undergarments engaged in a private grappling match'.

LITERATURE: H. Nishida, 1974, p. 1402, Fig. 2;
O. Impey, 1985, Pl. 106; New York, Japan Society,
1986, No. 95.

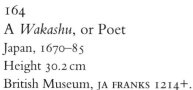

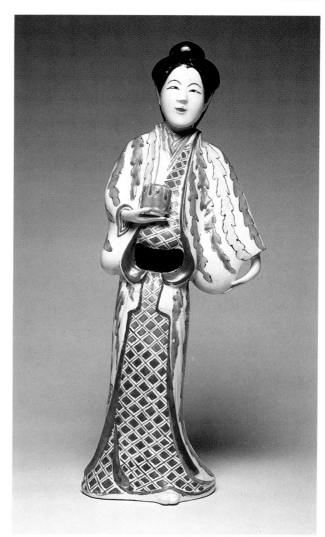

164
A *Wakashu*, or Poet
Japan, 1670–85
Height 30.2 cm
British Museum, JA FRANKS 1214+.

A figure of a young man dressed in a wrap-over kimono; one hand holds a fan tucked in his *obi* sash and the other, his sleeve. The kimono is painted in Kakiemon colours of blue, green, red and yellow with a wistaria tree and rectangles of stylised Chinese characters; the hair and *obi* are black.

Sometimes identified, although unreliably, with the figure no longer in that collection which is listed as 'Indian Queen' in 'My Lords Anty Roome' in the Burghley House Inventory of 1688 (No. 17 in this exhibition).

LITERATURE: S. Jenyns, 1965, Pl. 55B, where he states that it came from Burghley; T. Nagatake, S. Hayashiya, 1978, Pl. 47; Tokyo National Museum, 1987, Pl. 58.

165
Figure of a *Bijin*, or Beauty
Japan, 1670–90
Height 35 cm
Private Collection, on loan to the Fitzwilliam Museum, Cambridge, J.2.

She stands leaning slightly backward and with a smiling expression, holding a cup in her right hand and grasping a billowing sleeve with her left. Her hair is elaborately arranged with a loop at the back. She is dressed in a long kimono decorated in the Kakiemon style with a phoenix with long tail feathers which extend down its length and with cloud scrolls; with a black sash and an under-robe bearing a diamond-chequered pattern in red. The cup appears to be the remains of a damaged bottle.

Moulds for the making of these and similar figures have been found at the Aka-e-machi (enamellers' quarter) site in Arita. See note to No. 72.

166

166
Two Seated Figures of *Bijin*
Japan, 1670–90
Heights 26.8 cm
Victoria and Albert Museum, London, FE.33/4–1980.

Identical models, with animated expressions, seated at
ease with legs half folded beneath them, the right elbow
resting on a low table and the left hand touching the
ground. Their black hair is dressed in a central bun. They
wear richly-flowered kimonos with long sleeves and red
lining, open to reveal long, sashed robes chequered or
leaf-patterned in red and sprinkled with emblems.

These seem to be related to the standing figures such as
No. 165. From the H. M. Garner collection, one being
published in O. C. S. exhibition catalogue, 1956, No. 272
and S. Jenyns, 1956, Pl. 65B; and the two together by J.
Ayers, 1983, p. 54. A similar figure is in the Kina
pavilion at the Swedish Royal Palace of Drottningholm,
which was built in 1763: cf. S. Jenyns, 1937–38, Pl. 9B.

167
Two *Shishi*
Japan, 1670–85
Heights 16 cm
The Burghley House Collection, Stamford, Lincolnshire.

The *shishi* or lion-dogs are seated erect, one unsmiling
and the other with teeth bared, on studded oval drum-
shaped bases. They are decorated in enamels of the
Kakiemon palette, omitting yellow, and have red and
turquoise spotted coats, blue faces and tails and red
mouths; one sports a blue mane and his companion's
is in aubergine. The bases are decorated with formal
scrollwork.

G. Lang, 1983, No. 87, p. 32 writes that the 1688
Burghley Inventory refers to '2 Lyons' juxtaposed to the
'2 blue and white birds' located among 'China over ye
Chimney' in 'My Lords Dressing Roome'. Although the
description would seem vague these items were
discovered side-by-side in a display cabinet in the current

167

168
Two Tigers
Japan, 1670–1700
Heights 23.5 and 24 cm
Drayton House.

Seated on their hindquarters and both looking to the left with fierce expressions, their tails curled on their backs, and coloured in yellow enamel with black indications of fur, with white fronts and red jaws and ears. They are set on hollow tree stump bases painted in red and green with bamboo and sketchy washes.

Tigers were occasionally to be seen in Japan in travelling menageries; Japanese images of tigers almost invariably depict them as cat-like or even *shishi*-like rather than as the potentially ferocious beasts they are.

No tigers are listed in the Burghley House Inventory of 1688 (No. 17), yet a pair was sold from the house in 1888. This suggests that they may be later than the 1680s, and suggests continued acquisition of Japanese porcelain after the taking of the inventory.

master dressing room. Exceptional in lacking yellow (see No. 146), they may be early versions of the well-known larger figures. See also New York, Japan Society, 1986, No. 87. Other examples are known, e.g. at Drottning-holm: S. Jenyns, 1937–38, Pl. 6.

168

170
Exotic Bird
Japan, late 17th century
Height 42.5 cm
Lord Egremont, Petworth House, Sussex.

A large bird with prominent trefoil crest, curved beak, fierce eyes and talons sitting on a hollow tree stump. Its rich plumage is rendered in blue, red, turquoise-green, yellow and black enamels with a brilliant display of large feathers on the red breast, small blue and red feathers on the head and shoulders and a multi-coloured tail. The gnarled stump is mainly in brown.

Another example of the model in the Kurita Museum of Art, Ashikaga, has quite different colouring with green wing feathers: see T. Nagatake and S. Hayashiya, Tokyo, 1978, Pl. 179.

169
Figure of a Cockerel
Japan, 1670–1700
Height 28 cm
The Burghley House Collection, Stamford, Lincolnshire.

Modelled in a crowing attitude with head erect and beak open, standing on a flat rockwork base: its tail feathers fall in an arc to the base and form a third support. The plumage is picked out in a strong Kakiemon palette including orange red, deep turquoise, muddy yellow, blue and black; the base has a brown iron-oxide wash.

Published by G. Lang, 1983, No. 88; where No. 244 is a somewhat smaller, Chinese cockerel at Burghley in *blanc-de-Chine* porcelain. While the two are so similar as undoubtedly to be related, it would be difficult to say certainly which model came first. For an enamelled Delft copy in the Gemeentemuseum, The Hague, see C. J. A. Jörg, 1984, Pl. 144.

LITERATURE: New York, Japan Society, 1986, No. 90.

171
Duck, mounted in Ormolu
Japan, 1670–90
Length 20.4 cm
The National Trust: Clandon Park.

A swimming mandarin duck with long crest, upturned wings and open beak, set on an ormolu base. Predominantly coloured in red, it has blue, green and yellow wing and tail feathers, a pink under-side and red feet, with black markings on the feathers and head and yellow eyes. Moulded on the ormolu base are water plants, a small frog and a dragon's head rising from waves.

J. Cornforth and G. Jackson-Stops, 1971, p. 1006, Fig. 6 illustrate the two ducks at Clandon. In Japan, colourfully-enamelled ceramic models of this and other birds usable as boxes for incense, etc. had at this time recently been made famous by the celebrated Kyoto potter, Nonomura Ninsei.

As with the figures of tigers (No. 168) there were no duck listed in the 1688 Inventory of Burghley House, and yet lot 203 in the sale of 7th and 8th June 1888 was 'A Pair Of Figures Of Ducks, with coloured plumage'. Surely we can rely on Culpepper Tanner to have been able to identify both tigers and duck – even exotic duck such as mandarin.

172
Pair of Eagles, one having a Gilt-metal Crown
Japan, c. 1680–1700
Heights 55 cm; 56 cm
Grimsthorpe and Drummond Castle Trust.

The eagles are boldly and naturalistically modelled and are mould-cast, with hand-worked details; they have heavy curved beaks, fierce eyes and sharp talons and are perched on hollow tree-stump bases. Their plumage is mainly in shades of thin brown glaze, with a white half-circle round the eyes and white inside to the wing and tail, also the upper wing tips of one bird, the other however showing dark brown flecks. Brown-black is used on the beaks, eyes and claws; the tree-stump is streaked with reddish brown. On the right shoulder of each eagle is a small circular metal fitting, perhaps for a candle- or lamp-holder, and on the other a hole for a similar fitting. One eagle wears a small gilt-metal crown and in the other is a hole where probably a second crown was once attached.

Although eagles and hawks are popular subjects in Japanese painting of the 17th century, no porcelain models such as these are known there and they were surely made for export. Of impressive size and presence, they were much admired in Europe and in Eosander von Göthe's designs for the celebrated Porcelain Room at Schloss Charlottenburg, see Fig. 14, p. 61, a recognisable pair figure in a central position. In photographs taken in the 1930s they are no longer *in situ*; a pair are, however, reputed to survive in an East Berlin collection. In France, the catalogue of the Gaignat Sale on 14th

February 1769 included at No. 12 'Deux Beaux Aigles, de grandeur naturelle', and a surviving copy embellished with sketches by Gabriel de Saint-Aubin shows that these resembled No. 172 (see illustration, p. 185). For another pair at Waddeston Manor, see R. J. Charleston and J. Ayers, 1971, No. 99 and the references given there. These were among the very few Japanese models copied at the Meissen factory and one such eagle, lent from the Dresden Collection, appears here at No. 191.

173
Figure of a Hawk
Japan, early 18th century
Height 23 cm
British Museum, JA FRANKS 310.

The hawk is poised with its wings half-raised and talons flexed, its head forward and turned to the left. The tail and wing-tip feathers are enamelled in aubergine and black and the middle wings in green, yellow, red and gilt; the back and upper wing are in brown. The head feathers are picked out in sepia, with salmon-pink and black round the eyes and a gilt beak.

Possibly this originally stood on a rockwork base. The relationship between free-standing models such as this, or smaller versions of human figures such as No. 174, and the figures used as knops of the larger and later covered jars and bowls (e.g. No. 225), has yet to be explored.

174
Large Figure of an [?] Actor
Japan, early 18th century
Height 53 cm
Groninger Museum, Groningen, 1932.19.

A standing smiling figure in a histrionic pose grasping the lapels of his long robe, which is decorated with large sprays of flowering prunus and ornamental lozenges in blackish underglaze blue and red, salmon-pink, green and aubergine enamels; over this he wears a short blue coat with large peonies in red and gilt.

Imari figures of this sort survive in some number and variety in Europe, but they appear to have exercised little direct influence on the development of the porcelain figure there. See however No. 189 in the exhibition, inspired by a rather more accomplished Kakiemon-style model.

LITERATURE: C. J. A. Jörg, 1984, No. 87.

173

174

175
Figure of a Dog
Japan, 1670–90
Length 24 cm
The Burghley House Collection, Stamford,
Lincolnshire.

The dog (or puppy) stands with its head lowered and
facing to the left. The glazed body is mottled with
patches of iron-red, turquoise, yellow and black enamel,
and a red collar is fitted to the neck.

This may be the 'Large Marbled Mastife Dogg' listed in
the 'Tea Roome' in the 1688 Inventory.

LITERATURE: G. Lang, 1983, No. 9; New York, Japan
Society, 1986, No. 92.

175

176
Horse
Japan, 1720–40
Length 18 cm
Groninger Museum, Groningen, 1960.47.

Seated on its haunches on a shaped plinth with one foot
arched and head erect with ears pricked, wearing a
flowered saddle-cloth and a rosette by his tail (which
may have originally been of hair). The animal is painted
mainly in underglaze blue with piebald spots and with
dashes of red and black enamels. A blue scroll runs round
the plinth.

Published by C. J. A. Jörg (1984, No. 88) who remarks
that the source of the model was probably in white Delft
ware. Similar Japanese copies of Delft figures are those of
cows and the 'drinker on a barrel': for which, see No. 72.

176

177
Rooster and Hen
Japan, early 18th century
Heights 25 cm; 23.5 cm respectively
Private Collection, on loan to the Fitzwilliam Museum,
Cambridge, J.117 A & B.

A white rooster seated with head turned, beak open and
tail feathers erect on a tree-stump base with growing
fungus and plants. The white hen sits on a similar stump.
The heads of the birds are mainly in shades of red with
gilt beaks and a range of colours including underglaze
blue and red, black and green appear on the tail feathers

177

and on the wings of the hen; the bases are in dull brown with washes of green and blue.

Sherds of figures of cockerels were found among the waste heaps of the Aka-e-machi (the enamellers' quarter) in Arita in 1988.

178
Leaping Carp
Japan, early 18th century
Height 31.5 cm
Fitzwilliam Museum, Cambridge, C.43A–1962, bequeathed by the Hon. Lady Ward.

Leaping upwards and supported on its curling tail, which is set on a high rockwork base. The scales and fins are entirely coloured in underglaze blue and pale red enamel with light gilding and the open mouth is picked out in red and gold. Details of the base are in green and black.

In the sale of the collection of M. Gaignat, Paris, 1768, lot 122 was 'Deux Carpes de porcelaine du Japon, sur leurs rochers vernissés en partie'. In the famous annotated catalogue of Gabriel de Saint-Aubin there is a drawing of one of this pair which greatly resembles the model shown here: see the illustration to No. 172.

178

179
Pair of Leaping Carp
Japan, late 17th century
Heights 24 cm
Private Collection.

Leaping upwards with curling tails set on a wave base, their modelled scales and fins coloured with washes of underglaze blue and a pale purplish-pink enamel, the open mouths in red and the swirling waves in green, with details in gilt now partly worn away.

179

VIII The Japanese Style in Europe

This section shows in brief some of the more important ways in which the Japanese porcelains came to influence European ceramics. In Holland, where the makers of delftware – a form of tin-glazed earthenware – had long sought to match the qualities of late Ming blue-and-white, with its blue-painted designs and fine white porcelain body, this influence may well have begun with the arrival of Japanese imports about 1660. Owing to the collapse of the Ming dynasty, the Chinese wares had then been unavailable for over a decade and certain Delft wares now appeared which seem to ape the Japanese, in their sometimes rough and uncomprehending attempts to reproduce the Chinese styles. The Dutch East India Company had commissioned from Arita wares made in this ever-popular taste, while as shown in Section III, elements from Delft had also filtered into the Japanese designs. A new response at Delft is nevertheless indicated by their adoption of specifically Japanese forms – such as the double gourd vase No. 180 and the jar No. 271 – and by certain mannerisms of painting.

Such copying soon gave way to fanciful 'chinoiseries' or 'japonaiseries'; but as Section XII will show, whether in Holland, France, England, Germany or elsewhere, the 18th century makers of delftware or 'faience' long continued to find such excursions in the Japanese manner rewarding. By 1700, the enamels of the Kakiemon and Imari styles were being used at Delft and the coloured Japanese designs too were freely imitated; while with growing sophistication, and to meet the pressing demand, independent enamellers there

sought out plain oriental porcelains and over-decorated them in their own version of these attractive styles (Section XI).

A number of these independently-enamelled wares were acquired for the great collection of Augustus the Strong at Dresden and in his introduction John Mallet argues that they may have significantly influenced the Meissen factory to follow the same trend (Section XIII). Not for nothing did the king rename his 'Dutch Palace' there the 'Japanese Palace'. For two decades from 1730 Japanese styles were in high favour at Meissen and especially close copies of the Kakiemon were made.

From a variety of contemporary accounts it is clear that '…*la première qualité colorée du Japon*' as these now relatively 'antique' wares became known, were regarded by collectors in France as the most desirable of all porcelains, not excluding the Chinese; and in the mid century they still remained fashionable. It is this rich palette that dominates the 'oriental' output of factories such as Chantilly, under the patronage of the Prince de Condé, St Cloud, and Mennecy-Villeroy from about the 1730s, and their 'soft-paste' porcelains proved an ideal vehicle for its peculiar brilliance and charm – even if their decorators were often tempted to portray fantasies rather than the purely oriental designs.

The enthusiastic pursuit of Japanese styles at the newly-founded English factories from around 1750 is well documented in this exhibition. Both Chelsea and Bow made surprisingly faithful copies of the patterns, sometimes using Japanese rather

than the now much-admired Meissen pieces as
their models; the result may be studied more fully
in Section XIV. In all this, the influence of Japanese
vessel shapes, sometimes ingeniously many-sided
and sometimes austerely plain and beautiful, both
tested the potters' skill and brought them
inspiration. The way in which various factories,
from Meissen to Worcester, treated a single
Kakiemon type, the so-called 'Hampton Court'
jar, is itself illuminating (Nos 195 to 201).
J. G. A.

180
Blue-and-white Double Gourd Bottle
Holland, Delft, 1660–80
Height 38.5 cm
Fitzwilliam Museum, Cambridge, 2860,
Glaisher Bequest.

A tin-glazed earthenware bottle painted in blue with on
the lower bulb, a landscape after the Chinese 'Transitional'
style with tall, brush-like trees and islands of rocks and
foliage among which are groups of figures, some carrying
slender bottles and wearing curious hats; there are similar
scenes on the upper bulb. Round the waist is a border of
broken scrollwork and on the neck, one of stiff pointed
leaves.

How far the Delft painters of late-Ming-style landscape-
and-figure designs were inspired by their Japanese
versions is under debate, see Introduction, pp. 36–38
and Section XII; however, the shape here certainly
corresponds to an Arita, not a Chinese form. Compare
the Kakiemon-enamelled example No. 136 or, in blue-
and-white, D. F. Lunsingh Scheurleer, 1971, cover
illustration. A Chinese version appears there as Fig. 123.

181
Jar and Cover

Holland, Delft, 1680–1700, the contemporary
cover Japanese
Height 31.5 cm
Mark: CF. An unknown potter's or factory
mark.
Private Collection.

A tin-glazed earthenware oviform jar with
short neck, painted in underglaze blue and
enamels closely following the Kakiemon
style. Round the sides is a continuous design
of flowering chrysanthemum and other
plants, with a border of red triangles at the
foot and three formal blue-and-white borders
round the shoulder and neck.

Compare the Japanese covered jar from
Burghley House (No. 120).

182
Large Jar

Holland, Delft, 1670–80
Height 33.2 cm
Lady Victoria Leatham, Burghley House.

A tin-glazed earthenware ovoid jar tapering
to a small foot and with short neck. It is
painted in blue in Chinese 'Transitional' style
with a bizarre scene of orientals in a scattered
mountain landscape, some wearing exotic
hats and bearing parasols, with waterfalls,
temples and balustrades, brush-like pine trees,
palm and banana. Borders of scrollwork and
pointed leaves encircle the neck and foot.

183
Bottle

China, Jingdezhen, 1700–20, enamelled in
Holland, 1710–25
Height 21.5 cm
British Museum, OA 643.

A rather globular porcelain bottle with
tapering, tall neck and small foot. It was
decorated in China with three comic-looking
mythical beasts round the sides in underglaze
copper-red. The Dutch enamelled additions

181

182

comprise three large, rustic-looking European figures in purple tunics threatening the animals and between them, flowering trees in the Kakiemon style and palette growing from a field of plants. A stiff-leaf border in red rings the mouth.

Compare the subject matter of No. 262. These would appear to be among the earlier types of Dutch enamelling in Japanese styles.

184
Bowl
Germany, Meissen, *c.* 1730
Diameter 24.1 cm
Mark: crossed swords in underglaze blue and the incised and blackened mark of the Dresden Palace Collection, N:445.

Victoria and Albert Museum, London, 7327–1860, given by H.M. Queen Victoria in 1860.

A five-lobed bowl with foliated rim lined in brown. It is painted in green, yellow, blue, red, puce and brown enamels after a Kakiemon original with a flowering plant growing by rocks round the inside, and outside, with an extended spray of chrysanthemum and a smaller floral spray.

Compare the Japanese bowl from the same Museum bearing an early inventory mark of the Dresden Palace Collection, No. 116 in the exhibition, which is very similar in shape and design although the five lobes are sub-divided. The exact parallel, and perhaps the piece originally used as a model, is a bowl formerly in the de la Mare Collection which has the inventory mark 'N=3' with square: cf. O. C. S. exhibition catalogue, 1956, No. 96, illustrated. From this form surely derives also the beautiful four-lobed bowl with *deutsche Blumen* shown by R. Rückert, 1966, No. 591, which by now (*c.* 1745) passes as something quite European.

183

184

193

185
Large Dish
Germany, Meissen, c. 1735
Diameter 57.2 cm
Mark: crossed swords in underglaze blue.
Victoria and Albert Museum, London, c.75–1957, given
by Mrs Charles Staal in memory of her husband.

A plate with flat, serrated rim which is lined in brown
enamel. The enamelled decoration is divided into
separate Kakiemon- and Imari-style areas by a line
resembling a serrated leaf-edge. In the former is a

'squirrel' on a banded hedge with growing vines, with a
red fox and floral sprigs; the latter is a dense chequer-
board of diaper patterns in green, red, yellow, purple,
black and gilt.

The inspiration for the split-patterned design is revealed
by Meissen dishes of the same pattern which are
moulded in the form of two overlapping leaves: cf. R.
Rückert, 1966, Nos 250 and 292 (Ernst Schneider
Collection). A Japanese blue-and-white dish lent from
Dresden to this exhibition, No. 65 shows the source of
the form.

186

Beaker Vase

Germany, Meissen, *c.* 1730–33
Height 34.6 cm
Mark: AR monogram in blue on
the base.
British Museum, M&LA 1948, 12–3, 65,
Sir Bernard Eckstein Bequest.

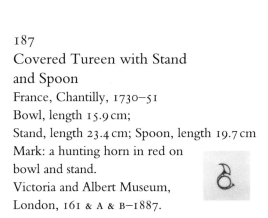

A broad, trumpet-shaped vase rising from a bowl-shaped
lower part with heavy foot. It is painted in bright enamel
colours in '*indianische Blumen*' style: flowering branches
issue from rocks by a terrace on which is a stork-like
bird with two smaller birds and a butterfly above, and on
the lower part are four lappets, each with a puce flower
with white foliage reserved on red, with green scale
panels between. A gilt band surrounds the foot.

The shape of the lower part of the vase is characteristic
of Arita porcelain, but in its decoration chinoiserie
fantasy has essentially taken over. The 'Indian flowers' of
Meissen at this time are in fact a cocktail of Chinese and
Japanese elements.

The mark 'AR' – for 'Augustus Rex' – was added to
porcelain originally intended for the royal palaces or as
royal gifts.

LITERATURE: H. Tait, 1962, Pl. XIII.

187

Covered Tureen with Stand
and Spoon

France, Chantilly, 1730–51
Bowl, length 15.9 cm;
Stand, length 23.4 cm; Spoon, length 19.7 cm
Mark: a hunting horn in red on
bowl and stand.
Victoria and Albert Museum,
London, 161 & A & B–1887.

An oval, four-lobed bowl with everted rim and
matching low domed cover with convolvulus-flower
knob, with curved spoon inserted through a hole at one
end and low, matching stand. Each part is painted after
the Kakiemon style in freshly-coloured enamels with
flowering plant sprays and insects.

LITERATURE: W. B. Honey, 1949, Pl.124E and 1952, p. 123.

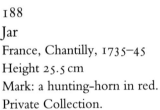

188

Jar

France, Chantilly, 1735–45

Height 25.5 cm

Mark: a hunting-horn in red.

Private Collection.

An ovoid vase with short neck and spreading foot, its sides fluted and with petal-shaped panels extending from shoulder to rim. It is painted with Chinese figure subjects executed, however, in a colourful Kakiemon-inspired enamel palette. On one side an enthroned emperor or noble in yellow robes holds a red cup to his lips, flanked by two attendants, one of whom is pouring wine into a cup held by a boy. On the reverse five figures, one holding chopsticks, sit at a table bearing food and drink; in between are butterflies and a blue bird.

A Japanese covered jar in the exhibition (No. 145) shows the prototype for the moulded pattern. The painted design of figures at a table was taken from an engraving in *Livre de Desseins Chinois Tirés d'Après des Originaux de Perse, de la Chine et du Japon* by Jean-Antoine Fraisse, painter to the Prince de Condé, a copy of which, dating from 1737, survives at the Musée Condé, Chantilly, see N. Ballu, 1958. See also Introduction pp. 50–52 and Figs 8 and 9.

189

Figure with a Gourd

France, Mennecy, 1740–50

Height 9.5 cm

Mark: D.V. in blue-black inside the hollow base.

Fitzwilliam Museum,

Cambridge, E.C.6–1942, bought from money given by Professor Stanley Cook, in memory of his wife.

A Japanese boy seated on a green-enamelled mound base and holding the yellow cords of a gourd bottle slung over his left shoulder. He has a smiling expression and wears a white robe dotted with black stars and over this, a sleeveless gown decorated on the back with a phoenix and flower sprays.

A variety of Japanese-inspired figure models were made in France, notably at Chantilly and Mennecy, during this time. In common with others this figure does not follow closely the Kakiemon colouring, but in modelling it clearly imitates the seated boys with gourds represented here by No. 162. Another version of it, illustrated in W. B. Honey, 1960, Pl. 44A, seems intended to provide a female counterpart.

190

Stag, mounted in Ormolu as a Candelabrum

Germany, Meissen, *c.* 1730; the mounts perhaps French,
1730–50

Height 18 cm

Mark: perhaps a 'caduceus' in blue.

Residenzmuseum, Munich, K.V. C 255.

A stag with branching horns and ears pricked, seated
with head turned to the left. Its coat is enamelled semi-
naturalistically in Kakiemon colouring with distinct areas
of green, yellow or blue and with scattered red or green
maple leaves; the horns are in puce-pink. Together with
its pair (not here exhibited), which faces to the right, the
model was pierced to hold a Chinese porcelain *lohan*
'rider', in this case now missing; its flat base is set on an
ormolu rockwork-and-foliage mound with lizards, etc.
from which rise two branches with flowers forming
candle-holders.

LITERATURE (for the pair): H. Brunner, 1966, Abb. 41
and 42, where the mounts are described as probably
French and the models as 'Chinese'. S. Jenyns, 1965, p. 9
refers to them as Japanese. On careful examination in
1972 however, the second stag was found to bear the
underglaze 'caduceus' mark of Meissen.

191
Eagle
Germany, Meissen, *c.* 1733
Height 49 cm
Porzellansammlung, Dresden, PE 680.

Modelled closely after a Japanese original, the eagle has a
curved, open beak, fierce eyes and sharp talons and is
perched on a hollow tree-stump base. Its plumage is
naturalistically rendered in enamels with the head and
neck feathers left white, the breast and legs coloured light
brown and the wing and tail feathers in graded tones of
light and dark brown with flecks of black; a lustrous
black is used for the eyes, beak and talons; the tree-stump
is reddish-brown with black mottling.

This eagle is said to have been modelled by Johann
Gottlieb Kirchner in 1733. It may possibly have been
intended to accompany other models of large animals
which he made for the Japanese Palace of Augustus in
Dresden; however, the King died in that year. A
Japanese eagle of the type of No. 172 will have provided
the original, although these have closed beaks. The pair
at Waddesdon cited in a note have white necks, like this
eagle. The model clearly became popular and it exists
both 'in the white' and in various coloured versions.
See C. Albiker, 1935, No. 689; also Washington, 1985,
No. 373 where a white example is shown and discussed
in relation to a Japanese eagle (No. 172).

LITERATURE: F. Reichel, 1981, Pl. 96; Tokyo, 1989, Pl. 59.

192
Octagonal Dish
Germany, Meissen, *c.* 1730
Diameter 25.2 cm
Mark: crossed swords in blue
enamel, and incised Dresden
Palace Collection mark N:37.
W

British Museum, M&LA FRANKS 28.

With panelled sides and flat rim with upturned lip lined
in brown. It is painted in enamels closely after a
Kakiemon original with a scene illustrating the 'Hob-in-
the-Well' story. On the rim is a formal border of blooms
and foliage.

This is perhaps the best known of the various designs on
Kakiemon dishes brought to Europe and subsequently
copied there. It tells the story of the 11th century

Chinese statesman Sima Guang, who as a child is reputed to have been very quick-witted. When a friend was drowning in a large pottery jar he picked up rocks and casting them at the jar, smashed it, thus allowing the water to escape and his friend to survive. This story was popular in Japan in the late 17th century where he was known as Shiba Onkō.

For the Japanese original, see No. 122. It was copied also by Dutch enamellers (see C. J. A. Jörg, 1984, No. 80) and in England, where the design acquired its popular title: see the Chelsea example No. 193.

193
Octagonal Dish
England, Chelsea, *c.* 1755
Diameter 22 cm
British Museum, M&LA 1938, 3–14, 65, Wallace Elliot Bequest.

With panelled sides and flat rim with upturned lip lined in brown enamel. It is painted in enamels closely after a Kakiemon original with a scene illustrating the 'Hob-in-the-Well' story.

For the Japanese original of this very popular pattern, see No. 122. It was copied at Meissen (No. 192) and also by Dutch enamellers (see C. J. A. Jörg, 1984, No. 80). The Chelsea factory's sale catalogue, first day's sale, 10th March, 1755, lot 77 refers to '... 10 octagonal soup plates, Hob in the Well'. The name is apparently taken from the popular farce 'Flora or Hob in the Well' by Colley Cibber, which was adapted in 1711 from the play by Thomas Doggett originally published in 1698.

194
Dish
England, Chelsea, *c.* 1753–55
Diameter 17.5 cm
Victoria and Albert Museum, London, C.374–1918, R. Clarke Edwards Gift.

A saucer dish with fluted sides and scalloped rim. It is painted in the Kakiemon style in red, blue and turquoise enamels and gilt with three birds, two of them perched on sprays of chrysanthemum and another flower.

193

194

195
Hexagonal Jar and Cover

Germany, Meissen, *c.* 1730
Height 30.9 cm
Marks: (on unglazed base) crossed swords in blue, and
painted mark in black of the Dresden Palace Collection
N:133. (and on cover) incised N:138.

   W   W

British Museum, M&LA Franks 25, Franks Bequest.

With slightly curving sides and shoulder and hexagonal
neck, the matching domed cover having a button knob.
It is shaped and painted directly after a Japanese
Kakiemon-style jar. Two differing flowering plants
appear on alternate sides and a band round the shoulder
shows three green birds in a floral scroll with red blooms,
in a scheme also employing blue and yellow enamels and
gilt. Round the neck is a red key-fret border; the cover
repeats the shoulder design.

For a Japanese jar that may actually have served as the
model for this, see F. Reichel, 1981, Pl. 33; it was
registered in the collection in 1721 as N:1 □. The
Japanese vases of this form show a number of design
variations, see note under Nos 151 and 155, and these
were followed not only at Meissen but notably also in
England: see Nos 196, 198, 199, 200 and 201 below.

LITERATURE: Sir A.W. Franks, 1896, No. 25.

195

196
Hexagonal Jar

England, Chelsea, *c.* 1753–55
Height 23.5 cm
Mark: an anchor in red
inside the rim.
Victoria and Albert Museum,
London, C.205–1935

Like No. 195 in its shape and enamelled and gilt
decoration, the jar directly imitates a Kakiemon-style
original. On alternate sides appear long-tailed *ho-ō* birds
(or phoenixes) perched on flowers and another flowering
plant; in three quatrefoils round the shoulder are
ascending birds reserved on a ground of blue scrollwork
with red blooms and on the neck, a red key-fret border.

The closeness of the imitation suggests copying of a
Japanese, rather than a Meissen model. Examples enough

196

were available in England and an identical Japanese pair is at Hampton Court Palace, along with other variants; so that the type has come to be popularly known as a 'Hampton Court' jar.

197
Hexagonal Jar
England, Chelsea, *c.* 1752–55
Height 24 cm
Private Collection.

The jar is made in tin-glazed soft-paste porcelain and is of 'Hampton Court' shape. Painted in enamels and gilt on the six faces are groups of 'oriental' figures, some Chinese and others more Near-Eastern in inspiration. In bands round the shoulder and lower part are formal plant scrolls on an iron-red ground, after a Kakiemon design, and on the neck is a key-fret border in red.

The oriental figures are copied from those seen on a pair of Meissen vases in the Rijksmuseum, Amsterdam and imitate the 'chinoiseries' of J. G. Höroldt and his followers: see Fig. 7, p. 44.

197

198
Hexagonal Jar and Cover
England, Chelsea, *c.* 1752–55
Height 26.5 cm
British Museum, M&LA PC II 21.

A covered jar, like No. 196 of 'Hampton Court' shape and again copying a Kakiemon-style original. The six sides are enamelled and gilt with designs representing the 'Three Friends of Winter' – pine, prunus and bamboo – in alternation with a pattern of foliage scrolls in turquoise-and-gilt on a red ground. The same scheme is repeated in a different order on the shoulder and cover; a leafy scroll encircles the neck.

Compare No. 152, a pair of Japanese jars of the same pattern, lent by Her Majesty the Queen, which are equipped with imposing ormolu mounts.

LITERATURE: R. L. Hobson, 1905, II, 21.

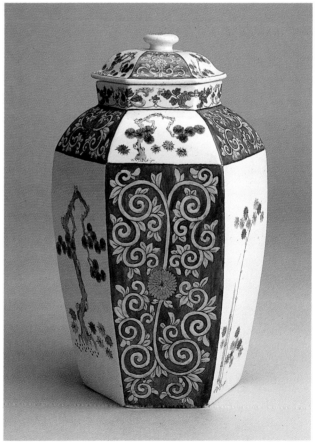

198

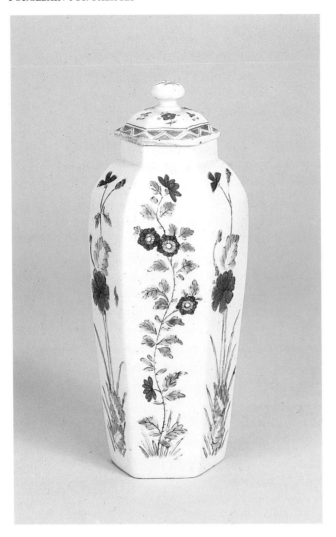

199
Small Hexagonal Jar and Cover
England, Chelsea, *c.* 1752–55
Height 16.5 cm
Private Collection.

A slender jar and matching cover echoing the 'Hampton
Court' jar shape, and painted in the customary Kakiemon
palette. The six sides bear an alternating pattern of tall
flowering plants and the cover shows six small flower
sprays and a chevron border in red. No gilding is used.

200
Hexagonal Jar and Cover
England, Worcester, *c.* 1775
Height 28.8 cm
Mark: a square seal in
underglaze blue.
British Museum,
M&LA 1921, 12–15, 8,
Frank Lloyd Collection.

With tapering sides, rounded shoulder, straight neck and
domed cover. Two large shaped panels, each spreading
over three sides and outlined in gilt C-scrolls and waves,
are painted in a fanciful derivation of the Kakiemon
style: in one are three exotic birds among flowering
plants growing from grassy lawns and in the other is a
comparable design, but with banded hedges and no birds;
two smaller panels on the shoulder and two rectangular
panels on the neck show flowering plants; all are set in a
ground of mottled scale-blue overlaid with gilt marbling.

LITERATURE: R. L. Hobson, 1923, No. 85.

201
Hexagonal Jar and Cover
England, Worcester, c. 1775
Height 37.9 cm
British Museum, M&LA 1923, 3–15, 33,
Frank Lloyd Collection.

With tapering sides, rounded shoulder,
straight neck and domed cover. It is
painted in fanciful imitation of the
Kakiemon style with on three sides a
'dragon' coiled in a flowering tree, a
long-tailed bird under a prunus with a
corn-sheaf below, and flowering stems of
chrysanthemum, and in between, with a
chrysanthemum medallion
set in a red ground with gilt trellis
work. On the shoulder, alternate panels
display flowers on a turquoise ground
and scrolling red foliage; flowering
branches encircle the neck.

LITERATURE: R. L. Hobson, 1923, No. 77.

IX Imari

In Europe we are in the habit of calling all coloured export porcelain made in Arita in the 17th and 18th centuries, with the exception of the wares singled out as Kakiemon, 'Imari'. This immediately introduces a difficulty in its separation of the coloured from the blue-and-white wares, which we call Arita, and which were, of course, made in the same kilns at the same time. It also encompasses a great variety of styles, dates, palettes and qualities, including things that look quite unrelated.

Kiln site material does not enable us to classify the export Imari wares by producer, because not only are enamelled sherds not found at kiln sites, but also the twelve or so kilns involved in the export trade made a wide variety of wares in a series of ill-defined quality (i.e. price) ranges. We should therefore attempt to classify the styles and palettes at the various stages of development or of date (if we are able), according to the market, and not according to the manufacture.

We are able immediately to single out some categories that are distinct. Some of the types often called Imari have already been discussed as 'Early Enamelled ware'. It is now generally recognised that much porcelain previously attributed to the Kutani kilns on the main island of Honshu (the so-called *ko-Kutani* wares) was in fact made in Arita. Those pieces that were made at Kutani did not reach Europe in the 17th and 18th centuries, being apparently made for export to South-East Asia and not for Europe, were possibly carried by Chinese junks and are not relevant to the discussion here, however intriguing the problems they raise. Some of the wares shown here as Early Enamelled ware have in the past been attributed to Kutani (Nos 75 to 78).

A major division occurs between those wares that use underglaze blue and those that do not. The latter class, a minority, tends to be of good quality and sometimes is of a very high standard indeed. In some ways this can be seen as a parallel to the Kakiemon wares, where the best quality body, the *nigoshide*, never bears underglaze blue. And, indeed, some of the finest Imari wares of this group stand up well to comparison with the Kakiemon (Nos 203 and 205). Cases are known where Kakiemon-style enamels appear on the same shapes as the finest Imari wares, which may be some indication of competition between kilns. Decoration on these fine wares tends to be sparse and well painted; flower patterns predominate. Gilding seems to be more lavishly used than it is on the Kakiemon, and the colours are immediately distinguishable. Much use is made of aubergine, of at least two greens and of a method of shading green into yellow. Sometimes large areas of matt black appear, though usually only on the more coarse pieces that use no underglaze blue (No. 215).

Different palettes occur within this class; some use red and gold only, others gold and black only, some have red, gold and green and others use wider ranges of colours. A pink wash, apparently made from colloidal gold, appears in the early 18th century and is used both for some wares of this group and for the polychrome groups.

Especially after about 1700, the great majority of the Imari wares are painted in underglaze blue that leaves space for specific overglaze enamel patterns to be added later. Such spaces are merely left blank, but the drawing of the rest of the pattern in underglaze blue dictates what must be added in enamel (Nos 220 and 222). Outlining in underglaze blue of a space to be enamelled is very rare in the Imari wares, though it is the rule in Nabeshima porcelain, which was not, however, made for the export market.

Sometimes in this period there is rich polychromy, more often there is red, blue and gold only, with black outlines to the enamelled areas. This latter group might be called the lowest common denominator of Imari porcelain; it was this type that was so commonly imitated in China, from about 1710, as Chinese Imari, though as this exhibition is at pains to demonstrate, much Chinese Imari was of far better quality, frequently imitating the best polychrome groups. The varieties without underglaze blue, however, and the Kakiemon were much less imitated in China.

A class that may or may not use underglaze blue, but that makes much use of coloured grounds in a rather dark red or in green and that bears a distinctive, formal, almost Baroque-style decoration may be distinguished as *kenjo-Imari*, 'presentation Imari'. Certainly with an origin in the early 18th century (Nos 216 and 217), this style persists probably throughout the 18th and into the 19th century.

There is a tendency for the polychrome Imari wares to be very richly decorated, for the entire surface of a vessel or dish to be covered with decoration; this is in contrast to the Kakiemon. To some extent this tends to increase with time, so that the later Imari wares may be more profusely decorated than the earlier ones, and also to increase the further down the market the pieces were. Thus, most but not all, very highly decorated Imari wares were made in the 18th century and were intended for a different (? cheaper) market than were the finely-painted pieces. We are, of course, not discussing here anything made after the mid 18th century.

O. R. I.

202
Mustard Pot and Two Salts

Japan, 1670–90

Mustard pot, height 12.3 cm; Salts, heights 6.6 cm and
3.9 cm

Victoria and Albert Museum, London C.73, 74 &
75–1970.

A globular mustard pot moulded as an opening lotus
flower with two ranks of petals on a ribbed conical stem,
and loop handle. The flat lid has contemporary
European gilt-metal mounts consisting of a knob in the
form of a turbanned boy and a rim fitting attached to the
handle with shell thumb-piece. In two sizes, the salts are
small, rimmed saucers raised on dome bases similarly
petalled and with three ball feet. All are painted *en suite*
in a palette of red, green and aubergine enamels and gilt
with various flower sprays and with chevron, petal and
scrollwork borders.

In both moulding and colouring these pieces are inspired
by, or ancestral to Chinese *famille verte* wares of the
Kangxi period. They may be assumed to precede
composite condiment sets in the more developed 'Imari
style' such as No. 241, which were in Europe before
1721. Japanese salt-cellars were (according to T. Volker,
1954, p. 156) first exported in 1669.

202

203
Bottle

Japan, 1670–90

Height 23.8 cm

Ashmolean Museum, Oxford, 1978.461, Reitlinger Gift.

An octagonal bottle with tall neck and low foot,
enamelled in red, yellow, green, turquoise, aubergine,
black and gilt with a flowering peony and a fruiting
persimmon tree spreading over the body, and a red scroll
on alternate sides of the neck.

Among the various bottles of this elegant shape and style
are a pair at Hampton Court Palace: see A. Lane,
1949–50, Pls 10 C, D. Two more are shown here in the
Porcelain Room, pp. 136–37, No. 7.

LITERATURE: Oxford, Ashmolean Museum, 1981, No. 224;
London, Royal Academy of Arts, 1981, No. 216.

203

204
Teapot and Lid
Japan, 1690–1710
Height 14.5 cm
British Museum, JA 1976, 12–6, 1.

A multi-lobed teapot with matching lid and
chrysanthemum-shaped knob, having a loop handle of
square section and faceted spout. It is enamelled in green,
yellow, red, aubergine and gilt with branches of tree
peony and a perching bird round the sides and lid, with
petal borders in red above and *karakusa* scrolls in green
on the neck, handle and spout.

Such is the quality of the moulded work that even the
foot is shaped to match.

LITERATURE: S. Jenyns, 1956, Pl. 38B.

205
Plate
Japan, 1700–20
Diameter 12.6 cm
Ashmolean Museum, Oxford, 1978.33, Reitlinger Gift.

A small plate with flat octagonal rim and gilt upturned
edge. It is painted in red, green, yellow, black and
aubergine enamels and gilt with a basket of flowers on a
low table to one side and butterflies; the outside is plain.

An Imari plate imitating the Kakiemon style.

206
Saké Kettle and Cover
Japan, 1690–1710
Height 16.5 cm
Ashmolean Museum, Oxford, 1978.499, Reitlinger Gift.

A globular saké kettle with flat-topped side spout,
arching overhead handle with gilt chrysanthemum-
flower pinions and close-fitting lid; three tiny feet project
at base level. It is painted in red, green, yellow,
aubergine and black enamels and gilt with a garden scene
where a flowering tree, bamboo and other plants grow
by a veranda with tasselled curtains and blinds. On the
cover, flowers overlie radiating chrysanthemum petals
extending over the kettle; red tendril scrolls decorate the
handle and spout.

This shape was much copied at Meissen.

LITERATURE: Oxford, Ashmolean Museum, 1981,
No. 223.

207
Saké Kettle and Cover
Japan, c. 1690
Height 16 cm
Private Collection.

A globular saké kettle with overhead handle and short
spout, decorated all over with a scrolling chrysanthemum
pattern in red and gilt on a green ground.

The use of red and green enamels only, without black or
underglaze blue for the drawn outlines, is quite unusual.

208
Pair of Incense Burners
Japan, 1690–1710
Heights 7 cm; 6.5 cm
Mark: Dresden Palace mark N: 52
□
Porzellansammlung, Dresden, PO 5258 and 498.

Small, low, round-sided jars with short neck and a pair of
side handles, the sides adorned with applied flowers and
leaves, as are the flat, infitting, perforated lids. The
flowers stand out in red or white among green leaves and
there are berries in red, blue or gold all on a dark red
ground.

These pieces are remarkable not only for the flowers in
full relief, but also for the red ground. For a piece of the
same shape, but with an uncoloured ground, see Oxford,
Ashmolean Museum, 1981, No. 219.

LITERATURE: Tokyo, 1989, No. 41.

206

207

208

210

211

209

Goblet

Japan, 1690–1710

Height 11.5 cm

Porzellansammlung, Dresden, PO 497.

A cup on a cylindrical stem with spreading foot, decorated outside with applied flowers and leaves and coloured in the same style as the incense burners, No. 208. Floral bands in red and green encircle the stems and foot.

210

Teapot and Lid

Japan, 1690–1710

Height 11.5cm

Mark: N:54 painted in black and incised.

☐

Porzellansammlung, Dresden, PO 503.

A teapot with rustic handle and spout, decorated in the same style as the incense burners, No. 208 with red peony flowers with gilt leaves in applied relief on a green ground and white flowers on red for the lid. Floral motifs are also reserved in the green-coloured ground.

A similar teapot was registered in the Dresden Palace Collection in 1721: see F. Reichel, 1981, Pl. 70. For another with an uncoloured ground, see Naples, Museo Duca di Martina, 1984, Pl. II. 25.

LITERATURE: Tokyo, 1989, No. 42.

211

Pair of Incense Burners

Japan, 1690–1710

Heights 15.5 cm

British Museum, JA 1940, 6–1, 13 & 14.

A pair of open-work boxes designed for burning incense, each in the form of an elaborately-modelled cage of tree peonies in bloom and in bud, with a *shishi* lion reclining on top, and with a square base to match. The flowers are in red, white and gilt with green and yellow leaves and aubergine and black stems; a chequer-board pattern decorates the flat bases.

212
Bowl

Japan, *c.* 1700
18.2 cm by 17.6 cm
Ashmolean Museum, Oxford, 1985.48, Jeffery Story and
Walter Cook Bequest.

A square bowl with indented corners and brown-glazed
rim, the inside decorated with a moulded wave pattern.
It is painted in red, green, yellow, aubergine and black
enamels and gilt with two scrolling peonies descending
from the rim inside, and outside, with a 'thunder-scroll'
pattern interlaced with flowering chrysanthemum and
prunus branches and clouds.

An identical bowl was registered in the Dresden Palace
Collection in 1721: cf. F. Reichel, 1981, Pl. 75.
Much later it was to be copied in England at Worcester,
though without the moulded decoration: see the bowl
from the Marshall Collection, No. 347.

212

213
Celadon Dish

Japan, early 18th century
Diameter 21.2 cm
Ashmolean Museum, Oxford, 1972.43.

A celadon-glazed saucer dish, painted in red, green,
yellow, aubergine and black enamels and gilt. The
asymmetrical design features a peony spray, with a
diaper-patterned palm leaf and a large butterfly.

Another dish of this unusual type from the Dresden
Palace Collection is published by F. Reichel, 1981, Pl.
72. Far from being uncommon, however, celadon has
been found at the sites of most Arita kilns.

213

214
Two Celadon Wall Vases

Japan, early 18th century
Lengths 16.8 cm
Private Collection.

They are shaped as elongated half-melons, with an
aperture for a flowering stem and foliage in relief at the
top. On the flat backs are many spur-marks.
Formerly in the collection of Margaret, 2nd Duchess of
Portland. It is difficult to imagine how wall-vases were
used in Europe, though they are not uncommon; see
No. 112 for a Kakiemon example. There are several at
Dresden, though none are illustrated by Reichel. (There
are also some Kyoto-ware wall-vases in Dresden, listed in
1719: see O. Impey, 1974.)

214

215

Lobed Dish

Japan, *c.* 1700
Width 27 cm
Private Collection.

A round-sided dish with rim shaped in two straight-pointed and two curved-pointed lobes, having a moulded pattern. It is decorated in enamels and gilt with two flat, irregular panels in black, red and gold overlaying a design of pine, prunus and peony painted mainly in green, red and aubergine. On the back are perfunctory red sprigs.

Formerly in the collection of Margaret, 2nd Duchess of Portland. The rather crude use of heavy, dark colours without underglaze blue was a style copied at Worcester.

216

Two Cylindrical Bottles

Japan, 1710–25
Heights 24.6 cm
Marks: *fuku* ('happiness') in blue.
Porzellansammlung, Dresden, PO 4795 and 4796.

Plain cylinders with a sloping shoulder and small tubular neck, one having a turned-out lip. They are decorated in underglaze blue and red, green, yellow, aubergine and black enamels and gilt. Both have shield-shaped panels and support scrolled enclosures framed in blue, one displaying a phoenix on a green ground and the other, a chrysanthemum spray on red, with the converse coloured ground below. On the first, the field between is filled with flower sprays and on the shoulder are a fan and a spray of hibiscus. On the second, growing prunus and bamboo decorate the sides and a formalised phoenix [?], the shoulder.

A distinctive style of formally-painted, almost Baroque-looking pieces with broad areas of strong, dark enamel is referred to in Japan as *kenjo-Imari* ('presentation-Imari').

LITERATURE: F. Reichel, 1981, Pls 68 and 69.

215

216

217
Covered Bowl

Japan, 1700–20
Diameter 24 cm
Mark: Dresden Palace mark N:2.
I
Porzellansammlung, Dresden, PO 4784.

A shallow bowl with rising sides and domed, overlapping
cover with 'foot-ring' handle. It is painted in the full
enamel palette of this Imari style. A broad band round
the sides displays flowering sprays and a plant with broad,
diaper-patterned leaves, while another on the cover
shows a floral scroll with brocade-type lappet panels;
above both are borders of waves and florets.

F. Reichel, 1981, illustrates this piece (Pl. 66) and records
that it was registered in the Dresden Porcelain Collection
in 1721. The style is distinctive, and may relate to the
kenjo-Imari (see No. 216).

218
Coffee Pot and Lid
Japan, 1710–25
Height 31 cm
Groninger Museum, Groningen, 1989–154.

After a Dutch model probably in metal, a tapering cylinder raised on three shaped feet with a low cover with pointed knob, which is secured by a metal chain to the flat loop handle; on the other face is a brass tap. Shaped panels boldly outlined in underglaze blue contain formalized lotus in red, green and gilt or in white on a strong red ground, with other ornaments drawn in red.

Coffee pots, usually three-legged, are common both in blue-and-white and in enamelled Imari. Usually there is one hole left for a tap to be fitted in Europe, occasionally there are three.

This example is decorated in a style influenced by the *kenjo-Imari* wares.

219
Dish
Japan, 1710–30
Diameter 28 cm
Private Collection, on loan to the Fitzwilliam Museum, Cambridge.

A saucer-shaped dish with twelve-sided rim, decorated in underglaze blue and a full palette of enamels and gilt. Two sprays of iris and other flowers curve round the well of the dish, penetrating a blue double circle in the centre; round the rim are alternate panels of blue-and-gold and leafy sprays. On the underside are flower sprays and four small medallions.

Imari porcelain matching underglaze blue with overglaze enamel comes in a bewildering variety of styles, of palettes of colour and ranges of quality and hence of price. The richly polychrome variety is usually well painted, the enamels conforming to the pattern laid out by the painter in blue. See, especially, Nos 220 and 226.

220

Bowl

Japan, 1700–20
Diameter 20 cm.
The Burghley House Collection,
Stamford, Lincolnshire.

Of chrysanthemum-flower form with
sixteen lobes and a wavy gilt rim,
painted in underglaze blue and in red,
green, turquoise, pale aubergine, yellow
and black enamels and gilt. On the
outside are two *ruyi*-shaped reserves,
one with a man resting in a boat, the
other with bamboo, prunus and peony
growing by rocks, on a ground of
entwined chrysanthemum and other
flowers. Inside is a central spray of
pomegranate surrounded by trailing iris.

A bowl of comparable type in the
Dresden Palace Collection was
registered there in 1721: F. Reichel,
1981, Pl. 65, p. 151.

LITERATURE: G. Lang, 1983, No. 113.

221

Pierced Bowl with openwork Rim

Japan, 1700–20
Diameter 24.6 cm
Her Majesty the Queen.

A shallow bowl with sides pierced with
interlaced rings, forming a wavy rim. It
is painted in underglaze blue and Imari-
style enamels with sprays of iris and
camellia inside and with three camellia
sprays round the outside.

Openwork rims had some popularity in
18th century European ceramics. See,
e.g. the Vienna bowl of similar pattern
(No. 309) in the exhibition; also a Bow
bowl with this rim and Kakiemon
decoration in the British Museum
(R. L. Hobson, 1906, No. 163).

222

Pair of Square Flasks

Japan, 1700–20

Mark: *shin* ('to brandish') in red

Heights 22.8 cm

Victoria and Albert Museum, London,

C. 1517, 1518–1910, Salting Bequest.

Square flasks with petalled collars round small necks and with chrysanthemum stoppers. They are richly painted in full Imari style with gilt-on-blue borders framing sprays of chrysanthemum, peony and prunus and a squirrel-and-vine design on the four sides, four red leaves round a gilt-on-blue shoulder and hexagon diaper on the neck. The stoppers are gilt.

Formerly at Blenheim Palace and included in the Duke of Marlborough's sale at Christie's on 9th August, 1886. There is a tendency in the early 18th century towards increasing heaviness and elaboration of design. This exhibition shows no extreme examples, though Nos 237 and 238 go a long way towards this.

223

Vase

Japan, 1700–20

Height 51.5 cm

Victoria and Albert Museum, London,

C. 1508–1910, Salting Bequest.

A tall baluster vase richly decorated in underglaze blue, red, green, yellow, manganese-purple and gilt with fan and poem-slip shaped panels of landscapes and trailing wistaria reserved on a ground of chrysanthemum and peonies in red and gold on deep blue.

A link clearly exists between this class of Imari and the Chinese 'powder blue' ground wares of Kangxi.

224

Large Bowl

Japan, 1700–20
Diameter 37.2 cm
Victoria and Albert Museum, London,
C. 1579–1910, Salting Bequest.

Richly decorated in underglaze blue
and in two shades of green, red, yellow
and manganese-purple enamels and gilt.
Inside is a chrysanthemum medallion
surrounded by iris and camellia sprays
and round the outside are three
medallions of wistaria and bamboo
reserved on a deep blue ground with
red-and-gold chrysanthemum sprays.

225

Large Octagonal Bowl and Cover

Japan, 1710–30
Height 44.5 cm
Marquess of Zetland.

A very deep receptacle with rounded,
rising sides and a matching domed
cover with *shishi* lion finial. It is richly
decorated in a full Imari palette with
two quatrefoil panels on each part, one
painted with cranes and their young
wading beneath pine and bamboo and
the other with a spotted *shishi*, set in a
deep blue ground with gilt scrollwork,
and lesser reserves featuring flower vases
and individual blooms; below is a
peony-scroll border.

An identical bowl is in Naples: Museo
Duca di Martina, 1984, Pl. II.18.

226
Large Jar and Cover
Japan, 1680–1700
Height 67 cm
Private Collection.

A high-shouldered jar with domed
cover and simple knob, boldly painted
round the body in underglaze blue and
enamels with chrysanthemum, peonies
and other flowers, and similarly on the
lid. On the shoulder are a peony-scroll
band in red and gold and one of
pomegranate in polychrome; on the
neck are formalized designs in eight
panels.

227
Small Garniture of Five Vases
Japan, early 18th century
Heights 29 cm; 17.3 cm
Private Collection.

A set of three covered oviform jars with
domed lids and figure finials and two
beaker vases. They are painted *en suite*
in underglaze blue, red enamel and gilt
with freely-drawn peonies and
chrysanthemum by balustrades and a
more formal decoration round the
shoulders and on the covers; on the jars
the designs are framed in blue or
divided by leaf motifs, with a stylized
scroll round each foot.

228

Pair of Large Covered Jars on Stands

Japan, early 18th century, the painted wood stands
English, late 18th century
Heights 88.5 cm; 89.5 cm; Stands, heights 23cm
The National Trust: Erddig.

Of baluster form with high domed lids and *shishi* lion
finials, painted identically in underglaze blue, red, green,
puce-pink and manganese-purple enamels and gilt.
Round the sides are a pair of eagles, on one side in flight
and on the other perching, among trees with clusters of
nuts growing by rocks, enclosed above and below by
large *ruyi*-shaped panels with flower heads separated by
roundels decorated with dragons or hares, with bands of
lappets and of butterflies round the shoulder and neck.
The lids are similarly decorated. The stands are
hexagonal, and carved in the Adam style with garlands,
scrolls and fluting picked out in green.

229

Large Dish

Japan, 1700–20
Diameter 54cm
Private Collection.

229

A deep dish with broad, spreading rim richly painted in
a full Imari palette of underglaze blue and enamels. In
the centre is a vase of flowers on a balustraded terrace
and in the surrounding band are two fan-shaped panels,
one with a peafowl on a shore with pines under a gilt
sky and the other with birds perched in a prunus, also
smaller panels with fish and red-and-gold peonies in a
ground of scrolling foliage in blue.

230

Large Dish

Japan, late 17th – early 18th century
Diameter 54.5 cm
Groninger Museum, Groningen, 1988.255.

230

A plate with broad, spreading rim. Painted in Imari
colours is a double-gourd shaped urn in the centre with
scrolling handles, containing a variety of flowers, and in
the broad surround are two scrolling leafy branches
springing from a single source, both above and below,
with smaller scrollwork filling the ground.

Evidently intended for the Western market, the design
of this dish occurs also in a blue-and-white version
(see No. 46).

231
Dish with the Arms of Van Buren
Japan, *c.* 1702–20
Diameter 36 cm
Groninger Museum, Groningen, on loan from the Netherlands Office for Fine Arts.

With broad flat rim, painted in underglaze blue, red and green enamels and gilt. In the centre are the arms of the Dutch family of Van Buren and round the well are eight cartouches containing alternately a vase of flowers or a growing plant, on a coloured ground with gilt trellis pattern. On the rim is a wavy band with sixteen pendant tassels set on another trellised ground with regularly-placed flower sprays.

Part of a large service comprising both 'dinner' and tea wares which belongs to the Department. In describing the piece C. J. A. Jörg, 1983, No. 85 points out that a conjunction of arms on a saucer provides evidence of association with a marriage that took place in 1702. Few such armorial services were apparently ordered from Japan, probably because they could now be obtained more cheaply in China.

232
Large Armorial Dish
Japan, 1710–25
Diameter 55 cm
Private Collection.

A broad-rimmed dish decorated in underglaze blue, red and gilt with in the centre an armorial device with mantling and a coronet, the shield and motto scroll being left blank. In a broad surrounding band are four medallions of flowers set among elaborate floral scrolls with perching birds among them, held aloft by four centaurs. The underside is plain.

231

232

The designs derive from the European Renaissance tradition; possibly it was intended that the arms should be completed for the eventual client by a Dutch enameller.

233

233
Large Dish
Japan, 1710–30
Diameter 55 cm
Lady Victoria Leatham,
Burghley House.

A broad-rimmed dish decorated in bright underglaze blue, red and black enamels and gilt with scenes of village and lakeside life. In the centre, two figures on a shore look up at ladies sitting in a pavilion by a lake with boats, houses and islands beyond, and round the rim is a village street with figures and a bridge, the scene repeated three times. Sprays of prunus and narcissus decorate the underside.

234

234
Large Dish
Japan, 1680–1700
Diameter 49.5 cm
British Museum, JA 1929, 11-11, 1.

A shallow broad-rimmed dish painted in a strong, dark underglaze blue enriched with red enamel and gilt. In the centre are two confronted four-clawed dragons forming a circle, framed by a heavy ring, and in a broad surrounding band are sixteen more dragons in various sinuous postures. On the reverse are three brocaded balls tied in ribbons, and palm leaves.

With this dish, the style is essentially 'blue-and-white' with minor additions of colour. Sherds of an identical dish were found in the excavations of the Aka-e-machi (the enamellers' quarter) in Arita in 1988.

235
Large Dish
Japan, 1690–1720
Diameter 54.6 cm
Her Majesty the Queen.

A rimmed dish, painted in underglaze blue and Imari-style enamels and gilt. In the centre, a roughly jar-shaped panel with lobed and pointed outline, apparently Near-Eastern in inspiration, shows a pair of cranes among prunus and bamboo. It is set within a larger panel with peony and chrysanthemum plants growing by rocks, again irregular and calligraphic in outline, on a ground of chrysanthemum scrolls in blue with red-and-gold blooms. On the reverse side are three peony sprays and on the base, a blue ring and many spur-marks.

236
Large Dish
Japan, 1690–1720
Diameter 53.5 cm
Her Majesty the Queen.

With sloping rim, painted in underglaze blue and Imari-style enamels. Above, a large, oval lobed panel with flowered streamer attached shows a house with a tree and a garden containing a phoenix and an ornamental rock. Two smaller fan and scroll-shaped panels below display peonies and pinks respectively, on a ground of scattered chrysanthemum branches and blooms. On the reverse side are sprays of chrysanthemum, peony and prunus and on the base, a blue ring.

237
Dish
Japan, 1710–30
Diameter 24.5 cm
British Museum, JA 533.

A saucer dish fluted in sixteen lobes with scalloped rim, decorated in underglaze blue and red, green, aubergine and yellow enamels and gilt. In the centre a bird perched on a rock looks up at a pine tree overhanging a turbulent stream, rendered here in pale pink and gilt. In the richly-decorated surrounding border are two cartouches outlined in blue and containing phoenixes, set within larger decorative panels, partly red and partly gilt, which are separated by blue grounds bearing chrysanthemum. On the outside are three flower sprays.

This dish was carefully copied at Meissen (see No. 307), where a 'pink lustre' pigment was employed.

239

238
Dish
Japan, 1720–40
Diameter 26 cm
Mark: six-character Chinese reign mark of the Jiajing
period (1522–66).
Victoria and Albert Museum, London, C.1101–1917.

A fluted dish with scalloped rim, painted in underglaze
blue and in blue, red, turquoise, pink and puce enamels
and gilt. In the centre is a ring of flowering prunus
branches in blue, red and gold within a wavy red border
and in sixteen radiating panels are diaper and floral
patterns in alternation, sprinkled with chrysanthemum
medallions. On the back are four sprays of flowers.

This pattern was copied at factories in England; a faithful
Worcester version is No. 350.

239
Bowl and Saucer Dish
Japan, c. 1730
Bowl, height 7.3 cm; Saucer diameter 17.8 cm
Private Collection.

Bowl and saucer with cartouches of gilt flowers on a red
ground framed in green against a background of
concentric squares which are overlaid with gilt figures,
above borders drawn in underglaze blue. The centres
with a seated sage; the back with *daikon* mark in blue and
red.

A Derby copy of a very similar bowl is No. 355.

240
Goblet
Japan, 1710–30
Height 9.9 cm
Private Collection.

A fluted cup rising from a flange moulded as a flower
with ranked petals over a slender stem and flat spreading
foot. It is painted in the full Imari palette with two
formal panels of gilt on red on the cup and sprays of
camellia in between, leaves on the stem, and similar
panels on the foot. The outer flower petals and part of
the foot are coloured in underglaze blue and the
mouthrim is brown-glazed.

The form is that of a European wine glass.

241
Condiment Set
Japan, 1700–25
Diameter 28.5 cm
Private Collection.

The set comprises five covered ewers for oil, vinegar, soy, etc. and a high-stemmed salt arranged on a flat-rimmed stand round a tall, hollow stem, each held in place by a raised ring. Four of the ewers have loop-handled lids and the fifth is pierced like a pepper-pot. The stand is decorated in somewhat linear style in underglaze blue, red and gilt with various floral designs, birds and scrollwork; the vessels and stem have floral designs which on the ewers frame circles with initials in gold identifying their contents.

The forms were probably derived from Dutch silver models. A comparable five-piece condiment set in the former Dresden Palace Collection illustrated by F. Reichel, 1981, Pl. 59 is recorded to have been acquired from the dealer Bassetouche in 1721.

242
Sauceboat
Japan, 1710–30
Length 24 cm
Private Collection.

Sauceboat derived from a European silver shape, with an open spout at one end and a small handle at the other. The interior is decorated in underglaze blue and overglaze enamels with peonies and grasses in a vase, the exterior with panels of phoenix and formal flowers.

Services of Japanese porcelain are rare –see the armorial dish No. 231; and few pieces as supposedly functional as this have survived.

LITERATURE: M. Vickers, O. Impey and J. Allan, 1986, Pl. 56.

243
Ewer imitating Dutch Silver
Japan, 1720–40
Height 29.9 cm
Ashmolean Museum, Oxford, 1985.15.

Of baroque form with scalloped rim
and spout moulded with scrollwork, a
rib round the body with similar
scrolling motifs, a heavy, flat scrolling
handle and hollow rectangular pedestal
foot. It is decorated mainly in red, pink
and light green enamels and gilt with
flowering plants, grasses and birds.

Based on a Dutch silver original of the
1730s, as demonstrated by M. Vickers,
O. Impey and J. Allan, Pl. 58. This
gives a useful dating for this distinctive
palette.

LITERATURE: D. Howard and J. Ayers,
1979, Fig. 110.

244
Bowl, with Silver Mounts
Japan, 1700–20, the mounts French,
1710–25
Height 11 cm
Bayerisches Nationalmuseum, Munich,
KER 1942.

A medium-sized bowl decorated in
kenjo-Imari style, the outside having
cartouches outlined in blue and
displaying multi-coloured phoenixes in
a band of chrysanthemum scrolls on a
strong red ground, with a flower-scroll
border below. There is a blue ring on
the base.

The silver mounts comprise a simple
reeded band round the rim and a high,
spreading foot with entwined ribbon-
and-ball moulded border, linked by
tapered, hinged straps with shell and
pendant in relief; also a pair of split-
scroll handles on either side.

LITERATURE: D. F. Lunsingh Scheurleer,
1980, Abb. 436; Munich, 1976.

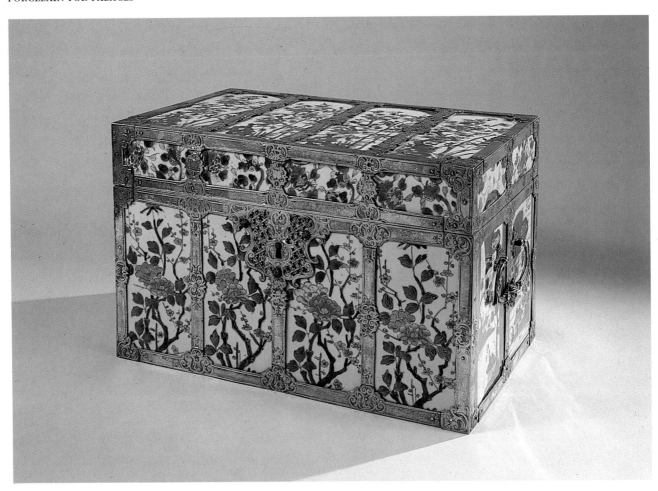

245

Flasks, mounted in Silver-gilt to form a Jewel Chest

Japan, end 17th century, the mounts Viennese [?],
c. 1725, re-stamped in 1806/1807
Length 37.5 cm; width 23.5 cm; height 23.5 cm
Vienna, Hofsilber- und Tafelkammer, 180. 122/021.

Five or more square porcelain flasks, decorated in Imari style have been dismantled and their sides incorporated in a silver framework. Four identical side panels painted with prunus branches make up the front and four with other plants form the top of the lid, the front and sides of which include further cut sections; the ends show two complete panels painted with landscapes. The framing consists of flat bands of chased *laub-und-bandelwerk* design with scrollwork at the corners and mid-points. On the front is an ornately-scrolled lockplate of trellis pattern and each end is fitted with a scroll handle with mask. The chest has a sandalwood lining.

From the collection of mounted oriental porcelains assembled by Charles-Alexandre de Lorraine (Governor of the Low Countries, 1744-80), much of which was

transferred to Vienna following his death. A most unusual example of the silversmith's use of porcelain, the chest is symptomatic of the vogue then current for adapting oriental wares to the more fanciful of court requirements.

LITERATURE: R. Ernst, 1924, p. 5; D. F. Lunsingh Scheurleer, 1980, Abb. 476; P. Parenzan, 1980, p. 6.

246

The Weld Family *Surtout de Table*

Covered bowls and ewers mounted in silver to form a Tureen Set
Japan, 1700–30, the mounts partly English, by Eliza Godfrey, 1755–56, with Netherlandish modifications by J. F. Van der Donck, Brussels, 1766–67
Height 44 cm; width 60 cm
Vienna, Hofsilber- und Tafelkammer, 180. 112/040–49.

The set comprises a central covered bowl or soup-tureen surrounded by four small tureens symmetrically disposed and by four ewers for condiments, all in Imari style, which are raised and supported on curving arms projecting from a central silver stand. The central bowl is panelled with flower subjects, with alternate sides on a coloured ground; the others display large half-chrysanthemums, while the covered, spouted ewers bear the letters O, S or A (for oil, soy or *azijn*, 'vinegar') in roundels set among floral sprays; each cover has a silver knob in the form of an artichoke. The porcelains sit on silver trays, the bowls also having silver basketwork supports; the whole is supported in the centre by four elegantly-scrolling feet.

The *surtout* was originally made for Thomas Simeon Weld (d. 1764), an English catholic, and his wife Mary (d. 1766), whose daughter Mary entered a convent in Bruges in 1757 and later, became its abbess. The central support and longer arms bear London hallmarks and the main basket and trays show their conjoined arms (see illustration). Charles-Alexandre de Lorraine, Governor of the Low Countries, 1744–80 may have acquired the piece from the family in 1766, in which year Van der Donck began work on remodelling the central basket and adapting the others, perhaps also adding the condiments. The 'Chinese Service' which he commissioned, and of which this evidently formed the centre-piece, together with much else of this sort was removed after his death to Vienna.

For an account of his patronage and further information concerning the *surtout* and its history see Brussels, 1987, No. II.14; also L. De Ren, 1984, pp. 121–36, Afb. 11.

LITERATURE: D. F. Lunsingh Scheurleer, 1980, Abb. 481.

247

Vessels, mounted in Silver to form a Fountain

Japan and China, 1700–30, the mounts Netherlandish by
J. F. Van der Donck, 1772
Height 45 cm
Vienna, Hofsilber- und Tafelkammer, 180. 112/035.

The fountain is composed of four Imari-style porcelains
mounted together. Above, part of a cylindrical vase of
'Chinese Imari' ware decorated with flowering plants is
covered by an inverted saucer with floral decoration,
silver-rimmed and topped by a leafy finial, and raised on
a silver band of large and smaller concave ovals over a
small bowl painted with chrysanthemum and other
sprays. The bowl has been pierced and fitted with three
animal-head taps, their keys shaped as an enclosed cross
of Lorraine - in reference to the patron of the work. A
silver, goblet-like section attaches the bowl to the central
pillar of a stand for a condiment set, which is circular,
with four rings to contain the condiment pots or cups.
Finally, the rim of the stand is encased in a heavy silver
band having three leaf-scroll feet.

One of two such table fountains preserved in the
Hofsilber- und Tafelkammer which belonged originally
to Charles-Alexandre de Lorraine and were transferred
after his death to Vienna, together with other items of
this kind such as the Weld family *surtout,* No. 246.

LITERATURE: Brussels, 1987, p. 64; L. De Ren, 1984,
pp. 121–36, Afb. 14.

247

248

Figure and other Porcelain, mounted in Silver to form a Candelabrum

Japan, 1690–1720, the mounts mid 18th century
Netherlandish with Viennese re-stamped marking of
1806
Height 30 cm [?]
Vienna, Hofsilber- und Tafelkammer, 180. 112/022.

An Imari porcelain figure of a woman in a kimono is
mounted on an inverted vessel which is supported on an
upturned dish. Over her head is a silver cap with flower-
bud finial from which are suspended the three arms of
the candelabrum, in the form of split scrolls with further
flat scrolls pendant below and rising to support candle-
holders. The inverted vessel has a globular body and
deep, dish-like upper part and is decorated with simple
floral scrolls in part-relief; below, the dish is raised on

248

three silver scroll feet attached to straps which secure plain bands and scrollwork encircling the rim and foot. A stemmed flower-bud is tucked in the arm of the figure.

Four such *flambeaux à personages* which belonged originally to Charles-Alexandre de Lorraine are in the collection, together with an elaborate silver-mounted centre-piece and other table decorations of various dates. For a vessel identical to that employed in the central section, compare S. de Bodt and J. Koldeweij, 1985, p. 378; the dish-like part is pierced with holes and the writers tentatively identify it as a flower-vase.

LITERATURE: D. F. Lunsingh Scheurleer, 1980, Abb. 477.

249
Pair of cut Square Bottles, in Ormolu Mounts
Japan, 1700–20, the mounts French, *c.* 1740–50
Heights 29.5 cm
Her Majesty the Queen.

Square flasks, no doubt originally with flattened shoulder and small mouth, but with these removed to create an open container. They are painted in Imari style with underglaze blue and enamel colours including a lustrous black-enamelled ground. A spotted green-and-gold *shi-shi* lion is seen beneath a colourful bank of peonies at the foot of a waterfall with a leaping carp, the design covering two faces of either side. The design is enclosed in an irregularly-shaped panel largely displacing the ground of floral scrolls in blue. The flasks are enhanced by finely-wrought ormolu mounts enclosing the rim and joined by a pair of leafy scrolling handles with branches and leaf clasps embracing the sides to meet the base mounting; this is richly scrolled in the Rococo style and supported on four scroll feet.

The porcelains show a rare use of the black enamel to parallel that of the *famille noire* style in China. The Rococo-style mounts are also of exceptional quality.

LITERATURE: D. F. Lunsingh Scheurleer, 1980, Abb. 470.

250

Covered Jar, mounted in Ormolu as a Pot-Pourri and Fountain

Japan, 1700–1730, the mounts probably French, 1800–1815

Height 43 cm

Her Majesty the Queen.

A high-shouldered ovoid jar with short neck and domed cover with pointed knob. The sides are decorated with three panels of prunus trees in moulded relief alternating with other, shaped panels painted in underglaze blue, red and gilt with bamboo, a bird, and long-leaved flowering plants. There are floral-scroll borders round the shoulder and foot and a blue band on the neck. The lid, which is painted with floral designs, is raised up on a pierced metal band to form the pot-pourri. The jar stands on a base with chased interlacing resting on three claw feet, and from its lower sides projects a simulated bamboo spigot topped by a flower cluster.

251

Two Dishes, mounted as a Table

Japan, c. 1700, the table mounting in Louis XVI style, perhaps English, early 19th century

Diameters 57 cm and 32cm; Table, height 81 cm

The Methuen Collection, Corsham Court, Wiltshire.

The dishes are mounted, one above the other, as a tripod table of wood veneer, with brass fittings, including lion heads and claw feet. They are decorated in underglaze blue, red and gilt. The larger dish shows a vase of flowers on a balustraded terrace in the centre, a peony scroll round the well and on the rim four cartouches of tree peonies with chrysanthemum heads between and gilt foliage on a blue ground. On the smaller dish below is again a vase of flowers in the centre and a blue border with panels of chrysanthemum and peonies.

LITERATURE: H. Nishida, 1974, p. 1402, Fig. 2; D. F. Lunsingh Scheurleer, 1980, Abb. 563.

X Chinese Porcelain in the Japanese Style

Having lost their rich export markets to Japan during the 1650s because of the fighting which raged between the Manchus and the remnants of the Ming, the Chinese potters of Jingdezhen were at pains to regain it when the rebuilding of their kilns enabled them to start mass production again in the 1680s. Though the Kakiemon style became very fashionable in Europe in the 18th century it was virtually never copied by the Chinese, and the teapot belonging to H. M. the Queen No. 252 and dish from the Walpole service No. 260 are rare exceptions. They must now have found that their *famille verte* designs were equally popular with the European merchants, and through the fact that the Japanese did not market their porcelain competitively the Chinese could easily undercut them.

With regard to the Imari style however, the Chinese took this up and made considerable quantities of armorial services for the European market. In his study of the subject, *Chinese Armorial Porcelain*, David S. Howard lists no less than forty services made for British families between 1700 and 1730 and many more in related styles; while others have come to light since. The majority of these are purely Chinese in manner, while using underglaze blue, iron-red and gold as their basic colour scheme, but the dish No. 259 is based on an actual Japanese design. The dishes Nos 255 and 257 are also close copies of Japanese originals, while the triple gourd vase No. 253, covered bowl and ormolu-mounted urn No. 258 are varied examples of the Chinese adapting the Imari style. This kind of use of the Imari colour scheme continued in China for export purposes up to the middle of the 18th century, and the type of decoration seen on the mug No. 261 served as a model for many European factories. In Italy and England, the majority of the Imari-style wares made in the second half of the 18th century may be said to have followed Chinese rather than Japanese originals.

A. du B.

252
Teapot and Lid

China, Jingdezhen, 1690–1700
Height 16 cm
Her Majesty the Queen.

A teapot of eight-lobed melon form
with rising spout, loop handle and
domed cover with knob, shaped and
decorated in close imitation of a
Japanese Kakiemon-style ware. The
upright panels are framed in underglaze
blue and enamelled with various
flowering plants; flower-scroll borders
encircle the shoulder and lid and lotus-
scroll foliage decorates the spout and
handle.

There are very few examples of direct
Chinese copying of Kakiemon-style
wares. A matching Japanese teapot from
the Jenyns collection is displayed in the
Fitzwilliam Museum, Cambridge;
S. Jenyns, 1965, Pl. 78A, also Pl. 78B for
another Chinese specimen. Both were
no doubt made to meet a Western
demand, for Japanese tea-making
procedures did not require such a pot.
As Jenyns argues (p. 33), the Chinese
version will have been supplied to the
Dutch in Batavia, if not to European
traders at other entrepôts.

252

253
Triple Gourd Vase

China, Jingdezhen, 1710–20
Height 38.4 cm
Mark: a double circle in underglaze
blue.
Victoria and Albert Museum, London,
C.1501–1910, Salting Bequest.

The vase is painted in the Imari style of
underglaze blue, red, green, yellow and
manganese-purple enamels and gilt.
Sprays of peony, iris, chrysanthemum
and hibiscus appear on the two lower
bulbs and branches of prunus on the
upper, with diapered borders round the

253

waists, footrim and mouthrim and stiff leaves on the neck.

LITERATURE: W. B. Honey, 1927, Pl. 119; C. Clunas, 1987, Pl. 20. A slightly different version at Dresden is illustrated by F. Reichel, 1981, Pl. 85.

254
Large Bowl
China, Jingdezhen, 1710–25
Diameter 35 cm
Mark: a square seal in blue.
The National Trust: Belton House.

A punchbowl of Chinese form, decorated in the Imari style of underglaze blue and enamels. Round the outside are flowering branches of peony and chrysanthemum flowers in three horn-shaped vessels tied with ribbons, lappet and scrollwork borders at the foot, and a band of trellis pattern with floral reserves at the rim both outside and inside, where the main motif is repeated.

254

255
Dish
China, Jingdezhen, 1710–25
Diameter 27 cm
Victoria and Albert Museum, London, C.1491–1910, Salting Bequest.

A saucer dish with moulded ribs in the form of a large pointed star creating eight semi-circular panels round the foliated rim. It is painted in the Imari style with underglaze blue, red enamel and gilt predominating and two shades of green, yellow and manganese-purple. In the centre is a colourful pomegranate within a lotus-scroll border in white on red, and in the panels are 'squirrel-and-vine' designs, with a diapered rim. On the underside are panels of prunus

The 'squirrel' is in fact the oriental tree rat.

255

256
Large Bowl and Cover
China, Jingdezhen, 1710–25
Height 21.4 cm; diameter 22.2 cm
Mark: a double circle in underglaze blue.
Victoria and Albert Museum, London,
C.1499 & A–1910, Salting Bequest.

The deep, straight-sided bowl and its
shallow cover are painted in the Imari style
of underglaze blue, red, green and yellow
enamels and gilt with a continuous design
of peony, iris and other plants and a large
stylised chrysanthemum bloom, its petals
done alternately in red and blue and with
foliage scrolls in white reserve or gilt.

256

257
Large Dish
China, Jingdezhen, 1720–30
Diameter 54 cm
Victoria and Albert Museum, London,
C.1474–1910, Salting Bequest.

A dish with broad, spreading rim painted
directly after an Imari dish in underglaze
blue and in green, red, yellow, manganese-
purple, blue and black enamels and gilt. In
the central medallion is a vase of flowers on
a balustraded terrace, framed by a blue band
with floral reserves. The surrounding
border has three panels of irregular outline
with peonies, birds and butterflies in *famille
verte* style alternating with three of
chrysanthemum and prunus blossom in red
and gold on blue. On the underside are
four flower sprays and a panelled border.

LITERATURE: J. Ayers, 1980, Fig. 204.
Smaller dishes of this pattern also exist. A
Japanese version of this size in the Museum
Boymans, Rotterdam is reproduced in the
Amsterdam, Museum Willet-Holthuysen
catalogue, 1972, Afb. 3. It was copied also
in Europe: see the plate from the
Poniatowski service made in Warsaw
faience for presentation to the Sultan of
Turkey, No. 285 in this exhibition.

257

258
Fountain, with Ormolu Mounts
China, Jingdezhen, 1715–30
Height 33.7 cm
Victoria and Albert Museum, London, 166–879.

A cylindrical vase has been cut at the shoulder and mounted in ormolu to form a covered coffee or chocolate urn. It is painted in the Imari style with chrysanthemum in a horn-shaped container in iron-red and gold and, round the foot and shoulder, with a seeded diaper border in underglaze blue.

The mounts, which are French work of the Régence period, include reeded bands for the lid and mouthrim, where folded handles are fitted, and a top plate with Rococo-style finial in the form of a coral-branch. Above the foot, the spigot is formed of bulrushes with acanthus leaves and the fountain stands on a floral ring with shell pendants supported on three elaborate scrolling feet.

LITERATURE: C. Clunas, 1987, Pl. 18.

259
Armorial Dish
China, Jingdezhen, 1710–20
Diameter 33.4 cm
Ashmolean Museum, Oxford, 1962·83.

An octagonal dish with projecting rim, shaped and painted after an Imari original. The central design was replaced by a European coat-of-arms with three birds on a shield and a scrolling helm, both in gilt on blue, and a bird as a crest, with the motto 'CORBEAU' above. In the surrounding border reserved on a blue ground are floral scrolls and shaped panels, one with a strange spotted animal and another with cranes by a pine tree, other smaller panels contain potted plants and floral motifs.

A dish of this type was copied also at Meissen in Germany, cf. R. Rückert, 1966, No. 316 where the unaltered central design is a vase of flowers. Possible identifications of the arms are discussed by D. Howard and J. Ayers, 1978, p. 141.

258

259

260
Dish
China, Jingdezhen, *c.* 1752
Diameter 31.5 cm
Private Collection.

Saucer-shaped, with sides moulded with eight spiral
flutes and with brown-glazed rim. It is painted in a fine
underglaze blue with, in the centre, a tiger looking up at
an arching bamboo and in the eight bordering panels
two dragons, two fabulous beasts breathing cloud scrolls,
peony, bamboo, pine, and prunus with a perching bird.
Round the underside is a 'classic' foliage scroll and on
the base, also painted in blue, is an English coat-of-arms.

The arms are those of Horatio Walpole, son of the
famous diplomat and diarist, and his wife Lady
Cavendish: see D. Howard, 1974, p. 585. Both the
design and the placing of the arms are exceptional. It
may be that a Japanese model was taken to China for
copying by Captain Richard Walpole of the East India
Company, who visited Canton in 1752.

261
Mug
China, Jingdezhen, 1730–40
Height 15.3 cm
Victoria and Albert Museum, London, c. 41–1966.

Reproducing the form of an English 'bell-shaped' silver
mug, with slightly everted lip, spreading foot and jutting
handle. Painted round the sides in underglaze blue, red
enamel and gilt are flowering peony and bamboo growing
by a rock, with a debased '*ferronerie*' border above. There
are formal floral borders on the handle and foot.

XI The Independent Decorators of Porcelain

As John Mallet has argued in his Introduction (pp. 40–44), the independent Dutch enamellers played a key part in the spreading of the Japanese style in Europe. Little is known as to the identity of the artists or even if they were all Dutch, or working always in Holland. Several distinct styles are involved and the greater part involve decoration after Kakiemon or Imari originals. They painted on white Japanese Arita porcelain, Chinese porcelain from Jingdezhen and Dehua, Meissen, and even, occasionally, on porcelain from other European factories.

In Holland, copies of the Imari style probably occur slightly earlier than those of Kakiemon and are usually painted on undecorated Arita ware. The large bottle No. 262 is typical both in its amusing introduction of European *Commedia dell' Arte* figures and in its fundamentally Imari palette and main design. The flask No. 263 is representative of a more common type of Dutch decoration: a direct copy of the Kakiemon original, it is more stiffly painted than either the Japanese or Meissen versions; the enamels are thicker, more opaque and stand proud from the glaze. Where Jingdezhen porcelain, which is mostly of the late Kangxi period, is used, there is often some original decoration, as with the two bottles Nos 183 and 264 to which the Dutch have made their own additions, in the former case with European figures among Kakiemon-type flowering plants and in the latter, with a direct

copy of a Kakiemon design over the existing spiral bands in iron-red. The *rouleau* vase No. 268, on which the Chinese intended the carved design of scrolling lotus as its sole ornament, received a coiled phoenix and floppy-legged dragons from the hand of its Dutch decorator; a Meissen square bottle (No. 267) is, interestingly, painted with a similar subject by the same painter. The plate with two large, perching parrots (No. 265) has very European birds and a rose tree of Chinese *famille rose* type, but the palette is that of Kakiemon. There has been some discussion as to the exact date and place of decoration of the Böttger porcelain cup and saucer No. 266, though Holland remains the likeliest source.

Among the more fascinating pieces in this section is the figure of *blanc-de-Chine* porcelain from Dehua No. 269, on which the enamelling is of exceptional quality, and which includes a relief panel picked out in the purest Imari palette. Suspicion was thus aroused that it might have been decorated in the East; the full range of colours used, however, points rather to its being Dutch work.

The other Dehua pieces (Nos 270 and 362) are interesting in that the decoration resembles that executed on Chelsea and Bow wares during the 1750s and, as W. W. Winkworth has noted, certain of these pieces are very English in style: in particular, the 'hunchback' quails are very similar to those on Bow porcelain.

A. du B.

262

262

Large Apothecary Bottle

Japan, early 18th century, enamelled in Holland, 1710–25

Height 48 cm

Ashmolean Museum, Oxford, 1978·1804, Reitlinger Gift.

A swelling bottle with tapering neck and a small flange below the lip, painted in red, green, purple and black enamels and gilt in a mixture of Imari and European styles. A Vandyke collar and lappets, medallions and scrollwork encircle the neck and shoulder and below are flying birds, flowering plants and banded hedges, alongside figures of Harlequin and Pulcinello, who are attacking *shishi* lions with sabres.

LITERATURE: Oxford, Ashmolean Museum, 1981, No. 235.

263

Square Saké Flask

Japan, early 18th century, enamelled in Holland, 1730–40

Height 20.3 cm

Ashmolean Museum, Oxford, 1978·513, Reitlinger Gift.

The flask was painted in Japan in underglaze blue with, on two sides, prunus sprays and birds, and later in Holland, on the other two in Kakiemon-style enamels, with parrots perching on boughs and flowering plants. On the slightly-rounded top are green foliage and white chrysanthemum on a red ground.

263

264

Bottle

China, Jingdezhen, 1710–25, with further enamelling added in Holland, 1725–35

Height 26.3 cm

Victoria and Albert Museum, London, c.343–1931.

A pear-shaped bottle with tall, spreading neck and a bulbous swelling below the rim. It is decorated from head to foot – excepting the bulb – with a spiralling line in red enamel. The Dutch enameller has added designs in the Kakiemon style, including a boy with a *shishi* lion on a lead and flowering plants and a floral scroll on the bulb.

264

The plate is painted in the Kakiemon style with two parrots in turquoise, red and yellow enamels, the feathers partly outlined in black and gilt; one bird is perched on a budding rose-tree and the other on a stump pecking at a cherry held in its claws. Round the rim is a tendril scroll in green with small red-and-gilt flowers.

The design is identical with that on a Delft bird-cage figured by H. Havard, 1878, p. 153. It was perhaps decorated at the workshop of Gerrit van de Kaade. See W. W. Winkworth, 1928, p. 302.

265

265
Plate
China, Jingdezhen, 1710–25, enamelled in Holland, 1725–35
Diameter 21 cm
Victoria and Albert Museum, London, 680–1907, Gulland Gift.

266
Teabowl and Saucer
Germany, Meissen, *c.* 1720–25, enamelled in Holland, 1725–35
Teabowl, height 4.5 cm; Saucer, diameter 13 cm
Ashmolean Museum, Oxford.

A cup and saucer of Böttger-type porcelain with moulded stiff-leaf border round the foot. The subsequent Dutch enamelling is in a Kakiemon palette, with the leaves in turquoise, blue and yellow outlined in black; below the rim of the cup and on the saucer are two running red dragons and two berried plants and inside the cup, a flower spray and six florets.

266

267
Bottle on Ormolu Base
Germany, Meissen, *c.* 1720, enamelled probably in
Holland, 1730–40, the ormolu base French, *c.* 1780
Height 21 cm
Private Collection.

A square bottle, pear-shaped with tall neck and low,
spreading foot. Painted in the Kakiemon style on two
sides are a coiled dragon and phoenix and on the others,
a pair of phoenixes in a roundel and a dragon with
spotted and striped tail.

One of a pair. Böttger's white porcelain, at first
undecorated, was not infrequently enamelled outside the
factory. A pair of identical square bottles painted with
chinoiseries by *hausmaler*, probably at Augsburg about
1730, is in the Munich Residenz: cf. R. Rückert, 1966,
Nos 115–16. The decoration here is probably by the same
hand that worked on the Chinese vase No. 268. The
Japanese prototype of the designs is seen in an octagonal
bowl at Sherborne Castle, cf. M. Hinton and O. Impey,
1989, No. 32, p. 55.

268
Cylindrical Vase
China, Jingdezhen, *c.* 1720 with enamelling added
probably in Holland, 1730–40
Height 27.3 cm
Private Collection.

Of *rouleau* form with short trumpet neck, decorated all
over with carved lotus-scroll pattern under the glaze and
with brown-glazed rim. The added enamelled decoration
is in the Kakiemon style, with on each side a maned
dragon alternating with a phoenix above a flowering
branch; round the shoulder is scrolling chrysanthemum
foliage in turquoise and three gilt flowers on a red
ground and on the neck are two flowering branches.

269

Dutch Merchant with Monkey

China, Dehua, *c.* 1700, the decoration added probably in
Holland
Height 30.5 cm
Victoria and Albert Museum, London, C.17–1951,
Basil Ionides Bequest.

A smiling figure seated with the left leg folded across,
one hand on his knee and the other (now missing) grasping
a knotted kerchief; the monkey clambers on his leg. Face
and hair are painted in red and black, the locks falling to
the shoulders under a red topee. He wears a long, gilt-
buttoned coat with leaf pattern in brownish-red, purple,
two shades of green and black over a shirt with blue
cuffs, green trousers and purple leggings.

The plinth has a gilt-framed Imari-style panel in relief
with two birds on a pomegranate branch by a blue rock,
picked out in red, green and gold.

Both painting and enamels here are of particular quality,
while the Imari-style panel is a peculiarly perceptive re-
creation on the part of the enameller. Certain of the
colours used seem, however, to confirm that the work
must be characterised as Dutch, and not that of some
unfamiliar oriental source.

LITERATURE: G. A. Godden, 1979, Fig. 195, who
identifies the model with the 'Dutch Tropers', evidently
in *blanc-de-Chine*, sold at 2*s.*6*d.* each from the cargo of
the English East Indiaman *Dashwood* in 1703; an example
is illustrated as Fig. 194.

270

Octagonal Cup

China, Dehua, 1700–20, enamelled in Europe, *c.* 1730–50
Height 6.8 cm
Ashmolean Museum, Oxford.

With straight, tapering sides thickly potted, and heavy
footring, the mouth rim lined in brown glaze; a moulded
petal-pattern border rings the foot. Painted after the
Kakiemon style in blue, red, green and yellow with some
drawing in black are designs of a red dragon twined round
a pole and growing prunus and bamboo.

It has been suggested that this type of enamelling,
occasionally found on *blanc-de-Chine* porcelain, may be
the work of a London decorator, but as yet there is no
adequate evidence for this.

XII Delft and Faience

The first Japanese porcelains would appear to have reached Europe about 1660 or a little earlier. The secrets of porcelain manufacture, therefore, had not yet been discovered there but for some time, and especially in Holland, copies of Chinese porcelains had been made in tin-glazed earthenware, the white tin-glaze providing an admirable surface on which to reproduce their mainly blue-painted designs. At this date, these were still mainly in the Chinese 'Transitional' style of a decade or more earlier but in some cases the resemblance, whether in shape or design, is closer to Japanese than to the original Chinese versions: for example, the Delft double gourd vase No. 180 clearly imitates a Japanese, not a Chinese form. As regards the painted designs the matter is more controversial, since it is known that the Dutch themselves sent out models to the East for copying. Thus, in 1635 the Governor in Formosa (Taiwan) had supplied the Chinese with '...numerous shapes and sizes all made of wood, mostly turned, and painted with all kinds of Chinese figures which they have declared to be able to copy'. When the supply from China dried up after the fall of the Ming dynasty, the Japanese were no doubt asked to fulfil the requirements with wares in a similar style; but how this was actually achieved is not known.

This phase of Japanese influence at Delft was seemingly short-lived and by the 1680s the blue-and-white designs were increasingly acquiring a more fanciful 'chinoiserie' character. In France, the makers of faience made less reference to the Japanese imports and the Nevers dish No. 276 is a somewhat rare example from this time. The mug made in London (No. 275), is equally rare as an example of the Japanese style in England, produced no doubt under the influence of Delft.

By the early 18th century entirely new opportunities for pursuing oriental styles were opened up by the introduction of enamels: the colours of the *petit feu*. Particularly at Delft the Imari style, with its prominent use of blue, iron-red and gilding became very popular and some striking wares were made, especially at the 'Greek A' factory between 1701–22 (Nos 279, 280 and 283). The Kakiemon style was less closely imitated and the plaque and butter tub, Nos 277 and 278, show how its refined designs were adapted at Delft to more heavy-handed brushwork.

Few European porcelain factories were founded before the middle of the 18th century and so faience continued to be made in many centres. In France, the Japanese style was nowhere very widely used, although the so-called '*à la corne*' pattern was popular at Rouen and Sinceny (No. 288). Nor are there many English examples of its use – although the Kakiemon 'banded hedge' is to be seen on the large Lambeth bowl No. 289, executed in its typically Delft-derived palette. Imari designs were taken up by various factories in Germany, as at Ansbach (No. 286) and as late as the 1770s, in Poland, where the 'Warsaw' service was commissioned. Sometimes, however, it was 'Chinese Imari' rather than the Japanese ware that they used as their model.

J. G. A.

A. du B.

271
Jar
Holland, Delft, 1660–70
Height 24.5 cm
Fitzwilliam Museum, Cambridge, 2870, Glaisher
Bequest.

An ovoid jar with short neck, painted in blue after the
Chinese 'Transitional' style with a landscape divided on
one side by cliffs and swirling clouds and containing two
pairs of standing orientals with parasols and a single figure
holding a large book (?), all among roughly-painted
rocks and plants, with islands topped by pine trees and
sailing-boats. Round the neck is a dentate border.

A not insignificant group of Delft blue-and-white
products from this period were, it is now believed, based
upon Japanese rather than Chinese models. See the
comparable jar discussed by F. Scholten, *Mededelingblad*, 3,
1987, p. 20, Afb. 6, in relation to an Arita jar that may
represent its source of shape and design; and see also the
jar, No. 37 in this exhibition.

LITERATURE: B. Rackham, 1935, No. 2870, p. 357 (as
'Frankfort-on-the-Main').

272
Bowl
Holland, Delft, dated 1665
Height 15 cm
Gemeentemuseum, The Hague, OC 14–85.

A bowl with deep spreading sides. Painted in blue round
the outside is a scene with a bowed figure in an oriental
landscape with swirling rocks and feathery pine trees.
Inside is the date 1665 written in a roundel framed by a
further ring.

LITERATURE: F. Scholten, *Mededelingblad*, 3, 1987, p.19,
Afb. 2 and 3.

273
Jar and Cover
Holland, Delft, 1670–80
Height 40.3 cm
Gemeentemuseum, Arnhem, on loan from the State-owned Art Collections Department, The Hague, v38-s.

An ovoid jar with short neck and flanged, domed cover with pointed ball knob, painted in blue. Panels round the sides with seemingly 'Transitional-style' landscapes in fact depict Biblical scenes with Western-style buildings, including *The Flight into Egypt* and *The Entry into Jerusalem*. They are separated by large crosses on a blue ground: a scheme repeated with panels of flowers round the shoulder and on the cover. Dentate and pointed-leaf borders surround the neck and foot.

An example of the so-called 'Feinmeister' style which has been ascribed to the Frankfurt factory in Germany (see discussion in the Introduction, p. 37). A similar jar is illustrated in a still-life painting by the Delft artist Cornelis de Man which – paradoxically – now belongs to the Historisches Museum, Frankfurt: see Fig. 5, p. 38, also F. Scholten, *Mededelingblad*, 3, 1987, pp. 22–23, Afb. 10–11.

LITERATURE: C. J. A. Jörg, 1984, No. 105.

274
Ewer
Holland, Delft, 1670–80
Height 22 cm
Gemeentemuseum, Arnhem, GM 2233.

With somewhat globular body, tall neck and cupped mouth. It is painted in blue with panels of lotus, prunus and other flowers reserved on a ground of floral scrollwork, with a broad leafy-scroll band round the neck, a lappet border round the rim and flowers on the handle.

The shape is Dutch in origin, while the decoration is purely Japanese in style. For a variety of Japanese porcelain ewers of similar pattern cf. D. F. Lunsingh Scheurleer, 1971, Afb. 71–76, pp. 22–23.

LITERATURE: C. J. A. Jörg, 1984, No. 107.

275

Mug

England, probably Norfolk House, Lambeth, late 17th
century

Height 8 cm

Fitzwilliam Museum, Cambridge, 1382, Glaisher Bequest.

With swelling body and broad straight neck with a small
loop handle. The mug is covered in a dark blue tin-glaze
and broadly painted in white with an oriental figure
seated in a landscape with rocks and pines, in Japanese
style. A border of scrolls and strokes encircles the neck
and white strokes decorate the handle.

Perhaps borrowed from the French factory of Nevers,

275

276

where it was very popular, the 'white-on-blue' style was of Persian rather than Far Eastern inspiration; F. Britton, 1986, No. 98, p. 135 states that sherds of their *bleu Persan* wares have been recovered from the Norfolk House site. For similar pieces ascribed to Lambeth, see F. H. Garner, 1948, Pl. 30, p. 15.

LITERATURE: B. Rackham, 1935, No. 1382, p. 77.

276
Large Plate
France, Nevers, 1670–90
Diameter 41 cm
Fitzwilliam Museum, Cambridge, 2309, Glaisher Bequest.

A flat-rimmed plate decorated in underglaze blue and manganese-purple with oriental figures by a balustrade and a banana plant in a landscape with towering crags and mist, rocks and pine trees spreading over on to the rim, which is lined in blue. Two holes pierce the foot rim, presumably for suspension.

LITERATURE: B. Rackham, 1935, No. 2309, p. 299.

277

277
Wall Plaque
Holland, Delft, early 18th century
Height 36.8 cm; width 30.5 cm
Victoria and Albert Museum, London, C.108-1965.

A roughly lozenge-shaped plaque with lobed profile and slightly-raised rim. It is painted in blue, green, yellow and orange-red with a tree bearing large Kakiemon-like chrysanthemum flowers and four parrot-like birds perching in the branches; a fifth bird is attacking another in mid-air. Within the rim is a wide green-and-blue border.

278

278
Butter Tub and Lid
Holland, Delft, 1730–40
Height 5cm; diameter 10 cm
Museum Het Prinsenhof, Delft, PDA 109.

A shallow tub with straight sides encircled by two double bands of ribbing and with two small upright loop handles at the rim; the flat lid is topped by a finial in the form of a snail on a leaf. It is enamelled in the Kakiemon style

with birds among pine, prunus, bamboo and other plants growing by a banded hedge.

While this shape exists also in Arita porcelain, it is likely to be based on a European wooden original. See No. 300 for a similar tub in Meissen porcelain.

LITERATURE: C. J. A. Jörg, 1984, No. 134.

279

Large Jar and Cover

Holland, Delft, 'Greek A'
factory of Pieter Adriaenson
Kocks, 1701–22
Height 48.2 cm
Mark: PAK monogram in red.
Victoria and Albert Museum,
London, 31–1889.

An ovoid jar with short neck and domed
cover. It is decorated in the Imari style of
blue, red, green and gold with large clumps
of growing chrysanthemum, peony and
other flowers and perching birds, and with
vignettes of oxen, fish or flowers reserved
in a blue ground on the shoulder. Borders
of 'precious objects' and of lappets decorate
the neck and foot. On the cover are further
panels on a blue ground.

LITERATURE: W. P. Knowles, n.d.,
Pl. XVIII.

280

Double Spice-box

Holland, Delft, 'Greek A' factory of
Pieter Adriaenson Kocks, 1701–22
Height 6.4 cm; width 10.8 cm
Mark: PAK monogram in red.
Victoria and Albert Museum, London,
C.262 to B, 1910.

The spice-box is boat-shaped with eight
sides and is divided into two compartments,
each with a lid and small knob. It is
decorated in Imari style with borders of
gilt blue petals and half-peonies or *ruyi*-
heads in red round the sides and top
adjoining blue borders with gilt scrollwork
at the rims, with flower sprays on the lids,
and a blue band across the centre with a
flower-head in reserve.

In shape, this spice-box is based on a
contemporary French silver original.

279

280

281
Plate
Holland, Delft, early 18th
century
Diameter 22.5 cm
Mark: AR in monogram,
perhaps for the painter
Ary van Rijsselberg,
working for the De 3
Vergulde Astonnekens factory, *c.* 1718–35.
Victoria and Albert Museum, London,
c.2350–1910, Salting Bequest.

A flat-rimmed plate painted in a
predominantly Imari palette of blue,
red, green, turquoise and gold. In the
centre is a turquoise long-tailed tiger
beside rocks and flowering peony and
round it, a broad band with four panels
reserved on a blue ground; two are
painted with a bird on a prunus branch
by a banded hedge and two with floral
sprays, with two chrysanthemum and
gilt leaves between each panel. On the
underside are flowers and leaves in red.

LITERATURE: W. P. Knowles, n.d.,
Col. Pl. F, p. 36.

281

282
Dish
Holland, Delft, early 18th century
Diameter 22.5 cm
Mark: AR in monogram, perhaps for the
painter Ary van Rijsselberg, *c.* 1718–35.
Gemeentemuseum, The Hague, OCD
62–1904.

A saucer dish painted in colours in a
pastiche of Imari styles with a quatrefoil
panel showing a comic dragon by a fence,
set among others of fan and hanging-scroll
shape containing plants, with scattered
chrysanthemum blooms and leaves.

282

283

Two-handled Bowl and Cover

Holland, Delft, 'Greek A' factory of Pieter Adriaenson
Kocks, 1701–22
Height 9.5 cm; diameter 16 cm
Mark: PAK monogram.
Gemeentemuseum, The Hague, OCD 3–71.

A bowl with everted rim, having square handles on
either side and an infitting domed lid with acorn knob. It
is decorated in the Imari style with buildings in
landscapes and flower sprays in elongated panels in red,
green and gold, separated by clouds and wavy bands in
blue and gold. Floral-scroll and simple diaper-pattern
borders encircle the rim and foot.

This copies, in both form and decoration, an incense
burner in Japanese porcelain. The bowls may have been
used as small tureens. For a three-legged Japanese
example in the Kakiemon style, see No. 124 and for a
Meissen example, No. 305.

LITERATURE: C. J. A. Jörg, 1984, No. 122; C. H. de
Jonge, 1970, Pl. 107 illustrates an unmarked example in
the Gemeentemuseum at Arnhem.

284

Plate

Holland, Delft, early 18th century
Diameter 35.5 cm
British Museum, M&LA 1889, 7–6, 62.

The plate is hexagonal with flat spreading rim and cut-
out corners, and is painted in the classic Imari style and
palette of blue, red and gilt with a vase of
chrysanthemum and peony on a tripod stand in the
centre framed by a scrollwork border. Radiating to the
rim in a broad band are panels with a pavilion by a lake
or with a bowl of flowers, alternating with others of gilt
trelliswork on blue or of blue-and-gold chequerwork.
Round the underside is a flower scroll in blue and red.

H. Syz (1970, Taf. II.3 and III.5) illustrates this plate
together with its closely similar Japanese model, which
bears a Dresden Palace Inventory mark applied during
the years 1721–27. Cf. also W. P. Knowles, n.d., Pl. IX;
C. J. A. Jörg, 1984, Pl. 121, p. 168.

285
Dish
Poland, Warsaw, Belvedere factory, *c.* 1776
Diameter 28.5 cm
Victoria and Albert Museum, London, 544–1897.

A flat-rimmed plate painted after the Imari style in blue, green, red, yellow and gilt. In the centre is a vase of flowers on a platform flanked by balustrades. Gilt inscriptions in Turkish on the vase and in four of the medallions in a surrounding band read: 'Obedience and Fidelity are due to Kings. From the King of the Lekhs at Warsaw to the Tsar of the race of Osman as a token of respect, this present is offered and sent'. Round the rim are three cloud-shaped panels of birds, butterflies and peonies set in a blue ground with red chrysanthemum and gilt foliage. On the underside are flowering shrubs and a diapered border.

From a service said to have been made as a present from Stanislas Augustus Poniatowski, King of Poland to Abdul Hamid I, Sultan of Turkey, in 1776 but not delivered until 1789. A large part of it remains in the Topkapi Saray Museum, Istanbul. See H. Chojnacka, 1981, p. 36.

A larger dish of Chinese porcelain with essentially the same design is No. 257 in the exhibition. For a Japanese original in the Museum Boymans, Rotterdam, cf. Amsterdam, Museum Willet-Holthuysen, 1972, No. 111.

286
Large Dish
Germany, Ansbach, first half of the 18th century
Diameter 37.9 cm
Victoria and Albert Museum, London, c.94–1924.

A flat-rimmed plate painted in the Imari palette of blue,
red enamel and gilt. A central medallion displays a lakeside scene with islands and distant mountains and is
surrounded by a broad ornamental border composed of
floral elements formally disposed.

287

Tureen and Cover

Germany, Fulda, perhaps by Carl Heinrich von
Löwenfinck, 1740–43
Height 30.5 cm; diameter 24.8 cm
Victoria and Albert Museum, London, C.133 & A–1951.

A drum-shaped tureen with cupped rim and side handles
in the form of leaping carp; the domed cover has another
fish as its handle. It is decorated in turquoise, green, red,
yellow, blue, purple and brown with branches of
flowering peonies, insects and butterflies following the
Chinese *famille verte* style and, round the cover, with
diapered borders. The fish handles show Japanese
inspiration in their modelling and colouring.

A tureen of similar form in Meissen blue-and-white
porcelain with added gilt ground dates from *c.* 1725–30
and may represent a prototype: see R. Rückert, 1966,
Nos 97 and 98. The shape was also used at Meissen and
Vienna painted in the Imari palette: for the latter, see
J. F. Hayward, 1952, Pl. 26B.

LITERATURE: K. Strauss, 1974, p. 17 and Fig. 8.

288
Dish
France, Rouen or Sinceny, 1740–50
Diameter 38.6 cm
Mark: AD monogram
in reddish brown,
perhaps for the
Sinceny
painter Daussy.

Victoria and Albert Museum, London,
165–1887.

A plate with rim lobed, ribbed and
foliated in a European silver form and
painted in yellow, red, blue and green
of the *grand feu*. The design, which is
sometimes called *à la corne*, is an Imari
pattern with a large horn-shaped vessel
filled with flowers to one side and a
banded hedge with prunus on the other,
on a ground sprinkled with blooms,
insects and a pair of birds.

The *chrysanthème à la corne* subject was
probably copied from Imari ware,
where it is common, but it may have
originated somewhat earlier in
Kakiemon-type wares such as a dish
from the Reitlinger Collection
illustrated by S. Jenyns, 1956, Pl. 60B,
where it appears alone. A plate copying
this design made at Tournai, *c.* 1763–74
is published in the Tokyo exhibition
catalogue, *Ceramic Road*, 1982, No. 112.

289
Bowl
England, Lambeth, *c.* 1730-40
Diameter 34.3 cm
Victoria and Albert Museum, London,
CIRC.203–1951.

A large bowl painted after the Kakiemon style in
blue, green, yellow and orange-red with on the
outside, four birds perching in flowering branches of
prunus and pine by a banded hedge, and scattered
insects. Inside are a pair of Chinese emblems tied in a
ribbon in the centre and blue scrollwork round the
sides.

288

289

256

XIII Continental Porcelain

As the first in Europe to discover the secret of true porcelain in 1708, the potters of Meissen near Dresden were to enjoy almost a monopoly of trade for much of the next forty years. Their wares would be decorated in many different styles, but for fifteen years from about 1725 Kakiemon was one of the most popular.

Sometimes the imitation was so exact that even Japanese scholars have in the past mistaken them for the originals (Nos 292 and 307). But the invention at Meissen went further and, for instance, the plate from a dinner service (No. 297) adds also to its typically Japanese design a European royal coat-of-arms in the centre. The type of design known at Meissen as *indianische Blumen*, which may be combined with chinoiserie and Imari patterns as well as being used, in the late 1730s and 1740s, to decorate the clothes worn by figures, is a mixture of Japanese and Chinese elements; though in the case of the beaker vase, No. 186 the shape is essentially a Japanese one.

Meissen produced many designs set in panels on coloured grounds from the 1730s and sometimes these portrayed Kakiemon designs (No. 294). In the case of the octagonal bowl No. 298, the coloured grounds of an unusual pale turquoise are alternated with panels of Kakiemon designs. The red dragon pattern appearing on a two-handled cup No. 296 poses something of a problem in that while it has been regarded as copying a Japanese original, the known Japanese examples of this design are probably of slightly later date. They are also painted on pieces of European rather than oriental shape. The

probability is that Meissen adapted this design from a polychrome Kakiemon prototype with both dragon and coiled phoenix and that the Japanese later copied the Meissen invention.

Meissen blue-and-white is comparatively rare except in everyday service ware, which is usually based on Chinese models. The square bottle No. 290 is Japanese in shape although the decoration is no more than 'oriental' in inspiration; the tankard No. 291, however, has a distinctively Japanese design. Imari patterns were used for the more ordinary table wares and for tea and coffee services, but do not appear to have found favour in the palaces of Augustus of Saxony. The covered box No. 306 is typical of these, as is the plate No. 307. This latter pattern was at one time called the 'Warsaw service' but the name is likely to be a dealers' term, arising from confusion with the service of Polish faience (No. 285). Imari patterns came back into favour towards the end of the 18th century, particularly for export to the Ottoman Empire.

Vienna, though it employed a version of *indianische Blumen*, found that the Imari patterns were more popular than the Kakiemon, and combined oriental design motifs with exaggerated Baroque forms (No. 311). Even the basket No. 309 which is identical in shape to a Kakiemon example at Burghley, is decorated in muted Imari colours. By the time the majority of German and other Northern European factories had started making porcelain the fashion for Kakiemon had virtually disappeared, but Imari designs lingered on, as in the Ludwigsburg dish

No. 322, the similar example from Loosdrecht, No. 323 and the Amstel plate No. 324.

Italian porcelain and faience were inclined to copy Chinese rather than Japanese designs, and where the Imari palette is used the influence of China can be seen (No. 321). On the other hand, France, having started to make soft-paste or artificial porcelain in the late 17th century, produced many pieces in the Kakiemon taste but normally eschewed Imari. The earliest were probably from St Cloud, which adopted the Kakiemon designs but was unable to reproduce the palette (Nos 312 and 313). Chantilly, whose patron, the duc de Condé had a large collection of Japanese porcelain, produced many Kakiemon style wares; some of them exactly copying Kakiemon motifs, but on shapes of their own (Nos 187 and 314), some using invented chinoiserie designs on Japanese shapes (No. 188) and some combining all three (No. 315). Chantilly, as well as some other factories, delighted in adapting Kakiemon designs to all manner of small objects such as snuff boxes, stick handles and knife and fork handles (Nos 316, 317 and 318). By the time the greatest of all French

factories had been founded at Vincennes (to be moved to Sèvres in 1756), these styles had virtually gone out of fashion; the teabowls and dish here (Nos 319 and 320) are examples of a very small number of pieces from this factory with Kakiemon decoration.

Figures of Japanese inspiration are rare in European porcelain. Some oriental-style examples in the chinoiserie tradition from Chantilly have their robes decorated with Kakiemon-type flowers, while the little Mennecy figure No. 189 can trace its ancestry back to the Kakiemon model from Burghley No. 162. The Meissen figures of orientals are even farther away from their Japanese counterparts. A few birds and animals however were closely copied, such as the magnificent eagle No. 191 which is lent from the Dresden Collection itself, and which was apparently produced from around 1733. The rare ormolu-mounted stag from Munich, No. 190, is probably of earlier date: one of a pair that were turned into candelabra, it bears the caduceus rather than the crossed swords mark.

A. du B.

290
Blue-and-white Bottle
Germany, Meissen, 1720–25
Height 16 cm
Victoria and Albert Museum, London, C.55–1948.

A square bottle, pear-shaped with a tall neck and
reinforced mouthrim, standing on a low, spreading foot.
The porcelain has a cream-white glaze and is painted in
greyish underglaze blue with oriental landscapes
incorporating pavilions, trees, plants and birds in a
framed panel on each side.

For the type of Japanese square bottle from which this
form derives, see No. 111. It was much in use for a time
at Meissen but this version, with its strongly accented
mouthrim and footrim, relates to an early type in Böttger
white porcelain (see Dresden, Staatliche Kunstsammlungen, 1982, Pl. I/68). After the 17th century,
painting in blue played a declining role in European
ceramics and it was eventually confined to the
commoner sorts of ware.

291
Silver-mounted Tankard
Germany, Meissen, c. 1730
Height 18.3 cm (to top of thumb-piece)
Silver marks: 'pineapple' for Augsburg, 1741–43 and HB,
used by Bartholomaus Heuglin (Heyglin), Master 1730,
d. 1742.
British Museum, M&LA 1939, 7–7,1, Franks Bequest.

A cylindrical tankard mounted with a silver-gilt cover
and base. It is painted in underglaze blue after the
Japanese style with round the sides, a bird perched on a
branch, a butterfly and flowering plants growing by
rocks; on the handle is a flowering branch. Bands of gilt
trelliswork encircle the rim and (formerly) also the foot.

The domed cover of Augsburg silver, once gilt, has a
shell thumb-piece and is chased with a seated deer under
a tree set in a Baroque cartouche, and in three smaller
cartouches with a running hound, a squirrel and a hawk,
all within a fluted border.

The gilding may have been added to the piece at
Augsburg before the silver mount was attached there.

292

Octagonal Bowl

Germany, Meissen, *c.* 1730

Diameter 18 cm

Marks: crossed swords in blue enamel and incised
Dresden Palace mark N: 256 filled in in black.

W

British Museum, M&LA, FRANKS 26, Franks Bequest.

A deep bowl with straight sides and projecting rim with
upturned brown lip, shaped and decorated after a Japanese
original. It is painted in Kakiemon-style enamels with an
ancient prunus on one side and bamboo growing by blue,
green and yellow rocks outlined in black on the other.
Round the rim is a border of flower-heads and foliage.

Octagonal Kakiemon bowls and dishes occur in various
sizes and shapes. Compare the small bowl from Burghley
House (No. 128).

LITERATURE: Sir A. W. Franks, 1896, No. 26.

293

Pilgrim Flask

Germany, Meissen, *c.* 1730

Height 22.5 cm

Mark: K.H.C. on the base.

Musées Royaux d'Art et
d'Histoire, Brussels, C. 1501–1910.

A flattened circular flask with a small spout on the
shoulder, short neck, small lid and spreading foot, each
fitted with a silver-gilt mount with dentate border. It is
decorated in a Kakiemon palette of enamels with a tiger
twined round a bamboo and an ancient prunus tree.

LITERATURE: Tokyo, 1982, No. 125.

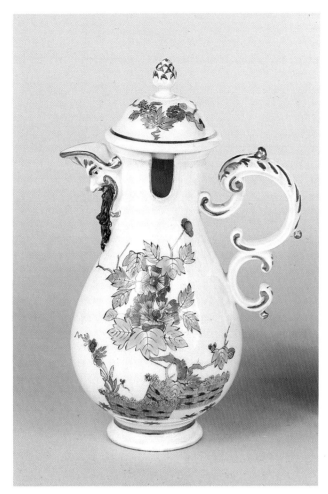

294
Chocolate Pot and Lid
Germany, Meissen, c. 1740
Height 16.5 cm
Mark: crossed swords in blue.
Cecil Higgins Art Gallery and Museum, Bedford, C. 891.

A cylindrical pot with tubular handle and spout set at
right angles on the shoulder, with domed lid and knob.
It is painted in the Kakiemon palette of enamels and gilt
with two quatrefoil panels reserved in a purple ground,
showing on one side a pair of quail and a prunus tree and
on the other flowers and foliage, with flower sprays on
the shoulder and smaller panels on the lid. Plants and
insects are reserved in the purple ground.

R. Rückert, 1966, Nos 407 and 409 illustrates a similar
coffee-cup and saucer, and a tea-caddy possibly from the
same service.

295
Condiment Pot and Lid
Germany, Meissen, 1735–40
Height 18 cm
Mark: crossed swords in blue.
Musées Royaux d'Art et d'Histoire, Brussels, 915 A–B.

A pear-shaped jug with an elaborate bearded-mask spout
and triple-scroll handle, having an aperture in the side for
a spoon and a domed lid with pineapple knob. It is
painted in the Kakiemon enamelling style and gilded
with a peony bush by a banded hedge and with flowers
on the lid.

The shape is based on a silver original.

LITERATURE: Tokyo, 1982, No. 123.

296
Two-handled Chocolate Cup
Germany, Meissen, 1734–39
Height 6.5 cm; width 11 cm
Mark: K.H.C. in purple on the base.
Private Collection.

A tall cup with slightly everted lip, the handles each
modelled as two Cs. Each side is painted with a dragon
in iron-red and gold, with 'endless knots' above the
handles; a small insect hides a flaw above one dragon.

The original service of this design was ordered for the
Hofsilberkammer in Dresden, between 1731 and 1734,
and the mark shows that this piece was in the Königliche
Hof-conditorei (Royal Court Store-room or Pantry).
The plates have twin phoenixes in the centres (compare
R. Rückert, 1966, No. 305). This pattern proved
popular and is still in production today. It has been
supposed to derive from a late 17th or early 18th century
Kakiemon original, but since known Japanese pieces all
appear to date from c. 1740 and are in Meissen rather
than Japanese shapes, it may be a Meissen invention. The
pattern was copied also at Chantilly, where it is known as
the *prince Henri* pattern.

297
Plate with the Royal Arms of Poland
Germany, Meissen, c. 1731
Diameter 23.4 cm
Marks: crossed swords in blue enamel, and incised
Dresden Palace mark N:22. filled in in black;

W

also the impressed mark of a star, that of the 'repairer',
Wildenstein.
British Museum, M&LA 1937, 1–11, 2, Monsieur A.
Wittekind Gift.

Painted in the centre are the Royal arms of Poland, in
white on red, with a gilt crown above. The remaining
decoration is in the Kakiemon style with a red-and-gilt
striped tiger and a bamboo, painted in colours and purple
lustre, which curves round the well of the plate.

Augustus III, King of Saxony and Poland, (1670–1733),
ordered several dinner services in the Japanese style. The
first, known as the 'golden lion' or '*jagd* service', has a
yellow ground and Kakiemon flowers and dates from
before 1730; services with the 'red tiger' were then
made, one bearing the arms of Saxony and the other
those of Poland, c. 1731, followed by another with the
arms of Saxony and Poland combined. See R. Rückert,
1966, Nos 451 and 452.

298
Octagonal Bowl

Germany, Meissen, *c.* 1735

Diameter 25.8 cm

Marks: crossed swords in underglaze blue, and incised

Dresden Palace mark N:480. filled in in black; also the

W

incised mark of the 'repairer', Rehschuh.

British Museum, M&LA 1931, 4–17, 2.

The bowl follows a popular Japanese octagonal shape.
Four sides bearing enamelled decoration in the
Kakiemon style alternate with four in plain light
turquoise: the first painted panel, which is repeated by
the third, shows flowers growing by purple rocks with a
praying mantis and a butterfly, the second, a long-tailed
bird perched on a flowering magnolia and the fourth, a
flowering and fruiting tree; all are outlined in gilt. Inside
are a similar flowering tree, four flower sprays and a red
foliage-scroll border.

The turquoise ground was known at the Meissen factory
as *seladon* or *seegrüner fond*.

299
Beaker Vase

Germany, Meissen, *c.* 1730

Height 30.2 cm

Mark: a caduceus in underglaze blue.

British Museum, M&LA Franks 43,

Franks Bequest.

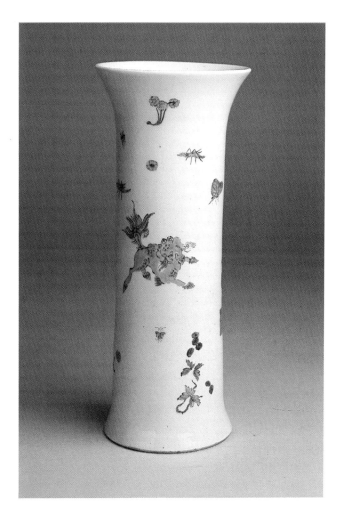

A slender cylindrical beaker with spreading lip and foot.
It is painted after a Kakiemon original with scattered
designs including a turquoise lion or *shishi* and a blue-
coated boy standing on a chequerwork ground; a bunch
of puce flowers with blue leaves tied with a ribbon and
smaller butterflies, insects and flowers appear in between.

The decoration, which corresponds to that of the
Kakiemon jar, No. 145 in this exhibition, appears also on
a Kakiemon beaker vase sold at Christie's on 7th March,
1989, lot 327.

LITERATURE: Sir A. W. Franks, 1896, No. 43.

301

300
Butter Tub and Cover

Germany, Meissen, 1738–40
Diameter 12.1 cm
Marks: crossed swords in underglaze blue inside in the
centre and impressed 23 on the base.
Private Collection.

The shallow tub is modelled after a wooden original
with ribbed sides and two pierced upright handles; the
flat cover has a pineapple finial. Painted on the cover in
enamels are a red crane with gilt crest by a trellis and a
flowering plant and a descending crane in blue and
yellow. Round the sides of the tub are two flowering
branches, a butterfly and foliage.

For the use of the same designs on a Chelsea plate see
No. 333 in this exhibition, and on a Japanese dish, H.
Nishida, Tokyo, 1977, Pl. 55.

301
Bowl

Germany, Meissen, c. 1730
Diameter 21.4 cm
Marks: crossed swords in blue enamel within a red ring,
and incised Dresden Palace mark N:450. filled in black.

W

British Museum, M&LA FRANKS 29, Franks Bequest.

Following a Japanese original, the bowl is fluted in
sixteen lobes with petalled rim outlined in gilt, and there
are gilt lacework borders at the rim and framing a central
medallion. Painted here in a palette of turquoise green,

blue, red, puce, yellow and black is a rural scene with
figures, a cow and a hill beyond, with buildings and tent-
like structures beneath cumulus clouds.

Round the outside are two figures seated at a table, a
sage and a boy on a terrace, and a pine tree by a fence
with a pair of phoenixes and clouds above. They are
divided by rockwork and flowering prunus.

The central scene, which appears in various forms on
Arita blue-and-white – cf. No. 67 in this exhibition – is
sometimes identified as 'Deshima Island'; in fact it
corresponds closely to Delft designs of the late 17th
century and undoubtedly depicts a landscape in Holland,
with sailing-ships in the distance.

LITERATURE: Sir A. W. Franks, 1896, No. 27; London,
1985, No. 9.

302
Tray
Germany, Meissen, *c.* 1735
Length 44.4 cm
Mark: crossed swords in blue.
Victoria and Albert Museum, London, C.621–1925,
Dingwall Gift.

A flat dish of irregular oval shape with scalloped rim and
handles at either end moulded and gilt in the Rococo
style. Painted after the Kakiemon style in enamel colours
across the surface is a tree stump by a banded hedge with
sprays of paulownia and hibiscus, with a long-tailed bird
flying above.

LITERATURE: W. B. Honey, 1946, Pl. XIVD and p. 63.

303
Teapot
Germany, Meissen, *c.* 1735
Height 11.8 cm
Mark: crossed swords in underglaze blue.
Victoria and Albert Museum, London, C.22–1956,
Tulk Bequest.

A melon-shaped teapot with lobed sides, an angular
handle with scrolled projections and a matching cover
with tall bud-shaped knob. It is sparsely enamelled in the
Kakiemon style with flying phoenixes and flower sprays
on the sides and the cover, the rim of which is lined in
iron-brown.

304

305

304
Cup and Saucer

Germany, Meissen, 1730–40
Cup, height 3.9 cm; Saucer, diameter 10.5 cm
Mark: crossed swords in underglaze blue.
Ashmolean Museum, Oxford.

A small cup and saucer, the cup having no handle. Both are enamelled in the Kakiemon style with peonies growing by rocks and with butterflies and insects; the rims are edged in brown.

305
Broth Bowl and Cover

Germany, Meissen, c. 1730
Width 18 cm; height 15.5 cm
Ashmolean Museum, Oxford, 1974.268.

A circular broth bowl with everted rim and two square projecting handles, standing on three cabriole legs; the cover is conical with a knob finial. It is painted in underglaze blue and enamel colours with on either side a lady standing beside flowering branches growing by a banded hedge. Round the rim is a formal floral design in blue and red; on the cover with its blue knob are a boy with a flower spray or kite on a string, a *shishi* lion and a flowering plant by rocks painted partly in pink lustre.

Based on a Japanese porcelain incense-burner form and with an assemblage of Kakiemon-style designs: cf. No. 104 in the exhibition. For another Meissen example see R. Rückert, 1966, No. 268.

306
Box and Cover

Germany, Meissen, c. 1735
Height 9.5 cm; width 16.5 cm
Mark: crossed swords in underglaze blue and a star.
Victoria and Albert Museum, London, c.154 & A–1928.

An oval box with two scroll handles and a domed over-fitting lid with a flower-bud knob. It is painted after the Imari style in underglaze blue, red, yellow, two shades of green, and gilt with flowering branches round the sides and in a panel on top, with a red-and-gold border round the lid and rim and floral sprigs on the handles.

For this essentially Meissen shape, compare R. Rückert, 1966, No. 319. The Imari style was less enthusiastically pursued at the factory than the ever-popular Kakiemon but some relatively close copies were made, as shown by the following exhibits.

307
Dish
Germany, Meissen, *c.* 1740
Diameter 23.7 cm
Mark: crossed swords in blue with
K below, K being the supposed
mark of the underglaze-blue
painter Kretschmar.
British Museum, M&LA FRANKS 38,
Franks Bequest.

A dish with lobed sides and a wavy rim, shaped and
painted in direct imitation of a Japanese Imari dish. In
the centre a bird perched on a rock looks up at a pine
tree overhanging a stream. The surrounding border is
richly ornamented, and incorporates two panels with
phoenixes in red, gold and pink lustre in cartouches
outlined in blue and set within further panels with a

part-red and part-gilt ground; in the remaining border,
chrysanthemum blooms with gilt foliage appear on a blue
ground. On the outside are three flower sprays in blue,
red and gold.

From what is sometimes known as the 'Warsaw service'.
For the Japanese Imari original, see No. 237.

LITERATURE: Sir A. W. Franks, 1896, No. 38.

308
Dish
Germany, Meissen, *c.* 1735
Diameter 15.5 cm
Mark: crossed swords in underglaze blue.
Private Collection.

A saucer dish with sides moulded in twenty-five flutes,
enamelled in Arita style in red, green, yellow, black and

308

309

310

gilt with a Chinese man and woman standing together in a medallion outlined in red. The border is painted with three sprays of carnation and the foliated rim is gilt.

While most European copies of Japanese porcelain are in the Kakiemon or Imari styles, very few emulate this particular palette.

309
Basket
Probably Austria, Vienna,
du Paquier factory, 1735–40
Diameter 24.1 cm
Mark: four garbled Chinese
characters in blue.
Victoria and Albert Museum,
London, C.76–1949.

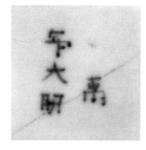

A shallow bowl with a pierced openwork border of intersecting circles at the rim. It is painted mainly in underglaze blue and in green, red and yellow enamels and gilt with a Kakiemon-style design of a phoenix perched on a branch of flowering peony and another hovering. On the back is a continuous leafy scroll in blue.

The Japanese version of this border is illustrated at Burghley, see G. Lang, 1983, Nos 74 and 75, who mentions a sketch in a surviving Kakiemon pattern-book. See too No. 221. It was extensively employed also at the English porcelain factories.

310
Dish
Austria, Vienna, c. 1750
Diameter 21 cm
Mark: a shield in blue.
Musées Royaux d'Art et d'Histoire, Brussels, L1174.

A deep saucer dish painted in close imitation of a Japanese Imari original. A vase of flowers flanked by a balustrade appears in the centre and in the well are three cartouches of mythical beasts on a gold ground, surrounded by flowering branches and three birds.

Unlike Meissen, the Vienna factory was more given to copying Imari than Kakiemon designs.

LITERATURE: Tokyo, 1982, No. 138.

311
Cistern
Austria, Vienna, du Paquier factory, *c.* 1735
Height 27.6 cm
Fitzwilliam Museum, Cambridge, E.C. 28–1942 , bought
from money given by Professor Stanley Cook, in
memory of his wife.

A three-sided urn-shaped cistern with tapering neck and
spreading foot, having mask heads at the corners and
fluted sides pierced by three small pipes for metal spigots.
It is painted in blue, red, pink, puce and green enamels
and gilt with prunus branches on the shoulder and
various flowers on the neck. The fluted areas are partly
picked out in the Imari palette of blue, red and gold.

The cistern is no doubt based on a European metal
original. Japanese influence presents itself only indirectly
in the painted design and colour scheme.

312
Tureen and Cover
France, St Cloud, 1730–40
Height 23.5cm; diameter 24.8 cm
Victoria and Albert Museum, London, C.445 & A–1909,
Fitzhenry Gift.

A low circular tureen with spreading base and two
grotesque mask handles, having a low domed cover with
acanthus-foliage knob; reeded bands in silverwork style
encircle the rims. The cream-coloured porcelain is
enamelled with designs partly in Kakiemon style and in a
colourful palette of blue, red, emerald-green, orange-
yellow and black, comprising flowering trees growing
by banded hedges and birds, also Chinese figures, a *qilin*,
and emblems.

According to Gauthier, based on a silver shape. The St
Cloud factory generally applied the Kakiemon-style
designs to its own preferred forms, and used a quite
modified range of colours for them.

LITERATURE: W. B. Honey, 1950, Pl. A and p. 12;
G. Savage, 1960, Pl. 7B; S. Gauthier, 1964, p. 72.

313

Trembleuse Cup and Saucer

France, St Cloud, *c.* 1735

Saucer, diameter 12.6 cm; Cup, height 7.1 cm

British Museum, M&LA FRANKS 338, Franks Bequest.

A tall cup with sides unevenly fluted and wavy, spreading rim, equipped with a branch-like handle; the matching saucer has a raised, matching ring in the centre to hold it. Painted on each part in enamels closely after the Kakiemon style are designs of bamboo, pine and prunus growing by banded hedges. In the centre of the saucer is a trefoil leaf painted in red.

LITERATURE: Sir A. W. Franks, 1896, No. 338.

313

314

Bourdaloue

France, Chantilly, 1730–51

Length 19 cm

Mark: a hunting horn in red.

Private Collection.

The small oval chamber-pot is of shell shape with a green-and-purple crabstock handle. It is enamelled in Kakiemon style with a blue *shishi* lion holding the string of an embroidered ball in its mouth, a flowering branch, a beetle and three small insects.

A shape also known at Vincennes, where the 1752 stock-list notes sixteen 'pots de Chambre forme de Limasson' ('snail-shaped chamber-pots'). S. Ericksen and G. de Bellaigue, 1987, p. 217.

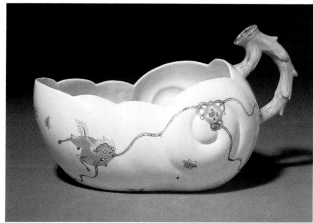
314

315

Seau à Bouteille

France, Chantilly, 1730–51

Height 16 cm; diameter 20 cm

Private Collection.

The *cache-pot* is cylindrical with a flanged rim at the top and bottom and two green-and-yellow lizard handles at the lip. It is enamelled in the Kakiemon style with a 'banded hedge and squirrel' design on one side and with chrysanthemum growing by rocks on the other. A border of flowers on a seeded ground appears above and a green band rings the base.

In the Japanese original the 'squirrel' is a tree-rat.

315

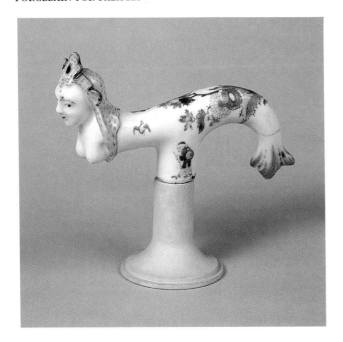

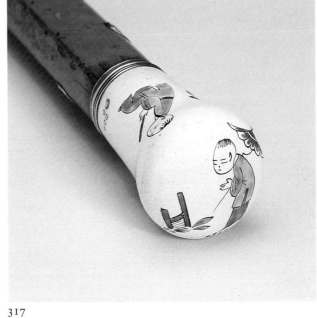

317

316

Cane-handle

France, St Cloud, 1730–40

Height 7.3 cm; length 14.9 cm

Victoria and Albert Museum, London, C.446–1909,
Fitzhenry Gift.

In the form of a mermaid with a blue and yellow hood
and elongated body from which projects a tube for
attaching to the cane. It is painted in an approximation
to the Kakiemon palette with a flowering spray of
chrysanthemum and other plants, a bird and an insect,
with figures of boys on either side, one with a fan and
the other with a gourd.

LITERATURE: W. B. Honey, 1950, Pl. 17B, p. 11.

317

Malacca Cane, with Porcelain Handle

France, Chantilly, 1730–51

Stick, height 93 cm; Handle, length 4.7 cm

Private Collection.

The knob-shaped handle is painted after the Kakiemon
palette with three oriental boys holding a stick, a fan and
a parasol and with fence posts and flowering foliage. It is
mounted to the stick with a reeded silver band and a
silver-mounted hole for a carrying thong below; the
bottom is mounted in brass and iron.

A   B   C

318

318

Two Dessert Forks and a Knife, with Handles of French and German Porcelain, 1730–40
Private Collection.

A: Villeroy, *c.* 1740

Two-tined French steel fork, length 19.4 cm

With flattened pistol-butt handle, enamelled with the Kakiemon 'quail pattern'.

B: Chantilly, *c.* 1730–51

Three-tined English steel fork, length 17.3 cm

With pistol-butt handle, enamelled with a sprig of prunus in the Kakiemon manner.

C: Meissen, *c.* 1740

Later English steel blade, length 22.3 cm

With pistol-butt handle moulded with the Sulkowski *ozier* pattern and enamelled with a bird and a *qilin* in the Kakiemon manner.

319

Five-lobed Dish
France, probably Vincennes, 1745–50
Diameter 12.7 cm
Victoria and Albert Museum, London, c.166–1933.

The saucer or *coupelle* has five-lobed sides and rim. It is decorated in a Kakiemon enamelling palette with a large central and five smaller medallions painted with a bird, a butterfly, fruit and flowers in red, blue, green and yellow; they are reserved on a trellised ground of red with blue dots and with flower-heads between. The rim is picked out in brown.

The unusual five-lobed form is surely inspired by a Kakiemon dish, such as for example S. Jenyns, 1965, Pl. 60A; a Meissen version also exists, however – although with different decoration – and was formerly in the Dresden Collection (cf. W. Williams, 1974, No. 49 and frontispiece). An identical dish in the Musée Céramique de Sèvres is illustrated by T. Préaud, 1978, Fig. 12. In that museum also are an oval Vincennes dish painted with the 'yellow tiger' pattern and a small jar with the 'squirrel-and-vine' pattern. Japanese decoration is otherwise virtually unknown at Vincennes or Sèvres.

319

320

Pair of Teabowls
France, Vincennes, 1745–50
Diameters 7.9 cm
Private Collection.

The bowls are of ogee profile with small foot, the rims shaped as four petal ends. Each is painted outside with three groups of three flower-heads above, and two groups of two below, and with two further groups of two flower-heads inside.

Although these could have been based on Japanese originals it is more likely that they copy Meissen cups. In either case the Vincennes profile is more conical.

321

322

321

Tureen

Italy, Venice, Cozzi factory, *c.* 1770
Width 28 cm
Mark: an anchor in red.
Fitzwilliam Museum, Cambridge,
E.C. 33–1945, given
by the Friends of the Museum.

An oval tureen moulded in Rococo style, with two
handles and four small legs joining a ring foot. Painted
outside in underglaze blue, red, green and yellow
enamels and gilt is a chinoiserie composition with a
pavilion and a bridge, a pair of small swimming ducks
and fantastic trees and plants. A border in blue, red and
gold encircles the rim.

The design is essentially a chinoiserie; the decorative
palette is after the Imari style. For a bowl with the same
design cf. A. Lane, 1954, Pl. 23C and p.18.

322

Oval Dish

Germany, Ludwigsburg, 1760–70
Width 36.5 cm
Mark: double C crowned over 3
in underglaze blue and
IP/4 impressed.
Fitzwilliam Museum, Cambridge,
MAR. C.39–1912, Marlay Bequest.

An oval dish with shallow well and broad, petalled
rim, painted in an Imari palette of underglaze blue, red
enamel and gilt. In the centre is a vase of flowers by a
balustrade within a blue border with six floral cartouches,
and extending to the rim are four shaped panels with
sprays of hydrangea, peony and twice-repeated
chrysanthemum, separated by motifs in blue and gold.

A rare example of the direct reproduction of a Japanese
design in Germany at this late date.

323

Oval Dish

Holland, Loosdrecht, 1778–82
Length 40 cm
Mark: MOL for Johannes de Mol.
Groninger Museum, Groningen, 1984–1.72.

The dish is shallow with a broad shaped rim. It is painted
in the Imari style of underglaze blue, red and gold with a
vase of flowers in the centre surrounded by flowering
prunus and wistaria and a phoenix below, and a blue rim
border with gilt scrollwork and floral insets.

The decorative scheme is derived from the Japanese.
Oriental motifs are few on Loosdrecht porcelain and
always faithful copies of the model. Thus it is not known
whether such porcelains were made as additions to
existing services, or were still being marketed despite
waning interest.

324
Plate
Holland, Amstel, 1785–1800
Diameter 25.3 cm
Mark: AMSTEL in underglaze blue.
Groninger Museum, Groningen, 1986.420.

The plate is decorated in an Imari palette of underglaze
blue, red, gold and black with a pine tree and wistaria in
the centre and a border of cartouches, three with
flowering plants beside a fence and three with formalized
peony blooms.

A direct copy of a Japanese Imari plate, an example of
which is in the Groninger Museum. Cf. C. J. A. Jörg,
1984. No. 159, who reproduces the mark.

XIV English Porcelain

The English porcelain factories of Chelsea and Bow were, together with Meissen and Chantilly, the only European sources for large quantities of wares in the Kakiemon taste. These were produced ten years after the fashion had waned on the Continent, and at Chelsea it was to last only from about 1750 to 1755, while at Bow it must have continued for another five years, Thomas Craft stating that his bowl was made 'about the year 1760' (No. 339). It is worth noting that most of these wares appear to have been taken direct from Japanese rather than Meissen originals.

The first five pieces of Chelsea and the butterfly dish No. 334 are direct copies of the Japanese in both shape and decoration (Nos 326 to 330) while the unusual sugar bowl and cover No. 331 is more probably an adaptation of a Japanese shape. Nos 332 and 333 are purely European in their shape and moulding but have Kakiemon-style decoration, the latter perhaps taken entirely from Meissen rather than from Japan. A Chelsea cup and saucer, No. 325, is a copy of the Meissen red dragon pattern No. 296 while the Bow vase No. 337, although copying a Kakiemon design is based on a Chinese Kangxi shape.

An interesting example of how the Bow partridge pattern travelled to Worcester and then on to Plymouth, is the jug No. 340, which allows one to surmise that a Bow decorator or decorators may have travelled to these two factories. Mr Lambe's advertisement of his auction of Bow porcelain in February, 1758 states that 'Some part of this Porcelain is very little inferior to the fine old brown Edge Japan and wants no other Recommendation than its own Beauty and Service'; and as against the earlier presumption that the English decorators had copied Japanese rather than Meissen originals, when referring to 'fine Partridge sets' – e.g. No. 338 – in his auction of April 1758 he adds '...which are most beautifully painted by several of the finest Masters from Dresden'. It is however doubtful that Bow ever employed any decorators trained at Meissen.

The salt-glaze teapot No. 343 is probably painted by a Dutch decorator and should be considered alongside those pieces discussed in that context (p. 239). Except for the palette and subject matter it bears a greater relationship to the Dutch *hausmalerei* than to similar designs on English porcelain. Few figure models made in England show signs of Japanese influence, but the Chelsea carp No. 341 and Staffordshire salt-glaze hawk No. 342 show how the potters in each place interpreted their Imari models.

By the time the English factories started production Japanese blue-and-white porcelain was less highly regarded than the later Chinese, and the dish No. 344 is a rare example of Chelsea (where in any case very little blue-and-white was made) combining a Japanese subject with a Chinese border design in this colour.

The Worcester factory adopted Kakiemon motifs in the 1760s only after they had gone out of fashion in London and on the Continent. With the exception of the so-called 'Joshua Reynolds' pattern No. 348, probably the 'fine old pheasant pattern' of the 1769 catalogue, they are a far cry from the Japanese originals though their source is still easily recognisable. They were generally used in combination with coloured grounds of which the 'scale blue' is the most common, as may be seen in the bough pot No. 349.

As regards designs in the Imari style, these remained uncommon at both Chelsea and Bow (Nos 345 and 346) but were often exactly copied at Worcester (Nos 347 and 354) and occasionally also at Derby (No. 355).

The Kakiemon designs disappear towards the end of the 18th century and have remained unfashionable until modern times; in spirit, they were no doubt out of tune with what followed. The more elaborate Imari styles, however, were taken up and adapted by Derby at the end of the century, and were again readapted by Spode and other Staffordshire factories in the course of the 19th century; remarkably enough, they have retained a place in the forefront of English porcelain production continuously until the present day.

A. du B.

325
Cup and Saucer
England, Chelsea, 1750–52
Cup, height 4.5 cm; diameter 6.3 cm;
Saucer, diameter 10.8 cm
Mark: a raised anchor.
Victoria and Albert Museum, London, C.1328 & A–1924,
E. F. Broderip Gift.

Both are octagonal and each is painted with two dragons and a pair of 'precious objects' in red and gold; inside the cup and on the saucer is a plum-blossom in red and green.

The design is based on the Meissen 'red dragon' pattern, see No. 296. More common is the red dragon dish on which a pair of red phoenixes in the centre complete the design. Both Meissen and Japanese examples of this are reproduced in Tokyo, Idemitsu Museum of Arts, 1984, Figs 100 and 101.

326
Octagonal Dish
England, Chelsea, *c.* 1755
Diameter 22.2 cm
Mark: an anchor in red.
British Museum, M&LA PC II 64,
Franks Bequest.

With panelled sides and flat rim with upturned lip, painted in enamels in the Kakiemon style. A black-striped yellow tiger coiled round a bamboo looks back at a flowering peony growing by a banded hedge; a leafy floral-scroll border in red with gilt blooms encircles the rim, which is lined in brown. Three firing spurs on the base imitate a common feature of Arita wares.

The Chelsea Porcelain Factory Sale of 15th March 1755, lot 5 included 'wheatsheaf and tyger dishes'.

The 'tiger and banded hedge' is one of the most copied of Kakiemon designs, and at Meissen was used for the earliest services made for Augustus the Strong of Saxony in 1728, curiously known as the *gelben Löwen* ('Golden Lion') service (E. Zimmerman, 1926, Fig. 15, p. 63). Repetitions followed, including further royal services in 1734 and 1738. See also the flask in this exhibition, No. 293.

A comparison of Japanese, Meissen (1728–30), Venetian Cozzi (1770) and Chelsea ('raised anchor') versions of the pattern is made by H. Syz, 1970, Pl. VI.

LITERATURE: R. L. Hobson, 1905, II, 64; H. Tait, 1962, Pl. XXXII.

327
Decagonal Dish
England, Bow, *c.* 1756–58
Diameter 14 cm
Victoria and Albert Museum, London, C. 68–1964.

With panelled sides and flat rim with upturned lip lined in brown. It is painted in the Kakiemon style in turquoise, red, blue and brown enamels and gilt. A woman is seated by a veranda on which rests a bird cage, with two flying birds, a book at her side and a rolled-up, tasselled curtain above.

For a simplified Japanese original of this design, see the cup and saucer at Burghley House, No. 127 in the exhibition and for a Chelsea version, where the veranda is reversed, see No. 328. The dish is illustrated by J. V. G. Mallet, 1965, Pl. 26B together with Chelsea and Japanese examples for comparison; and he observes that it may have been copied from a 'Japan octogon cup and saucer lady pattern' which Lady Cavendish lent to Bow in 1756.

The pattern was also known at Chantilly (P. Alfasse and J. Guérin, 1930, Pl. 31B). Two Chinese saucer-dishes in the Musée des Arts Décoratifs, Paris are decorated in Holland with a variant of the pattern in which a male figure with a basket of fruit stands to the right of the lady.

328
Cup and Saucer
England, Chelsea, *c.* 1750–53
Saucer, width 14.8 cm; Cup, height 6.4 cm
Private Collection.

Both cup and saucer are shaped with the rim repeating
the irregular profile of a peach and the sides
correspondingly moulded. They are painted in green,
red, yellow and blue enamels after a Kakiemon design
with a scene of a woman seated by a veranda with a
small birdcage and two flying birds, framed by looped
curtains with pendant tassels.

Compare the Bow version of this design, No. 327 and
also a Japanese version, No. 127. J. V. G. Mallet, 1965,
pp. 17–18 suggests that this pattern is covered by the
description 'Old Lady Pattern', in which case this design
was still included in the 1756 Chelsea sale. The adjective
'old' refers to the pattern, not the lady.

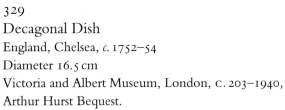

329
Decagonal Dish
England, Chelsea, *c.* 1752–54
Diameter 16.5 cm
Victoria and Albert Museum, London, C. 203–1940,
Arthur Hurst Bequest.

A shallow dish with flat rim and upturned lip lined in
brown. It is painted after a Japanese Kakiemon-style dish
in underglaze blue, red, yellow and green enamels and
gilt with two spiky-tailed birds and a flowering tree
growing behind a banded hedge, and a border of formal
flowers in red and gold.

This pattern is more commonly found at Chelsea
employing an overglaze blue enamel. It is discussed by
J. V. G. Mallet, 1965, Pl. 27, together with a Japanese
example from the Reitlinger Collection.

330
Decagonal Bowl
England, Chelsea, *c.* 1752–55
Diameter 19 cm
British Museum, M&LA, PC II 101, Franks Bequest.

With flat projecting rim and upturned indented lip,
shaped and painted in enamels after a Kakiemon-style
bowl. Round the outside is an extended landscape with
pine, bamboo and prunus (the 'Three Friends') flanked
by a standing and a flying crane, also a 'flaming' tortoise
among rocks. Inside in the centre is a coiled dragon

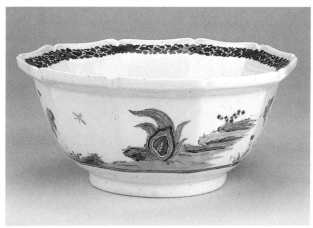

330

flanked by flower sprays, and on the rim, a leafy floral scroll
with five gilt blooms. On the base are three firing spurs.

The 1755 sale catalogue of the factory lists as lot 6 on the
5th day: 'Two ten square basons of the flaming tortoise
pattern, and 2 ditto butterflies old pattern'.

The so-called 'flaming tortoise' is the Japanese
minogame, a venerable water-creature with weed growing
from its shell. A Japanese use of the design is seen on
No. 123; while No. 158 (q.v.) is a *minogame* with rider.

LITERATURE: R. L. Hobson, 1905, II, 101.

331

331

Sugar Bowl and Cover

England, Chelsea, *c.* 1752–55
Height 11.5 cm
Victoria and Albert Museum, London, C. 3 & A–1966.

The eight sides of the bowl each end in a pointed gable
and the cover is pleated to fit. Alternate sides are painted
in the Kakiemon style with a stylised foliage scroll in
white and gold reserved on a red ground and with
flowers or 'precious objects' in blue, green and red
outlined in black. The cover has a burnished gilt cherry
knob surrounded by leaves; the interior is plain.

The 1755 Chelsea sale catalogue lists as lot 55 on the
10th day a tea set including '…a sugar bason octagon red
pannel pattern', which surely describes this piece.

Japanese use of the design may be seen in an octagonal
cup at Burghley House: G. Lang, 1983, No. 61. A cup
and saucer showing the distinctive Meissen treatment of
1730–35 is reproduced by R. Rückert, 1966, No. 327.
An entire Meissen service of the pattern is, however, said

332

to have been presented by the Queen of Prussia to Caroline, the wife of George II (see Christie's sale, 28th March 1969, lot 10).

332
Dish or Stand for a Sauceboat
England, Chelsea, *c.* 1752–55
Length 23 cm
British Museum, M&LA, PC II 65, Franks Bequest.

An oval dish of Rococo silver shape with shell mouldings. It is painted in the Kakiemon style with a red-and-gold dragon coiled round a bamboo and looking down at a red tiger which returns its gaze; below are two ancient prunus branches.

This design is probably the 'twisted dragon pattern' referred to in the Chelsea sale catalogue, 14th March, 1755, lot 37 and 15th March, lot 72. In shape, the dish is based on silver originals by Nicholas Sprimont made as stands for sauceboats, examples of which with his mark and date letter for 1746/47 are in the Boston Museum of Fine Arts, Katz Collection. For a sauceboat on an identical stand cf. J. C. Austin, 1977, Figs 40 and 41.

LITERATURE: R. L. Hobson, 1905, II, 65.

333
Plate
England, Chelsea, *c.* 1755
Diameter approx. 20 cm
Mark: an anchor in red.
Private Collection.

With flat rim and moulded in eight broad and narrow lobes extending to the upturned lip, which is correspondingly foliated and lined in brown enamel. Mould-impressed sprigs of chrysanthemum decorate the rim panels and centre, supplementing Kakiemon-style enamelled designs which include a large standing red crane in the centre and flying cranes and flowering plants by hedges on the rim.

This kind of moulded relief flower decoration at Chelsea has been identified as 'damask'd'. Both form and patterns imitate those of the celebrated Gotzkowsky service in Meissen porcelain which was modelled by Eberlein in 1741–44: cf. R. Rückert, 1966, No. 464. Japanese moulded patterns do not seem to have been much copied.

The same standing red crane appears on the Meissen butter tub, No 300.

333

334
Plate
England, Chelsea, *c.* 1752–55
Diameter 22 cm
Private Collection.

With flat rim shaped in five lobes and with upturned lip. It is painted in blue, turquoise and red enamel with large butterflies, two in the centre and five on the rim.

S. Jenyns, 1965, Pl. 60A illustrates a Japanese five-lobed dish with this Kakiemon design.

283

336

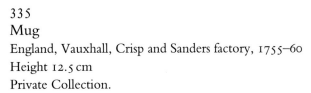

335
Mug
England, Vauxhall, Crisp and Sanders factory, 1755–60
Height 12.5 cm
Private Collection.

A cylindrical mug, the rim edged in brown, with a
slightly spreading base and reeded handle. It is painted in
a Kakiemon palette of blue, turquoise, red, grey, yellow
and gilt with a pair of peacocks, one sitting in a prunus
tree and the other perched on a blue rock surrounded by
fencing.

LITERATURE: B. Watney, 1989, Pl. 205A.

336
Cup and Saucer
England, Longton Hall or Scotland, West Pans,
c. 1755–60
Cup, height 5.2 cm; Saucer, width 13 cm
Private Collection.

A hexagonal cup and saucer enamelled in the Kakiemon
palette of blue, red and green with a pair of quail beside
a prunus tree, flowers and clumps of grass. In the centre of
the cup, which has a handle, are a blue rock and flowers.

An almost identical saucer in the Victoria and Albert
Museum is attributed to West Pans, where William
Littler carried on his work after the Longton Hall factory
closed in 1760.

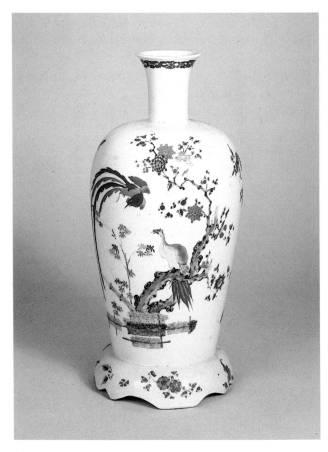

337
Vase
England, Bow, c. 1755
Height 26.5 cm
Private Collection.

An oviform vase with narrow flared neck and domed
foot with cut-out rim, after a Chinese *famille verte* model.
It is painted in Kakiemon-style enamels and gilt with a
pair of pheasants perched and in flight among prunus
trees and bamboo beside a banded hedge; there are

scattered flowers on both the vase and its foot and a border of red scrolling foliage below the mouth.

Compare the Chelsea use of the same pattern (No. 329). A comparable, but smaller Bow vase with different Kakiemon designs is shown by A. Gabszewicz and G. Freeman, 1982, No. 55.

338
Leaf Dish
England, Bow, *c.* 1760
Length 30 cm
Private Collection.

An oval dish formed as two over-lapping leaves, with clearly-defined veins and serrated edge. It is painted in blue, green and red enamels with a pair of quail under a prunus tree and a border of scrolling foliage in red and gold.

Leaf dishes were made at most of the English porcelain factories. For a Japanese blue-and-white dish of this form, see No. 65. A comparable Meissen leaf dish of 1725–30 decorated in blue enamel is reproduced by F. Reichel, 1981, Pl. 93 and an enamelled version of 1730–35 by R. Rückert, 1966, No. 250.

339
The Thomas Craft Bowl
England, Bow, *c.* 1760
Diameter 22 cm
British Museum, M&LA PC I 62.

A shallow bowl with rounded sides and a high foot, its mouthrim bound in brass to contain two cracks which are riveted. It is enamelled and gilt with an essentially English design which is however executed in the Kakiemon palette. Round the rim both inside and outside are four floral swags with floral pendants between and scattered sprays below, and inside in the centre is a flowered monogram of a double 'TC'.

The 'Craft' bowl is a major document of the Bow factory's history. The Museum retains a box contemporary with and specially made for the bowl, which is inscribed:

This bowl, was made at Bow China Manufactory, at Stratford-le-Bow in the County of Essex, about the year 1760, and painted there by Thomas Craft, my Cypher is in the Bottom;– it is painted in what we used to call the old Japan taste, a taste at the time much esteemed by the then Duke of Argyle; there is near 2 peny-weight of

Gold, about,; 15*s*.; I had it in hand at different times about three months, about 2 weeks twice was bestowed on it, it could not have been manufactured, &c, for less than £4, there is not its Similitude; I took it in a Box to Kentish town, and had it burned there in Mr Gyles's Kiln, cost me 3*s*..., it was cracked the first time of using it... The signature 'T. Craft, 1790' ends the account.

LITERATURE: R. L. Hobson, 1905, I.62; W. B. Honey, 1949, p. 139; British Museum, 1959, No. III.

340
Jug
England, Plymouth, 1768–70
Height 14 cm
Victoria and Albert Museum, London, 3092–1901,
Jermyn Street Collection.

A pear-shaped jug with pinched spout, painted in
Kakiemon enamel colours and gilt with a pair of quail
under a prunus tree, chrysanthemum plants and an insect.

Plymouth was the first English factory seriously to make
hard-paste porcelain; its successors in this were Bristol
and New Hall.

341
Vase in the form of Two Carp
England, Chelsea, 1760–65
Height 17.1 cm
British Museum, M&LA PC II 8, Franks Bequest.

Modelled after the style of Imari originals, with one fish
leaping up and supported on its tail and a smaller fish
below. Both are glazed plain white. Their fins and scales
are well defined and their open mouths offer receptacles,
perhaps for flowers. The base is unglazed.

For a coloured pair of Imari carp vases on moulded wave
bases, see No. 179.

LITERATURE: R. L. Hobson, 1905, II, 8.

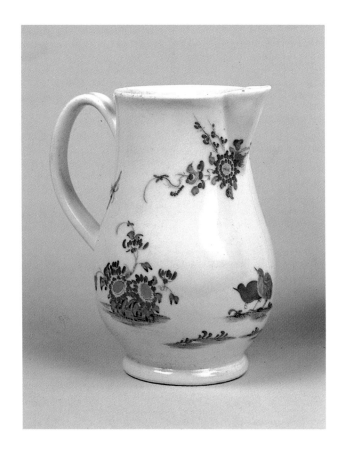

342
Figure of a Hawk in Salt-glazed Stoneware
England, Staffordshire, mid 18th century
Height 18.7 cm
British Museum, M&LA PC G 46, Franks Bequest.

The bird is press-moulded and stands looking front on a rocky base; there is some black speckling on the white body. The beak, eyes and rockwork base have a metallic iron-brown glaze and the glazed underside is hollow, with a brown border inside.

This model may be compared with the Japanese figure of a blue-and-white hawk on a brown rock, No. 156.

LITERATURE: R. L. Hobson, 1903, No. G46.

343
Teapot and Cover in Salt-glazed Stoneware
England, Staffordshire, 1750–60
Height: 13.3 cm
Mark: the numerals 1–12 in a circle incised.
British Museum, M&LA 1942, 4–11, 3, Rev.
G. A. Schneider Bequest.

A teapot with reeded globular body and tapering octagonal spout; the cover has an acorn-shaped finial. It is enamelled in the Kakiemon style with on one side, two birds and flowering plants growing by a double banded hedge, and on the other, a bird on a bamboo, a pinetree, and rocks by a banded hedge. Under the spout, a black-striped yellow tiger snarls at a bird above its head; both spout and handle are painted with floral motives.

Cf. B. Rackham, 1951, Pl. 51A, who suggests that the decoration was carried out by Dutch enamellers, either in Staffordshire or in Holland.

344
Blue-and-white Plate
England, Chelsea, *c.* 1755
Diameter 22.8 cm
Mark: an anchor within a circle in underglaze blue.
British Museum, M&LA PC II 56, Franks Bequest.

A deep plate with flat rim foliated in five lobes and with
upturned lip. It is painted after a Kakiemon-style design
in the centre with two long-tailed phoenix-like birds
perched opposite a flowering tree growing by rocks; the
well is plain and on the rim are five panels with flower
sprays reserved in a trellis-pattern ground, rather in the
Chinese taste. On the base are three firing spurs.

LITERATURE: R. L. Hobson, 1905, II, 56.

345
Fluted Dish
England, Chelsea, *c.* 1760
Diameter 20.8 cm
Mark: an anchor in gold.
British Museum, M&LA PC II 60, Franks Bequest.

With sides moulded in sixteen lobes and a wavy rim, painted after a Japanese Imari original in underglaze blue, enamels and gilt. In the centre are curving sprays of chrysanthemum and another flower and radiating to the rim are panels of varying size and design, including three with prunus or millet and others with brocade patterns or blue-and-gold trellis, with scattered chrysanthemum blooms. On the underside are three flowering branches.

On the base are three firing spurs, a double blue circle and the mark.

Japanese dishes of comparable design are Nos 237 and 238. It makes its appearance at Chelsea in the 1756 sale catalogue, lot 23, 7th day as 'a rare old Japan pattern blue and gold'. Before 1760 an underglaze blue, rather than gold, anchor mark will have been used. The pattern was later adopted at Worcester and Derby, while its exact precursor exists also in 'Chinese Imari': cf. Tokyo, Idemitsu Museum of Arts, 1984, Figs 125 and 126, with a Worcester variant, Fig. 127.

LITERATURE: R. L. Hobson, 1905, II, 60.

346
Plate
England, Bow, c. 1755
Diameter 18.4 cm
Victoria and Albert Museum, London, c.529–1906,
Sidney Vacher Gift.

The plate is painted in the Kakiemon style in underglaze
blue, red, green, yellow and greyish-purple enamels
outlined in black and with gilding. In the centre are
pomegranates and tree-peonies growing by rocks, and on
the rim sprays of prunus, flowering plants, ferns and rocks.

For a Meissen dish bearing a quite similar design with a
bird on a rock, dated to c. 1730, see W. Williams, 1974,
No. 67.

346

347
Square Bowl
England, Worcester, c. 1765–70
Width 23.5 cm
Ashmolean Museum, Oxford, 257, Marshall Collection.

With lobed sides, square at the rim, which is lined in
brown enamel. It is enamelled in the Arita style with
flowering branches inside in red, green, yellow and gilt
amongst key-patterns in iron-red, green and puce. The
exterior is similarly painted, with a prunus tree and
flowering plant.

This design is based on an Arita prototype (No. 212):
cf. F. Reichel, 1980, Pl. 76 for an example at Dresden.
The same shape and design were used at Derby in the
mid 1770s.

347

348
Sugar Bowl and Cover
England, Worcester, 1765–70
Height 11.5 cm
Mark: a square seal in underglaze blue.
Private Collection.

A fluted bowl with a domed lid and flower-bud finial. It
is painted in Kakiemon colours with on one side a
pheasant perched on a turquoise rock beside flowering
shrubs and on the other, two insects. The lid is similarly
decorated, and the rim lined in brown.

This design, with a blue border, was known as the
'Joshua Reynolds pattern', possibly because the artist
owned a similar service.

348

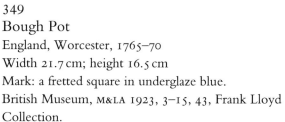

349
Bough Pot
England, Worcester, 1765–70
Width 21.7 cm; height 16.5 cm
Mark: a fretted square in underglaze blue.
British Museum, M&LA 1923, 3–15, 43, Frank Lloyd
Collection.

A flower holder of lobed shape and Rococo design with
three panels framed by scrolls in relief on its front, the
sunken top surrounded by raised shell-like scrollwork
and with pierced holes and a larger aperture. The front is
painted in the Kakiemon style with flowering plants
growing from banded hedges and grass. The left-hand
panel shows a secretary bird and the right, a serpent-like
dragon confronting a similar bird; the panels are outlined
with gilt C-scrolls and like those of the top, are reserved
in a scale-blue ground.

The 1769 sale catalogue of the Worcester factory
includes pieces 'of the very rich mazarine blue and gold,
fine old wheatsheaf pattern'.

LITERATURE: R. L. Hobson, 1923, No. 87.

350
Plate
England, Worcester, 1765–1770
Diameter 24.8 cm
Mark: a simulated Chinese character in blue.
Victoria and Albert Museum, London, 3193–1901,
Jermyn Street Collection.

A fluted plate with scalloped rim painted in the Imari
style with sixteen panels in underglaze blue, blue enamel,
iron-red, turquoise, pink, puce and gilding with diaper
and floral patterns in alternation, and scattered
chrysanthemum medallions. In the centre is a wavy-
edged medallion with a ring of flowering prunus
branches in blue, red and gold. On the back are four
sprays of flowers.

The design is based on a Japanese original, compare
No. 238; which bears an apocryphal Chinese reign mark.
    The sale of '… a large and elegant Assortment of the
Worcester porcelaine by Mr Christie on Thursday the
14th of this instant December 1769 and five following
days (Sunday excepted)' included 'Twelve beautiful
plates, old mosaick japan pattern £2.15s…'.

351
Bowl
England, Worcester, *c.* 1770
Diameter 19.6 cm
Ashmolean Museum, Oxford, 188,
Marshall Collection.

With sides moulded in sixteen flutes
and a scalloped and gilt rim. The
interior is painted with an unusual
Imari-style design showing four red
chrysanthemum heads with green leaves
on a turquoise ground; round the
border are three double panels with
trellis and Y-diaper patterns in red and
gilt, partly superimposed on which are
green ground panels enriched with
formal designs, trailing ribbons and *ruyi*-
heads. On the exterior is a sparing
design of foliage in red and gold, with a
border of turquoise gadroons.

LITERATURE: H. R. Marshall, 1954,
Pl. 10, No. 185.

352
Butter-dish and Cover
England, Worcester, *c.* 1770
Height 8.3 cm; width 11.7 cm
Victoria and Albert Museum, London,
C.418 & A–1935.

A shallow circular tub with straight
sides, two ear handles and a domed lid
with flower knob. It is painted in the
Imari style in green, red, blue, yellow,
greyish-purple and gilt with scroll-like
panels, radiating panels of diaper work,
dragons among scattered flowers and
chrysanthemum heads. Flowering plants
and an insect are painted inside.

Scroll-like panels of this sort are seen on
the Imari vase, No. 223.

353
Punch Pot and Cover
England, Worcester,
c. 1775
Height 22.5 cm
Mark: an imitation
Chinese Ming dynasty mark in
underglaze blue.
British Museum, M&LA 1923, 3–15, 24,
Frank Lloyd Collection.

A large, globular pot painted in the
Imari style with six half chrysanthemum
roundels petalled alternately in
underglaze blue, red and green enamels
and gilt, and four blue medallions with
gilt trellis-work. Under the spout is a
running fox and the inscription,
'TALLY HO'. The cover is decorated
in matching style.

The 1769 Worcester sale catalogue
includes 'six caudle cups and saucers of
the fine old Japan fan pattern, £1.19*s.*':
see Nightingale, 1881.

For a comparison of a cup and saucer
with this 'fan' pattern and an Imari
model, see H. Syz, 1970, Taf. V, Fig. 9.
It is prominent also on the 'Chinese
Imari' bowl No. 256.

LITERATURE: R. L. Hobson, 1923,
No. 59.

354
Plate
England, Worcester, *c.* 1770
Diameter 22.3 cm
Ashmolean Museum, Oxford, 727,
Marshall Collection.

Painted in the Imari style in underglaze
blue, red and pink enamels and gilt with
in the centre four carp leaping from the
waves, with stylized clouds above. In
the surrounding border are six petal-
shaped panels with flowering plants and
fences, reserved on a blue ground, with
gilt scrolling foliage. The reverse has
three flower sprays in red and blue.

For an example of this plate reproduced
beside its Japanese original, cf. Tokyo,
Idemitsu Museum of Arts, 1984, Figs
143 and 144.

355
Small Bowl

England, Derby, *c.* 1765
Diameter 11.5 cm
British Museum, M&LA PC V 73, Franks Collection.

A deep bowl with everted lip, painted outside with three leaf-shaped panels containing lotus sprays in gold on a red ground framed in underglaze blue and green enamel, on a ground of square key-fret in red; below is a fungus scroll border in blue. Inside on the bottom is a peony spray, with a cell-diaper border in red and gold at the rim. A fungus scroll in underglaze blue decorates the base.

For the precise origin of this design in Imari ware see the bowl and dish, No. 239 in the exhibition.

LITERATURE: R. L. Hobson, 1905, V, 73.

356

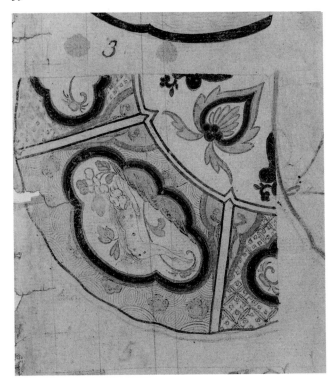

356
Small Plate

England, Derby, *c.* 1775
Diameter 17.8 cm
Mark: a square seal in blue enamel.
Ashmolean Museum, Oxford, 184, Marshall Collection.

With wavy, moulded border, painted in overglaze blue, red and gilt in the centre with formal paulownia and lotus buds; the surrounding border is divided into four, with a leaping *shishi* in a cartouche on a green-and-gilt trellis ground alternating with formal flowering foliage in a similar cartouche among puce scrollwork. On the underside is a formal foliage design.

This design was taken from an Arita prototype, and appears as No. 3 in the pattern book of the Derby factory: see illustration. It was directly copied at Worcester: cf. H. R. Marshall, 1954, No. 121, Pl. 7.

357
Tea Set
England, Derby, 1810–25
Teapot, length 25 cm; Cups, heights 4.5 cm; Saucers,
diameters 13 cm
Mark: crossed batons and D under a crown.
Private Collection.

The set comprises a teapot, cream jug, sugar bowl and
slop bowl and four cups and saucers and forms part of a
larger service. It is decorated in underglaze blue, red
enamel and gilt with the popular design known as the
'King's pattern'.

This teaset is included to represent the undiminished
fashion for Japanese Imari-style designs in English
porcelain of the early 19th century. Various factories
maintained the tradition and, remarkably, these designs
still remain highly popular for wares made for the table
today.

XV The 'Quail' Pattern

One of the commoner motifs on Kakiemon porcelains shows one or two small birds on the ground with various plants – stalks of millet, chrysanthemum, prunus blossoms, and occasionally mixed groups of flowers. These birds are the quail (Japanese *uzura*), romantically associated very often with autumn, with moonlight, and with grassy plains of Musashino (near modern Tokyo). On a more mundane level, both quail and their eggs were enthusiastically eaten in Japan, as elsewhere in the Old World.

The motif was by the mid 17th century a stock one, reaching decorative pattern books for artisans, which by later in the century were being produced in the woodblock medium as well as by hand. These were simplified versions of the works of the Tosa School of painters, who had since the 15th century been official artists to the Imperial Court at Kyoto. In the mid 17th century, under the leadership of Tosa Mitsuoki, they included among their productions 'bird and flower' paintings, *kachōga* (No. 358), in a detailed and naturalistic style ultimately derived from the courtly painters of Song Dynasty China in the 12th century. Among these subjects were quail, associated with various plants, of which several are by or attributed to Li Anzhong (fl. 1119–31). The Tosa artists tended even to use dyed silk to simulate the old browned silks of Song China.

Although often rather simply represented in Kakiemon, they were readily understood by any Japanese for what they were; when, however, the pattern was copied in Europe it was soon misinterpreted. It was to be among the most popular of many adaptations, the version with one bird in blue and the other in red under a prunus tree (as in No. 360) inspiring a number of factories. Among the earlier pieces on which it occurs is the Meissen sugar bowl No. 364; Chantilly soon followed and here the pattern is usually combined with that of two storks (No. 366). The dating of the Delft plate No. 363 is still imprecise but, as pointed out in the Introduction, p. 40–44, it seems likely that the Dutch enamellers were pioneers in the copying of Kakiemon designs in Europe.

In England, because of their size, the quail were imagined to be partridges. Thus 'partridge octagon plates' are entered in the account books of the Bow works for 1756, together with a memorandum by the manager 'to buy partridge, either alive or dead'; and 'nurl'd partridge' and 'nurl'd open partridge' appear at regular intervals in the 1755 sale catalogue.

This was perhaps the design most used during the late 1750s, adorning pieces that are sometimes Japanese and sometimes entirely European (No. 369) in shape. The Chelsea teapot No. 367 on the other hand mixes the two coloured quail with the 'quail and millet' pattern. At Bow, a border of foliage in red with gilt florets was frequently added. The Bow style was evidently much followed at Worcester (No. 369) and also at Plymouth (No. 340), although in each case more often without the red border.

The other version of the quail subject commonly found is one in which the two birds are in natural colours and appear by a clump of millet (No. 359). This does not seem to have been employed at Meissen or at Chantilly; it has its exact counterpart however at Chelsea (No. 368), while it was charmingly adapted at Bow (No. 370). At Worcester, nine different quail patterns in all may be distinguished.

L. R. H. S.

A. du B.

296

358
Quail and Millet

Hanging scroll in ink and colours on silk
Japan, Tosa School, late 17th or early 18th century, with
a false signature and seal of Tosa Mitsuoki (1617–1691)
Painted area, height 77.7 cm; width 28.6 cm
British Museum, JA, ADD 33.

The quail and millet was one of Mitsuoki's most
celebrated subjects. Under the normal Japanese system,
apprentice artists in the Tosa School would have copied
the master's works, both in his lifetime and after it,
including copies of the signature and seal. The signature
reads 'Tosa Sakon Jōran Mitsuoki Hitsu' and the seal
'Tosa Jōshō'.

359
Octagonal Dish

Japan, c. 1700
Width 25.5 cm
Ashmolean Museum, Oxford, 1978.574, Reitlinger Gift.

A dish with everted rim and upturned lip with brown
edge, painted in the Kakiemon enamel palette with two
quail in red and gold beneath flowers and millet stalks.
A border of half-florets runs round the rim; the outside
is plain.

LITERATURE: Oxford, Ashmolean Museum, 1981, No. 186;
London, Royal Academy of Arts, 1981, No. 220.

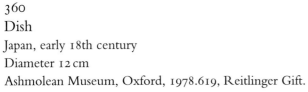

361

360
Dish
Japan, early 18th century
Diameter 12 cm
Ashmolean Museum, Oxford, 1978.619, Reitlinger Gift.

A small saucer dish painted in the Kakiemon enamel palette with a blue and a red quail under a prunus tree and with scattered flowers.

361
Dish
Japan, early 18th century
Diameter 14.7 cm
Mark: a commendation seal mark.
The Burghley House Collection, Stamford, Lincolnshire.

A saucer dish painted in underglaze blue with three large quail in the centre and a border with panels of 'precious objects' and flowers reserved on a blue floral ground. On the reverse are floral sprays. Three firing spurs on the base surround the mark.

LITERATURE: G. Lang, 1983, No. 7; New York, Japan Society, 1986, No. 43.

362

362
Vase
China, Dehua, late 17th century; with enamel decoration
added in Europe, mid 18th century
Height 16 cm
Private Collection.

A cylindrical vase of 'rollwagon' shape with short waisted
neck and two lion-mask handles. The plain *blanc-de-
Chine* porcelain is decorated closely after the Kakiemon
style with a pair of quail by a flowering prunus on one
side and flowers in pots on the other.

The enamelling on this piece will have been added either
in Holland or, according to one school of opinion as yet
unsubstantiated, in England.

363

363
Delftware Plate
Holland, Delft, 1720–35
Diameter 22.4 cm
Mark: AR in red, believed to be that of Ary van
Rijsselberg.
British Museum, M&LA AF 3179, Franks Bequest.

An almost flat plate, painted in the centre with two quail
beside growing millet and flowering plants and two
flying insects and with a border of formal foliage
medallions, all in turquoise-green and red enamels and
gilt. On the reverse are six flower sprays in red.

LITERATURE: For the mark, see C. H. de Jonge, 1970,
p. 167.

364

364
Sugar Bowl and Cover
Germany, Meissen, 1730–40
Height 11.7 cm; diameter 9.5 cm
Mark: crossed swords in underglaze blue inside, and
impressed mark of the thrower Seidel.
Victoria and Albert Museum, London, C.25 & A–1956,
Tulk Bequest.

An octagonal box with vertical sides and a domed cover
facetted to match, with reeded loop handle. It is painted
in the Kakiemon palette with a pair of quail, a prunus
tree and other plants. The rim of the cover is picked out
in brown.

365
Tureen and Cover
France, Chantilly, 1735–45
Diameter 30.5 cm
Mark: a hunting horn in red.
Ashmolean Museum, Oxford, 1980.1, Phillips Gift.

With two handles in the form of mastiff heads with
gaping mouths, the cover with finial in the form of an
apple. Round the sides painted in Kakiemon-style
enamels are two quail with millet, flower sprays and
insects, and above is a border in the *famille verte* style with
six shaped panels each containing two quail on a ground
of green 'cracked-ice' pattern with scattered prunus
blossoms. The border is repeated on the cover and inside
is a single spray.

The Chantilly factory made extensive use of the 'quail'
motif, applying it to many forms and often ingeniously
varying the Japanese scheme of colours or, as here,
combining a Japanese with a Chinese style. Ten various
uses of the quail pattern, included among them this
tureen, are illustrated by W. Williams, 1974, Nos 1–10.

366

Teapot and Lid

France, Chantilly, *c.* 1735

Height 10 cm

Mark: a hunting horn in red.

Cecil Higgins Art Gallery and Museum, Bedford, C. 1028.

In the shape of a horizontally-lobed melon, the stem flattened to make a loop handle and the opposite end drawn out into a spout, the lid having a knob in melon form. Painted round the sides in the Kakiemon palette of enamels are pairs of quail and of storks, both among flowering plants, with scrolls and sprays on the handle and under the spout. On the lid are paulownia flowers and two birds in green and blue.

LITERATURE: W. B. Honey, 1950, Pl. 20B; G. Savage, 1960, Pl. 17B.

367

Teapot and Lid

England, Chelsea, *c.* 1752

Height 13.7 cm

Cecil Higgins Art Gallery and Museum, Bedford, C. 254.

An octagonal pot supported on four feet which are together moulded in the form of a flowering branch, with two 'strawberry' leaves in moulded relief by the handle and blooms under the spout. The matching lid is in the form of a serrated leaf with its stem coiled to form a handle. The teapot is painted in Kakiemon-style enamels with two quails between growing millet and bamboo on one side (and one only on the lid), and on the other a bird in flight, plants and insects.

In shape, the lower part of this teapot resembles a Chinese pickle-tray illustrated by J. C. Austin, 1977, Pl. 69, who shows it has a *blanc-de-Chine* original: cf. P. J. Donnelly, 1969, Pl. 39C.

painted in the Kakiemon palette with the 'partridge pattern'; the shells are in red, blue, green and gold and the dolphin in greenish grey, dull rose-pink and red.

This quail design incorporating large prunus flowers is the most popular of the Japan patterns on Bow porcelain (see also No. 338); it was subsequently copied also at Worcester, No. 371. In this form it appears to have no exact counterpart either at Meissen or in Japan.

369

368
Octagonal Dish

England, Chelsea, *c.* 1753–55
Diameter 26.2 cm
Mark: an anchor in red.
British Museum, M&LA PC I 34, Franks Bequest.

With panelled sides and a flat rim with upturned lip. Enamelled in the centre are two red, gold, black and sepia quail with yellow beaks by growing millet and flowers and on the rim a border of half-florets, with the lip picked out in brown. There are three firing spurs on the base.

Of all the Western versions of Kakiemon designs it is perhaps those of 'red anchor' Chelsea that adhere most closely to the original. The 1755 sale catalogue of the factory lists as lot 34 on the sixth day: 'Four octagon sallad dishes old partridge pattern with border', which evidently correspond to this dish.

LITERATURE: R. L. Hobson, 1905, No. II, 63.

369
Dolphin Centre-piece

England, Bow, *c.* 1755–60
Diameter 18.4 cm
Victoria and Albert Museum, London, C.1986–1924, E. F. Broderip Gift.

Formed of three shells each on a small foot and a central dolphin handle with shells and seaweed at its base. It is

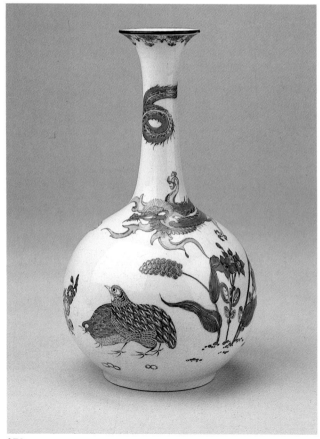

370

370
Bottle Vase
England, Bow, *c.* 1755–60
Height 20.3cm
British Museum, M&LA PC I 34, Franks Bequest.

The globular body is enamelled with two quail in red,
sepia and gilt among growing millet and flowers, and a
coiled dragon in red and gold encircles the slender neck.
Above this a border of half-florets is painted below the
spreading rim, which is lined in brown.

The origin of this quail design, as on the Chelsea dish
No. 368, may be traced to the Japanese dish No. 359,
while the dragon is also from the Japanese repertoire.

LITERATURE: R. L. Hobson, 1905, I, 34.

371

371
Jug
England, Worcester, *c.* 1765
Height 17.5 cm
British Museum, M&LA 1936, 7–15, 105, presented by
F. Howard Paget, Esq.

The jug is pear-shaped and broad-mouthed with a spout
in the form of a bearded mask. It is enamelled in the
Kakiemon style with a pair of quail, a prunus tree and
other flowering plants, insects and flowers round the
sides and a border of scrolling red foliage interspersed
with gilt florets at the rim; the mask is partly in puce.

372
Sugar Bowl, Cover and Stand
England, Worcester, 1765–75
Bowl, height 12.1 cm; Stand, diameter 18.4 cm
Victoria and Albert Museum, London, 281, A & B–1876.

A fluted bowl with a domed lid with flower-bud finial
and saucer-shaped stand to match, painted in Kakiemon
colours and gilt with a design of quail and prunus. The
cover and stand have an additional Rococo-style border
in turquoise blue and gold.

372

Bibliography

Elizabeth Adams, *Chelsea Porcelain*, London, 1987.

Elizabeth Adams and David Redstone, *Bow Porcelains*, London, 1981.

Carl Albiker, *Die Meissner Porzellantiere im 18. Jarhundert*, Berlin, 1932; 2nd edn., 1959.

P. Alfassa and J. Guérin, *Porcelaine Française du XVIIe au milieu du XIXe siecle*, Paris, 1932.

John C. Austin, *Chelsea Porcelain at Williamsburg*, Williamsburg, Virginia, 1977.

Louise Avery, 'Chinese porcelain in English Mounts', *Metropolitan Museum of Art Bulletin*, N.S.2, New York, 1944.

John Ayers, *Far Eastern Ceramics in the Victoria & Albert Museum*, London, 1980.

John Ayers, *Oriental Art in the Victoria & Albert Museum*, London, 1983.

John Ayers, 'Early Collections of Japanese Porcelain in Europe', *International Symposium on Japanese Ceramics*, Seattle Art Museum, 1972, pp. 107–18.

Nicole Ballu, 'Influence de l'Extrême-Orient sur le style de Chantilly au XVIII Siècle', *Cahiers de la Céramique et des Arts du Feu*, 11, 1958.

Bernard von Barsewich, 'Unterglasurblau-malerei', *Keramos*, 121, I, 1988.

H. Belevitch-Stankevitch, *Le Goût Chinois en France au temps de Louis XIV*. Appendix: *Relation de l'Embassade du Chevalier de Chaumont à la Cour du Roi de Siam, 1686*, Paris, 1910.

G. de Bellaigue, 'Chinoiserie at Buckingham Palace', *Apollo*, May, 1975.

Claus Boltz, 'Hoym, Lemaire und Meissen, Ein Beitrag zur Geschichte des Dresdner Porzellansammlung', *Keramos*, 88, April, 1980.

Gerhard Bott (ed.), *Die Grafen von Schönborn*, Germanisches Nationalmuseum, Nürnberg, 1989.

C. R. Boxer, *The Dutch Seaborne Empire*, London, 1965.

C. R. Boxer, *The Portuguese Seaborne Empire*, London, 1969.

F. Britton, *London Delftware*, London, 1986.

Jean-Baptiste Broebes, *Vues des palais et maisons de plaisance de Sa Majesté le Roy de Prusse*, Augsburg, 1733.

Herbert Brunner, *Chinesisches Porzellan im Residenzmuseum*, Munich, 1966.

Françoise Chapard, 'Cicaire Cirou, Premier Maître Porcellainier de la Manufacture de Chantilly', *Musée de Condé*, I, 1971.

R. J. Charleston, 'Covered Vases for the Drawing-Room', *Country Life*, 11th June 1959, pp. 1308–1309.

R. J. Charleston, 'Porcelain as Room Decoration in 18th century England', *Antiques*, December, 1969, pp. 894–99.

R. J. Charleston and John Ayers, *The James A. de Rothschild Collection at Waddesdon Manor. Meissen and other European and Oriental Porcelain*, London, 1971.

Xavier de Chavagnac and Gaston de Grollier, *Histoire des manufactures françaises de porcelaine*, Paris, 1906.

Halina Chojnacka, *Fayanse Polskie XVIII–XIX Wieku*, Warsaw, 1981.

T. H. Clarke, 'Sir Charles Hanbury Williams and the Chelsea Factory', *Transactions of the English Ceramic Circle*, Vol. 9, II, 1988, pp. 110–20.

Craig Clunas (ed.), *Chinese Export Art and Design*, Victoria & Albert Museum, London, 1987.

Gerald Coke, *In Search of James Giles*, Wingham, 1983.

Copenhagen, Nationalmuseet, *Ethnographic Objects in the Royal Danish Kunstkammer 1650–1800*, Bente Dam-Mikkelsen and Torben Lundback (eds), 1980.

John Cornforth and Gervase Jackson-Stops, 'The Gubbay Collection at Clandon', *Country Life*, 29th April, 1971, p. 1006.

H. A. Daendels, *Catalogus tentoonstelling Japans blauw en wit porselein op Hollandse bestelling en in de Japanse smaak*, Museum Het Princessehof, Leeuwarden, 1981.

C. H. De Jonge, *Delft Ceramics*, London, 1970.

L. De Ren, 'Tafelzilver van prins Karel Alexander van Lotharingen bewaard te Wenen', *Antiek*, 19/3, October, 1984.

Diary of Richard Cocks, Cape-Merchant in the English Factory in Japan 1615–22, Edward Maude Thompson (ed.), 2 Vols, Hakluyt Society, London, 1883.

J. L. Dixon, *English Porcelain of the 18th Century*, London, 1952.

P. J. Donnelly, *Blanc de Chine, the Porcelain of Tehua in Fukien*, London, 1969.

Franz Adrian Dreier, 'The *Kunstkammer* of the Hessian Landgraves in Kassel' in Oliver Impey and Arthur MacGregor (eds), *The Origin of Museums*, Oxford, 1965.

Dresden, Staatliche Kunstammlungen, *Porzellansammlung im Zwinger*, by Ingelore Menzhausen and Friedrich Reichel, Dresden, 1982, (4 Auflage, 1988).

Nicole Duchon, *La Manufacture de Porcelaine de Mennecy Villeroy*, le Mée-sur-Seine, 1988.

Joe Earle, 'Japanese Export Lacquer Tankard', *Orientations*, April, 1983, pp. 24–27.

J. Elliot, *The City in Maps: urban mapping to 1900*, British Library, London, 1987.

Svend Ericksen and Geoffrey de Bellaigue, *Sèvres Porcelain*, London, 1987.

A. M. L. E. Erkelens, 'Delfts aardewerk op Het Loo', *Nederlands Kunsthistorisch Jaarboek*, 31, 1980.

R. Ernst, *Führer durch die ehemaligen Hoftafel- und Silberkammer*, 2nd printing, Vienna, 1924.

A. Feulner, *Frankfurter Fayencen*, Berlin, 1935.

H. P. Fourest, *Delftware*, English Edition, London, 1980.

Jean-Antoine Fraisse, *Livre de Desseins Chinois Tirés d'Après des Originaux de Perse, de la Chine et du Japon*, (copy dated 1737).

Sir A. W. Franks, *Catalogue of a Collection of Continental Porcelain lent to the Bethnal Green Museum*, South Kensington Museum, London, 1896.

A. Gabszewicz and G. Freeman, *Bow Porcelain. The Collection formed by Geoffrey Freeman*, London, 1982.

F. H. Garner, *English Delftware*, London, 1948.

S. Gauthier, *Les Porcelainiers du XVIIIe Siècle français*, Paris, 1964.

H. E. van Gelder, 'De Kunstenaars van ons Oud-Delfts Aardewerk', *Mededelingenblad nederlandse vereniging van vrienden van de ceramiek*, 12, 1958.

Anne George, *Japanese Influence on 18th Century English Porcelain, the Albrecht Collection*, London, 1988.

Geoffrey A. Godden, *British Porcelain: an illustrated guide*, London, 1974.

Geoffrey A. Godden, *Oriental Export Market Porcelain and its influence on European Wares*, London, 1979.

H. Havard, *Histoire de la Faience de Delft*, Paris, 1878.

H. Havard, *La Céramique Hollandaise*, 2 Vols, Amsterdam, 1909.

S. Hayashiya, *Nihon no toji, 9: Kakiemon*, Tokyo, 1974.

S. Hayashiya, *Nihon no toji, 8: Ko-Imari*, Tokyo, 1975.

John F. Hayward, *Viennese Porcelain of the du Paquier Period*, London, 1952.

R. L. Hobson, *Catalogue of the English Pottery in the British Museum*, London, 1903.

R. L. Hobson, *Catalogue of the English Porcelain in the British Museum*, London, 1905.

R. L. Hobson, *Catalogue of the Frank Lloyd Collection of Worcester Porcelain of the Wall Period*, British Museum, London, 1923.

R. L. Hobson, *Handbook of the Pottery and Porcelain of the Far East*, 3rd Edition, British Museum, London, 1948.

W. B. Honey, *Guide to the Later Chinese Porcelain*, Victoria & Albert Museum, London, 1927.

W. B. Honey, 'Dutch Decorators of Chinese Porcelain', *Antiques*, February, 1932.

W. B. Honey, *European Ceramic Art: I. Illustrated Historical Survey*, London, 1949.

W. B. Honey, *English Pottery and Porcelain*, 4th edition, London 1949.

W. B. Honey, *French Porcelain of the 18th century*, London, 1950.

W. B. Honey, *European Ceramic Art: II. A Dictionary*, London, 1952.

W. B. Honey, *Dresden China*, London, 1954 edition.

W. B. Honey, *Old English Porcelain*, (revised edition), London, 1977.

Hugh Honour, *Chinoiserie: the vision of Cathay*, London, 1961.

David S. Howard, *Chinese Armorial Porcelain*, London, 1974.

David Howard and John Ayers, *China for the West*, 2 Vols, London, 1978.

Motosuke Imaizumi, *Old Arita and Ko Kutani*, Tokyo, 1974.

Oliver Impey, 'A Tentative Classification of the Arita Kilns', *International Symposium on Japanese Ceramics*, Seattle Art Museum, 1972, pp. 85–90.

Oliver Impey, 'Kyoto-ware hanging wall vases in the Johanneum', *Oriental Art*, XX, 4, 1974, pp. 431–35.

Oliver Impey, *Chinoiserie. The Impact of Oriental Styles on Western Art and Decoration*, London, 1977.

Oliver Impey, 'Collecting Oriental Porcelains in Britain in the Seventeenth and Eighteenth Centuries', *The Burghley Porcelains*, Japan Society, New York, 1980.

Oliver Impey, 'Shoki-Imari and Tianqi; Arita and Jingdezhen in competition for the Japanese market in porcelain in the second quarter of the seventeenth century', *Mededelingenblad nederlandse vereniging van vrienden van de ceramiek*, 116, 1984.

Oliver Impey 'Japanese export lacquer of the seventeenth century', *Lacquerwork in Asia and beyond: Colloquies on Art and Archaeology in Asia*, 11, Percival David Foundation, London, 1981.

Oliver Impey, 'Japan; trade and collecting in seventeenth-century Europe', *The Cabinet of Curiosities*, Oliver Impey and Arthur MacGregor (eds), Oxford, 1985.

Oliver Impey, 'Celadon porcelain from Arita', *Mededelingenblad nederlandse vereniging van vrienden van de ceramiek*, 130/31, 1988.

Oliver Impey, 'The beginnings of the export trade in Japanese porcelain', *Hyakunenan Toji Ronshu*, 3, Arita, 1989.

Hermann Jedding, *Meissner Porzellan des 18 Jahrhunderts in Hamburger Privatbesitz*, Museum für Kunst und Gewerbe, Hamburg, 1982.

Soame Jenyns, 'The Polychrome Wares associated with the potters Kakiemon', *Transactions of the Oriental Ceramic Society*, 1937–38.

Soame Jenyns, *Japanese Porcelain*, London, 1965.

C. J. A. Jörg, *Pronk Porcelain: Porcelain after designs by Cornelis Pronk*, Groningen, 1980.

C. J. A. Jörg, *Porcelain and the Dutch China Trade*, The Hague, 1982.

C. J. A. Jörg, 'Een Japanse fles met de initialen F. W.' *Antiek*, 23rd year, 7, 1989.

W. Pitcairn Knowles, *Dutch Pottery and Porcelain*, London, n.d.

Salomon Kleiner, *Representation au naturel des chateaux de Weissenstein au desus de Pommersfeld, et celui de Geubach...*, Augsburg, 1728.

Regina Krahl, *Chinese Ceramics in the Topkapi Saray Museum Istanbul*, John Ayers (ed.), II, London, 1986.

Arthur Lane, 'Queen Mary II's porcelain collection at Hampton Court', *Transactions of the Oriental Ceramic Society*, 25, 1949–50, pp. 21–31.

Arthur Lane, *Italian Porcelain, with a note on Bueno Retiro*, London, 1954.

Saul Levy, *Maioliche Settecentesche*, 2 Vols, Milan, 1962 and 1964.

R. W. Lightbown, 'Oriental Art and the Orient in Late Renaissance and Baroque Italy', *Journal of the Warburg and Courtauld Institutes*, 32, 1969.

Daisy Lion-Goldschmidt, 'Les porcelaines chinoises du palais de Santos', *Arts Asiatiques*, 25, 1984.

Louis L. Lipski and Michael Archer, *Dated English Delftware*, London, 1984.

London, *International Ceramics Fair and Seminar*, 'Documentary Continental Ceramics from the British Museum', 9, 1985.

Mrs Donald MacAlister (ed.), *William Duesbury's London Account Book*, London, 1931.

F. Severne Mackenna, *Chelsea Porcelain, the Triangle and Raised Anchor Wares*, Leigh-on-Sea, 1948.

F. Severne Mackenna, *Chelsea Porcelain, the Red Anchor Wares*, Leigh-on-Sea, 1951.

J. V. G. Mallet, 'A Chelsea Talk', *Transactions of the English Ceramic Circle*, Vol. 6, I, 1965.

J. V. G. Mallet, 'John Baddeley of Shelton Part I', *Transactions of the English Ceramic Circle*, II, 1966.

Joseph Marryat, *A History of Pottery and Porcelain*, London, 1863.

H. Rissik Marshall, *Coloured Worcester Porcelain of the First Period*, Newport, Monmouthshire, 1954.

Arnold Mountford, *Staffordshire Saltglazed Stoneware*, London, 1971.

T. Nagatake, S. Hayashiya (eds), *Sekai toji zenshu, Ceramic Art of the World, Vol. 8, Edo Period III: Imari and Nabeshima Wares*, Tokyo, 1978.

T. Nagatake, *Ko-Imari*, Saga, 1959.

T. Nagatake, *Kakiemon*, Arita, 1968.

Naples, Museo Duca di Martina, *Kakiemon e Imari*, 1984.

J. E. Nightingale, F.S.A., *Contributions towards the History of Early English Porcelain*, Salisbury, 1881.

Hiroko Nishida, 'An Import for Exotic Tastes: Japanese Porcelain in England', *Country Life*, 6th June, 1974, pp. 1402–1406.

Hiroko Nishida, *Nihon toji zenshu (Pageant of Japanese Ceramics)*, Vol. 23, Ko-Imari, Tokyo, 1976.

Hiroko Nishida, *Nihon toji zenshu (Pageant of Japanese Ceramics)*, Vol. 24, Kakiemon, Tokyo, 1977.

Kōji Ōhashi, 'A recent study on Hizen trade ceramics from kiln sites', *Idemitsu Museum of Arts Bulletin*, 64, 1989.

Oxford, Ashmolean Museum, *Eastern Ceramics and other Works of Art from the Collection of Gerald Reitlinger*, 1981.

Peter Parenzan, *Ehemalige Hoftafel- und Silberkammer*, Vienna, 1980.

Dr Erika Pauls-Eisenbeiss, *German Porcelain of the 18th Century*, London, 1972.

John A. Pope, 'The Origins of the Landscape Style in Arita Blue-and-White', *International Symposium on Japanese Ceramics*, Seattle Art Museum, 1972, pp. 124–28.

Tamara Préaud, *Sèvres des Origines à nos Jours*, Fribourg, 1978.

Bernard Rackham, *Catalogue of the Schreiber Collection of English Pottery and Porcelain*, Vol. II, Victoria and Albert Museum, London, 1930.

Bernard Rackham, *Catalogue of the Glaisher Collection of Pottery & Porcelain in the Fitzwilliam Museum*, Cambridge, 1935.

Bernard Rackham, *Early Staffordshire Pottery*, London, 1951.

Friedrich Reichel, 'Holländische Überdekore auf chinesischen Porzellan', *Dresdner Kunstblätter*, 9 Jahrgang, Heft 6, 1965, pp. 82–86.

Friedrich Reichel, *Early Japanese Porcelain, Arita Porcelain in the Dresden Collection*, English edition, London, 1981.

L. Reidemeister, 'Die Porzellankabinette der Brandenburgisch-Preuszischen Schlösser', Part 1, *Jahrbuch der Preuszischen Kunstsammlungen*, 54, 1933, pp. 262–72; Part 11, 55, 1934, pp. 42–56.

H. H. Ressing, 'Frankfurter Fayencen aus der Zeit des Barock', *Mededelingenblad nederlandse vereniging van vrienden van de ceramiek*, 134, 1989/2, pp. 13–18.

Rainer Rückert, *Meissener Porzellan 1710–1810*, Ausstellung in Bayerischen Nationalmuseum, Munich, 1966.

Rainer Rückert and Johann Willsberger, *Meissen. Porzellan des 18. Jahrhunderts*, Vienna, 1977.

W. J. Rust, *Nederlands porselein*, Amsterdam, 1952 (reprint 1978).

W. J. Rust, 'Een Classificatie van Amsterdams Bont', *Mededelingenblad nederlandse vereniging van vrienden van de ceramiek*, 41, December, 1965, pp. 9–43.

Sigrid Sangl, 'Hoffhandwerk und Wohnkultur unter Lothar Franz und Friedrich Karl von Schönborn' in Gerhard Bott (ed.), *Die Grafen von Schönborn*, Germanisches Nationalmuseum, Nürnberg, 1989.

George Savage, *Seventeenth and Eighteenth Century French Porcelain*, London, 1960.

A. R. Lunsingh Scheurleer, *Niederlandische Fayence*, Munich, 1984.

D. F. Lunsingh Scheurleer, 'Japans porselein met blauwe decoraties uit de tweede helft van de zeventiende en de eerste helft van de achttiende eeuw', *Mededelingenblad Vrienden van de Nederlandse Ceramiek*, 64/65, 1971/2–3.

D. F. Lunsingh Scheurleer, 'Seventeenth-century Japanese Export Porcelain decorated in Underglaze Blue', *International Symposium on Japanese Ceramics*, Seattle Art Museum, 1972, pp. 118–23.

D. F. Lunsingh Scheurleer, Chinese Export Porcelain, *Chine de Commande*, English edition, London, 1974.

D. F. Lunsingh Scheurleer, *Chinesisches und Japanisches Porzellan in europaischen Fassungen*, Braunschweig, 1980.

D. F. Lunsingh Scheurleer, 'Een Japans Fonteinje', *Mededelingenblad nederlandse vereniging van vrienden van de ceramiek*, 58, p. 71.

Th. H. Lunsingh Scheurleer, 'Documents on the furnishing of Kensington House', *Walpole Society*, 38, 1962, pp. 15–58.

Frits Scholten, 'Vroege Japonaiserie in Delft, 1660–1680', *Mededelingenblad nederlandse vereniging van vrienden van de ceramiek*, 128, 1987/3, pp. 17–25.

Frits Scholten, 'Frankfurt Revisited', *Mededelingenblad nederlandse vereniging van vrienden van de ceramiek*, 134, 1989/2, pp. 19–23.

Elka Schrijver, 'Amsterdams Bont', *Apollo*, November, 1964, pp. 396–97.

Richard Seyffarth, *Johann Gregorius Höroldt*, Dresden, 1981.

Masako Shono, *Japanisches Arita-porzellan im sogenannten 'Kakiemonstil' als Vorbild für die Meissner Porzellan manufactur*, Munich, 1973.

Linda R. Shulsky, 'Two porcelain collections; Kensington and de Voorst', *The Journal of the History of Collections*, 2, 1, Oxford, forthcoming, 1990.

Linda. R. Shulsky, 'Queen Mary's collection of porcelain and Delft and its display at Kensington Palace based upon an analysis of the inventory taken in 1697', *Bulletin of the American Ceramic Circle*, forthcoming, 1990.

Anna Somers Cocks, 'The non-functional use of ceramics in the English Country-house during the eighteenth century', *Studies in the History of Art*, 25, 1989.

Jean Louis Sponsel, *Kabinettstucke der Meissner Porzellan-Manufactur von Johann Joachim Kandler*, Leipzig, 1900.

Arthur Spriggs, 'Oriental porcelain in Western paintings, 1450–1700' *Transactions of the Oriental Ceramic Society*, 36, 1964–66.

Konrad Strauss, 'Seltene Deutsche Fayencen in Ausländischen Museen, VII: Victoria & Albert Museum, London', *Keramos*, Heft 66, December, 1974.

Hans Syz, 'Some Oriental Aspects of European Ceramic Decoration', *Keramik-Freunde der Schweiz, Mitteilungsblatt*, 80, March, 1970.

Hetty Terwie, 'De Scheveningen-bordjes outmaskerd?', *Antiek*, 23rd year, 9, 1989.

Peter Thornton, *Seventeenth-century Interior Decoration in England, France and Holland*, New Haven and London, 1978.

Toban Kamotsu Cho 1709–1711, published by Naikaku Bunko, 2 Vols, Tokyo, 1971.

Tokyo, Idemitsu Museum of Arts, *The Inter-influence of Ceramic Art in East and West*, 1984.

Jan Van Dam, 'Geleyersgoet en Hollants Porseleyn, Ontwikkelingen in de Nederlandse Aardewerk-Industrie, 1560–1660', *Mededelingenblad nederlandse vereniging van vrieden van de ceramiek*, 108, 1982/4, pp. 13–26.

J. D. Van Dam, 'Vroege uit Delft (1625–1655) en de Invloed op Japans Porselein (1660–1670)', *Mededelingenblad…*, 135, 1989/3, pp. 4–18 and 29–30.

A. Vecht, *Frederik van Frytom*, Amsterdam, 1968.

Michael Vickers, Oliver Impey and James Allan, *From Silver to Ceramic*, Oxford, 1986.

Minke A. de Visser, 'Chineesh Porselein in Holland met Kakiemon decor vorziern', *Oud-Holland*, Jaargang LXXI, Aflevering I–IV, 1956, pp. 212–16.

T. Volker, 'Porcelain and the Dutch East India Company', *Mededelingen van het Rijksmuseum voor Volkenkunde, Leiden*, 11, 1954.

T. Volker, 'The Japanese porcelain trade of the Dutch East India Company after 1683', *Mededelingen van het Rijksmuseum voor Volkenkunde, Leiden*, 13, 1959.

Voyage of Captain John Saris to Japan 1613, Sir Ernest M. Satow (ed.), Hakluyt Society, London, 1900.

Bernard Watney, *English Blue and White Porcelain of the Eighteenth Century*, London, 1973.

Bernard Watney, 'The King, the Nun, and Other Figures', *Transactions of the English Ceramic Circle*, Vol. 7, Part I, 1968, pp. 48–58.

Bernard Watney, 'The Vauxhall China Works, 1751–1764', *Transactions of the English Ceramic Circle*, Vol. 13, Part 3, 1989.

Otto Walcha, *Meissen Porcelain*, English edition, Dresden, 1981.

F. M. Wieringa, *De Verenigde Oostindische Compagnie in Amsterdam*, University of Amsterdam, 1982.

W. W. Winkworth, 'The Delft Enamellers', *Burlington Magazine*, LII, June, 1928.

W. W. Winkworth, 'European Kakiemon: A Japanese Theme that was Copied on Chinese porcelain', *Antique Collector*, October, 1970, pp. 216–20.

V. Woldbye and Bettina van Meyenburg (eds), *Konkylien og Mennesket*, Copenhagen, Museum of Decorative Art, 1983.

Giles Worsley, 'The Chinese pavilion at Oranienbaum', *Country Life*, 183, 16th Nov, 1989.

W. M. Zappey, A. L. den Blaauwen, A. W. A. van der Goes and A. C. Pronk, *Loosdrechts Porselein*, Zwolle, 1988.

Ernst Zimmermann, *Meissen Porzellan*, Leipzig, 1926.

Ernst Zimmermann, 'Nachdekorierung von chinesischen Porzellan in Europa', *Der Kunstwanderer*, 1928–29, pp. 202–207 and pp. 212–16.

EXHIBITION CATALOGUES

Amsterdam, Willet-Holthuysen Museum, *De Japanse Porseleinkast, Japans exportporselein uit de 17e en 18e eeuw*, 1972.

M. Bauer, *Frankfurter Fayencen aus der Zeit des Barock*, Museum für Kunsthandwerk, Frankfurt am Main, 1988.

Berlin, *Europa und die Kaiser von China*, 1985.

Kordula Bischoff and Dr Baron Ludwig Döry, *Keramika 2, Frankfurter Fayencen des 18 Jahrhunderts*, Historisches Museum, Frankfurt am Main, 1984.

Brussels, Bibliothèque Royale Albert Ier, *Charles-Alexandre de Lorraine, Gouverneur général des Pays-Bas autrichiens*, 1987.

Richard S. Cleveland, *200 Years of Japanese Porcelain*, St Louis, 1970.

Dresden Staatliche Kunstsammlungen, *Meissen Frühzeit und Gegenwart, Johann Friedrich Böttger zu Ehren*, 1982.

English Ceramic Circle, *English Pottery and Porcelain*, commemorative catalogue, Victoria & Albert Museum, London, 1948.

Barbara Brennan Ford and Oliver R. Impey, *Japanese Art from the Gerry Collection in the Metropolitan Museum of Art*, New York, 1989.

Fraeylemaborg, Slochteren, *Aziatische ceramiek uit vijf eeuwen*, 1977.

Hamburg Museum für Kunst und Gewerbe, *Blaumalerei aus Drei Jahrhunderten*, 1989.

Mark Hinton and Oliver Impey, *Kakiemon porcelain from the English Country House*, Ashmolean Museum, Oxford (and Christie's, London), 1989.

Holland Village Museum, *The Dutch East India Company in the 17th century. Life and work of Zacharias Wagenaer (1614–68)*, 1987.

C. J. A. Jörg, *Interaction in Ceramics: Oriental Porcelain & Delftware*, Hong Kong, 1984.

Klaber & Klaber, *Oriental Influences on European Porcelain*, London, 1978.

Gordon Lang, *The Wrestling Boys*, an exhibition of Chinese and Japanese ceramics from the 16th to the 18th century in the collection at Burghley House, 1983.

Martin Lerner, *Blue & White. Early Japanese Export Ware*, Metropolitan Museum of Art, New York, 1978.

London, British Museum, *Bow Porcelain 1744–1776. A Special Exhibition of Documentary Material to commemorate the Bicentenary of the retirement of THOMAS FRYE Manager of the factory and 'inventor and first manufacturer of porcelain in England'*, 1959.

London, Royal Academy of Arts, *The Great Japan Exhibition: The Art of the Edo Period 1600–1868*, 1981.

Munich, *Kurfürst Max Emanuel, Bayern und der Europa um 1700*, 1976.

New York, Japan Society, *The Burghley Porcelains*, 1986.

Oriental Ceramic Society, *Japanese Porcelain*, London, 1956.

Paris, Grand Palais, *Faiences Françaises XVIe–XVIIIe Siècles*, 1980.

Seattle Art Museum, *Ceramic Art of Japan, One Hundred Masterpieces from Japanese Collections*, 1972.

Tokyo N. H. K. and Japan Ukiyo-e Society, *Ceramic Road*, 1982.

Tokyo National Museum, *Masterpieces of Japanese and Chinese Art from the British Museum*, 1987.

Tokyo, *Drei Jahrhunderts Porzellan aus Arita und Meissen. Eine Ausstellung aus der Deutsches Demokratischen Republik*, 1989.

Victoria, B. C., Art Gallery, *The Flowering of Japanese Ceramic Art*, 1983.

Washington, National Gallery of Art, *The Treasure Houses of Britain*, Gervase Jackson-Stops (ed.), New Haven and London, 1985.

Winifred Williams, *The Kakiemon Influence on European Porcelain*, London, 1974.

日本部門への序文

宮廷の磁器：ヨーロッパの日本ブーム　1650〜1750年

東洋陶磁器研究会が日本の陶磁に全面的に注目し、史上初の日本磁器展覧会を開いたのは1956年のことでした。大きな意味では、偉大な学者でコレクターでもあった故ソーム・ジェニンズのインスピレーションによるその展覧会が、欧米のみならず日本においても、輸出された日本磁器に対する関心を再び呼び起こすきっかけとなったのです。今回の催しは全体的に当時よりも大がかりな企画で、ヨーロッパの美的感覚と磁器製造の発展に日本磁器が与えた大きな影響を探求しています。

17世紀中期から18世紀中期まで、ヨーロッパの邸宅や宮殿には日本や中国の磁器がよく見かけられました。東洋文化が流行する中で、王侯貴族が磁器を収集すると同時に漆の家具も購入し、その結果、室内装飾に磁器が広く使われるようになったのです。今日非常に多くの磁器が残っている理由の一つが、ここにあることは疑いもありません。本展覧会は、ヨーロッパに輸入された日本磁器の多様さを実際に公開し、磁器収集ブームがどれだけ広まっていたか、西欧の陶芸家がそれをどの様にして手本に使ったかを示すことを目的としています。

日本からの輸入が本格的に始まったのは、およそ1659年、オランダ東インド会社が65,000個あまりの磁器をバタビアからアムステルダムに送ってからでした。それまで東洋磁器の主な産地はマカオで、ポルトガル人が一世紀前からここで中国製の染付（青花）を購入していました。桃山時代までにはポルトガルと日本の貿易も盛んになり、その中で南蛮風の漆器が注文されていました。そして日本で磁器が手に入るようになる数年前に、オランダとイギリスの商人がこれに加わったのです。

1644年、明朝の衰亡によって中国産の磁器が手に入らなくなり、日本市場を独占し、長崎で貿易を行っていた新興のオランダ東インド会社は日本に目をつけました。注文を受けた有田では、その結果この新しい産業の拡大が促進され、数多くの染付が製造されました（No.30〜72）。その中には西洋風の形をしたものも多く、時には西洋風の装飾が施されることもありました。しかし、インピー博士が論じているように、初期の時代からヨーロッパ人が高く評価したのは彩色豊かな色絵磁器で、これらは特に需要がありました（No.73〜98）。

初期有田の色彩は、徐々に「柿右衛門」として知られる色絵磁器に発達していきましたが、磁器窯の組織は複雑で、それが一つの窯で発達したのではなかったのは明かです。初期有田からもう一つの道を経由して発達した特徴ある磁器は、染付を豊富に使った、西欧でも「伊万里」の名で知られる磁器です。柿右衛門はヨーロッパに輸出された磁器の中では比類なく、展覧会でも最大のグループを構成しています（No.100〜155）。その特徴は、濁し手に施した新鮮で鮮やかな色彩と、左右非対称の簡素な図柄にあります。人や動物や鳥を象った人形もあり、一つのグループにまとめて展示されたもの（No.156〜179）の中には非常に珍しい品もあります。伊万里の部門（No.202〜251）では初期の品から、その後発達した彩色も豊富で金を塗った大型の焼物まで広範に揃えました。磁器貿易はその後徐々に衰え、1740年代には事実上過去のものとなっていました。

輸出された磁器の多くは、初めは実用上の理由から、そして後には器が置かれる豪華な宮殿などの装飾に適するように、ヨーロッパで銀や金箔をかけたブロンズの台にはめ込まれました。これらの流行の移り変わりは展示品や関連する記述によって示しました。また、特別ディスプレーでは、1700年頃の西欧の典型的な「磁器の部屋」の雰囲気を再現しています。

東洋磁器ブームのもう一つの重要な産物は、倣製の過程にあります。明朝の染付を模倣することを目的としていたオランダやその他の国の「デルフト焼」は、その後短期間日本の磁器に習い、柿右衛門や伊万里を模倣した品を作り、あるいは東洋磁器に絵付を加えていました（No.262〜289）。1709年から、ドイツ・ドレスデン近郊の王立磁器制作所マイセンで優れた質の磁器が作られるようになり、続いてヨーロッパ各地に磁器窯が広がりました（No.290〜324）。柿右衛門の形や文様はこれらの窯でこぞって倣製され、フランスでは特にシャンティ、サンクルーで数多く作られました。1750年頃までには英国でも磁器が流行し、チェルシー、ボウ、ウスターなどに新しい窯ができました（No.325〜357）。

本展覧会を意義あるものとするため、展示品はヨーロッパ各地の最も古く、かつ最も有名なコレクションの多くから借用しました。

ジョン・エアーズ

I 初期の日欧貿易

1. 六曲屏風「葡萄牙船長崎入港」 日本・桃山時代 彩色 部141cm×348cm ロンドン・ビクトリア＆アルバート博物館

2. ロンドン貿易商社ギルド 1614年12月20日 日本漆器輸入覚書 ロンドン・インド政庁図書館

3. 螺鈿漆箪笥 日本 1620年頃 85.5cm×57cm 大英博物館

4. 蓋付きジョッキ 螺鈿漆 日本 1610〜1620年 高さ18.5cm ロンドン・ビクトリア＆アルバート博物館

5. 「オランダ東インド会社アムステルダム本社」 銅版 オランダ 17世紀後期 アムステルダム・国立美術館版画部

6. 「オランダ東インド会社アムステルダム造船所」 銅版 オランダ 1692年またはその直後 アムステルダム・国立美術館版画部

7. 1778年頃のオランダ東インド会社商船「ドルフィン」号 （模型） 長さ137cm 高さ115cm グリニッジ・国立海運博物館

8. 世界地図 ヨハネス・ファン・クーレン 銅版手彩色 アムステルダム 1682年 高さ51.5cm 幅60cm 大英博物館

9. 「海から見たバタビア」 ヨハネス・ファンブーンズ 銅版手彩色 オランダ 1660年 41.5cm×92.5cm ハーグ・アルヘメーンライクサルチーフ

10. 日本地図 ヤン・ヤンソン 銅版 アムステルダム 1659年 55cm×45.5cm 大英図書館

11. 長崎地図 木版 日本 1680年頃 61cm×30.5cm 大英図書館

12. 「出島」 A. モンタナス 銅版「日本全図」より ロンドン版 1670年 大英図書館

13. 出島蘭館風景絵巻 長崎派 18世紀後期 大英博物館

14. 長崎唐人居住区風景絵巻 長崎派 18世紀後期 大英博物館

15. 「奥津清美寺」 安藤広重 東海道五十三次より 木版 およそ1847〜1851年 大英博物館

16. ロンドン・東インド会社におけるフリゲート艦「フリート」号積送品販売（日本と中国産の陶磁器も見られる） 1704年9月19日 ロンドン・インド政庁図書館

17. バーリーハウス家財目録中の中国製および日本製磁器 1688年 装丁本 31cm×21cm バーリーハウス

II 初期伊万里

18. 有田と唐津の窯跡で発見された破片12個 オックスフォード・アシュモリアン博物館

19. 青磁広口瓶 1620〜1630年 高さ15cm オックスフォード・アシュモリアン博物館

20. 染付山水皿 1630年頃 口径19.2cm

21. 染付「福」文字徳利 おそらく天神森窯 1640〜1650年 高さ15cm オックスフォード・アシュモリアン博物館

22. 釉裏紅瓶 おそらく広瀬窯 1620〜1640年 高さ13cm

23. 染付桃型皿 1650年頃 口径30cm オックスフォード・アシュモリアン博物館

24. 折り紙型染付皿 1630〜1640年 幅16.5cm

25. 染付蓮文皿 おそらく天神森窯 口径約15.3cm

26. 染付皿 1650〜1660年 口径20.5cm

27. 褐釉染付皿　山小屋窯　1630年頃　口径15cm　オックスフォード・アシュモリアン博物館

28. 染付草文皿　おそらく丸尾窯　1650年頃　口径35cm　オックスフォード・アシュモリアン博物館

29. 青磁釘彫牡丹文大皿　1650年頃　口径47cm

Ⅲ　染　付

30. アルバレロ型薬瓶　17世紀中期　高さ26.5cm

31. 明末風花文皿　1660〜1680年　口径54cm　フロニンゲン・フロニンゲル博物館

32. 明末風皿　「VOC」のモノグラム入り　1660〜1680年　口径39.5cm　オックスフォード・アシュモリアン博物館

33. 皿　「VOC」のモノグラム入り　1660〜1680年　口径34.3cm大英博物館

34. 花水文花型向付　1660〜1680年　口径10.8cm　バーリーハウス

35. 藍釉色絵瓶　1660〜1670年　高さ18.7cm　大英博物館

36. オランダ製銀蓋付藍釉水注　1660〜1670年　高さ15.5cm　フロニンゲン・フロニンゲル博物館

37. 明末風山水文壺　1660〜1680年　高さ24.5cm

38. 明末風山水壺　1660〜1680年　高さ28.5cm　バーリーハウス

39. オランダ風水注　明末風唐人図　1660〜1680年　高さ25.5cm　オックスフォード・アシュモリアン博物館

40. 「Dr VAN Dr Hof」の銘入り薬瓶　1670〜1690年　高さ25.5cm

41. 独風水注　1670〜1690年　高さ21.3cm　大英博物館

42. オランダ製銀蓋付欧風花文ジョッキ　1670〜1690年　高さ27.8cm　大英博物館

43. 菊牡丹文瓶　1660〜1680年　高さ44.5cm　オックスフォード・アシュモリアン博物館

44. 竹文大鉢　1660〜1670年　口径46cm

45. 鳳凰花文皿　1680〜1700年　口径55cm

46. 皿　1680〜1700年　口径55cm　フロニンゲン・フロニンゲル博物館

47. 松竹鳥文蓋付鉢　1680〜1700年　口径32cm

48. 山水文壺　1680〜1700年　高さ44cm　シャーボーン城

49. 松梅文壺　1680〜1700年　高さ49.8cm

50. 瓶　1670〜1690年　高さ28cm　オックスフォード・アシュモリアン博物館

51. 銀線細工台付色絵二重小箱　1660〜1680年　高さ4.6cm　口径6.4cm　バーリーハウス

52. 獅子文筒瓶　1660〜1680年　高さ25.2cm

53. 「VOC」のモノグラム入り磁器瓶9本を入れたオランダ製木箱　1670〜1690年　長さ26cm　アムステルダム・国立美術館

54. 蓋物　1660〜1680年　高さ48cm　ケンブリッジ・フィッツウィリアム博物館

55. 菊文壺　1670〜1690年　高さ30.5cm　バーリーハウス

56. 蓋付山水花文角瓶　1670〜1690年　高さ29cm

57. 花文壺一対　17世紀後期　高さ21.2cm

58. 鈴蘭梅文蓋物一対　17世紀後期　高さ14.3cm

59. 大鉢　1700年頃　口径52cm

60. 蓋付花文角水注　ヨーロッパ製銀箔台付　1680〜1700年　高さ17cm

61. 水籠図向付　1680〜1700年　長さ15.9cm

62. 皿　1680〜1700年　長さ13.5cm　バーリーハウス

63. 茄型小箱　およそ1700年　長さ7.8cm　バーリーハウス

64. 貼付水車文皿　1700年頃　口径21cm

65. 葉型皿　17世紀後期　長さ32cm　ドレスデン・磁器博物館

66. 花鳥文水注　1690年頃　長さ13cm　大英博物館

67. オランダ風景絵皿　17世紀後期〜18世紀初期　口径19cm　オックスフォード・アシュモリアン博物館

68. 欧風海運風景図深鉢　18世紀初期　口径20.2cm　バーリーハウス

69. オランダ風景図葉型皿　17世紀後期〜18世紀初期　口径12.6cm　バーリーハウス

70. 皿　「コーネリス・プロンク」風　1740年頃　口径27cm

71. 椰子の木型壺2点　フランス風(?)オルモル脚付　17世紀後期〜18世紀初期　高さ33.6cm　英国女王陛下

72. 樽上のオランダ人型酒樽　18世紀中期　高さ36cm　大英博物館

IV　初期色絵磁器

73. 花文壺　1660〜1670年　(?)　高さ30cm　大英博物館

74. 蓋物　1660〜1670年　(?)　高さ31cm　大英博物館

75. 瓶　1660〜1680年　オックスフォード・アシュモリアン博物館

76. 山水文瓶　1660年頃　高さ26.3cm　大英博物館

77. 菊文瓶　17世紀後期　高さ42.5cm　ロンドン・ビクトリア&アルバート博物館

78. 草文瓶　1660〜1680年　高さ24.5cm

79. 窓絵箱　1660〜1670年　口径22.6cm　大英博物館

80. 壺から作ったジョッキ　オランダ製銀箔台と中国磁器製蓋付　1660〜1680年　高さ14cm　オックスフォード・アシュモリアン博物館

81. 染付色絵瓶　1660〜1670年　高さ23.1cm　オックスフォード・アシュモリアン博物館

82. 明末風絵皿　1660〜1670年　口径32.4cm　オックスフォード・アシュモリアン博物館

83. 花文茶碗　1660年頃　口径11cm

84. 染付色絵広口瓶　1660年頃　高さ9.5cm　オックスフォード・アシュモリアン博物館

85. 明末風染付色絵大皿　1660〜1680年　口径41.5cm　大英博物館

86. 窓絵壺　1660〜1680年　高さ52cm　大英博物館

87. 色絵ジョッキ　ヨーロッパ製銀箔縁　1660年　高さ15cm　バーリーハウス

88. 菊文蓋物　1670年頃　高さ27.7cm　オックスフォード・アシュモリアン博物館

89. オランダ風花文ゴブレット2客　1670〜1690年　バーリーハウス

90. 生け花文Ⅲ　1670〜1680年　口径32.8cm　オックスフォード・アシュモリアン博物館

91. 貼付布袋文「ケンディ型」水注　1660〜1680年　高さ19.7cm　オックスフォード・アシュモリアン博物館

92. 柿右衛門風深鉢　1680年頃　口径32.6cm　オックスフォード・アシュモリアン博物館

93. 柿右衛門風山水文蓋物　1660〜1680年　高さ46cm　ロンドン・ビクトリア＆アルバート博物館

94. 柿右衛門風深鉢　1670〜1690年　口径28cm　ロンドン・ビクトリア＆アルバート博物館

95. 蓮蕾型柿右衛門色絵ワインカップ　1680年頃　高さ10cm　オックスフォード・アシュモリアン博物館

96. 桶型壺　17世紀後期　高さ22.8cm　オックスフォード・アシュモリアン博物館

97. 色絵Ⅲ　1660〜1680年　口径27cm

98. 鳳凰牡丹文水注　ヨーロッパ製金箔台付　1660〜1680年　高さ12.5cm　ケンブリッジ・フィッツウィリアム博物館

Ⅴ　磁器の陳列

99. 磁器陳列用日本漆飾り棚　1680年頃　金箔木製スタンド（おそらく英国製）1660〜1690年　棚：幅90cm　高さ160cm

会場には、およそ1700年頃のヨーロッパの、室内装飾に磁器を使った典型的な「磁器の部屋」を復元したディスプレーがあります。

Ⅵ　柿右衛門

100. 欧風水注　1670〜1690年　高さ20.5cm　大英博物館

101. 竹梅文水注　後に金箔金属台を装着　1680〜1700年　高さ20cm

102. 蓮文カップと受け皿　1670〜1690年　カップ高さ4.2cm　受け皿口径10.8cm　オックスフォード・アシュモリアン博物館

103. 梅文水注　1680〜1700年　長さ11.2cm　ロンドン・ビクトリア＆アルバート博物館

104. 三脚香炉　1700年頃　高さ11.3cm

105. 藤文箱　1700年頃　高さ12cm　オックスフォード・アシュモリアン博物館

106. 菊文カップと受け皿　1680〜1700年　カップ高さ4.2cm　受け皿口径10.8cm　オックスフォード・アシュモリアン博物館

107. 染付色絵山水文Ⅲ　口径19.9cm　オックスフォード・アシュモリアン博物館

108. 松唐草文インク壺と「サンダ」　1700年頃　長さ9.7cm/9.4cm　フロニンゲン・フロニンゲル博物館

109. 染付花文六角箱　1690〜1700年　幅19cm

110. 染付色絵花文水注　金箔金属台付　1680〜1700年　高さ14cm　オックスフォード・アシュモリアン博物館

111. 花文角徳利　17世紀後期　高さ22.2cm　オックスフォード・アシュモリアン博物館

112. 壁掛け花瓶　17世紀後期　高さ20cm　オックスフォード・アシュモリアン博物館

113. 花文角瓶　1680年頃　高さ14.5cm　オックスフォード・アシュモリアン博物館

114. 竹梅文小皿2枚　1700年頃　口径9.5cm

115. 牡丹文深鉢　1700年頃　口径25cm　オックスフォード・アシュモリアン博物館

116. 深鉢　1690〜1710年　口径23.5cm　ロンドン・ビクトリア＆アルバート博物館

117. 蓋付深鉢　1690〜1710年　口径22cm　大英博物館

118. 菊文茶碗　1690〜1710年　高さ8cm　オックスフォード・アシュモリアン博物館

119. 菊文竹節瓶　17世紀後期　高さ18cm　大英博物館

120. 染付色絵菊文蓋物　1690〜1700年　高さ26cm　バーリーハウス

121. 皿　1680〜1700年　口径21.2cm　オックスフォード・アシュモリアン博物館

122. 司馬温公物語図八角皿　1700年頃　口径20.4cm　オックスフォード・アシュモリアン博物館

123. 十角皿　1690〜1700年　口径24cm　オックスフォード・アシュモリアン博物館

124. 十角皿　1700年頃　口径19.3cm

125. 皿　1700年頃　口径11.4cm　オックスフォード・アシュモリアン博物館

126. 染付竜虎文皿　1690〜1710年　口径31.4cm　オランダ・デルデン・スティッヒティング城

127. 八角カップと受け皿　1700年頃　口径7cm/12.5cm　バーリーハウス

128. 花文八角小鉢　1690〜1710年　口径10.5cm　バーリーハウス

129. 染付色絵四方皿　18世紀初期　14.6cm四方　銘：福

130. 染付色絵十角皿　1700〜1725年　口径19cm　銘：福　オックスフォード・アシュモリアン博物館

131. 染付花文八角小鉢　1690〜1710年　口径10.5cm

132. 染付花文深鉢　1690〜1710年　口径22cm　銘：福

133. 染付絵皿　1700年頃　口径31.1cm　銘：福

134. 染付絵皿　18世紀初期　口径31.5cm　銘：福　オックスフォード・アシュモリアン博物館

135. 松竹梅文壺　1670〜1690年　高さ44cm　シャーボーン城

136. 瓢壺　1670〜1690年　高さ40cm

137. 壺　1670〜1690年　高さ47cm　英国女王陛下・ハンプトンコート宮殿

138. 蓋物　1670〜1690年　高さ61cm　ドレスデン・磁器博物館

139. フランス製オルモル台付角瓶　1670〜1690年　高さ13.5cm　英国女王陛下

140. 金箔金属台付船型（おそらく香炉）　長さ22.8cm　英国女王陛下

141. 鯉（壁掛け花瓶）　噴水としてフランス製（?）オルモル台に装着　17世紀後期　高さ33cm　ブリュッセル・王立美術歴史博物館

142. 三脚燭台　1670〜1690年　高さ31cm　大英博物館

143. 染付色絵皿　17世紀後期〜18世紀初期　口径55cm

144. 染付壺　1670〜1680年　高さ47cm

145. 蓋物　17世紀後期　高さ35.5cm　オックスフォード・アシュモリアン博物館

146. フランス製オルモル台付獅子型燭台　1670〜1690年　高さ34cm　ミュンヘン・宮殿博物館

147. フランス製オルモル台付象型時計　1670〜1690年　高さ44.5cm　ミュンヘン・宮殿博物館

148. 角瓶　1670〜1690年　高さ27.5cm　ケンブリッジ・フィッツウィリアム博物館

149. 148番に似た角瓶2本　フランス製オルモル台付　1670〜1690年　高さ約39cm　パリ・ルーブル美術館

150. 馬図深鉢2点　1810年頃英国製オルモル台に装着　18世紀初期　高さ22.2cm　オックスフォード・アシュモリアン博物館

151. 松竹梅文六角蓋物2点　1810年頃フランス製オルモル台に装着　1670〜1690年　高さ50.5cm　英国女王陛下

152. 六角蓋物　1670〜1690年　高さ約31cm　英国女王陛下・ハンプトンコート宮殿

153. 菖蒲文六角蓋物　1670〜1690年　高さ38cm

154. 染付六角蓋物　1660〜1680年　高さ37.2cm　ロンドン・ビクトリア＆アルバート博物館

155. 花文六角蓋物　1670〜1690年　高さ31cm　大英博物館

Ⅶ　人　形

156. 褐釉台付染付鷹　17世紀後期　高さ18cm　バーリーハウス

157. 青磁座り羅漢2体　17世紀後半　高さ19cm/20.5cm　ナショナルトラスト・アーディグ

158. 亀上の仙人　柿右衛門色絵　1660〜1670年　長さ18.5cm　バーリーハウス

159. 柿右衛門色絵象　1670〜1690年　長さ24cm　ケンブリッジ・フィッツウィリアム博物館

160. 柿右衛門色絵象　1670〜1687年　高さ28.5cm　バーリーハウス

161. 柿右衛門黒象　1670〜1690年　長さ約40cm　ロンドン・ビクトリア＆アルバート博物館

162. 太鼓上の仙人　1670〜1685年　高さ14cm　バーリーハウス

163. 二力士　1670〜1685年　高さ30.7cm　バーリーハウス

164. 若衆　柿右衛門色絵着物　1670〜1685年　高さ30.2cm　大英博物館

165. 美人像　柿右衛門色絵着物　1670〜1690年　高さ35cm　ケンブリッジ・フィッツウィリアム博物館

166. 二美人座像　柿右衛門色絵着物　1670〜1690年　高さ26.8cm　ロンドン・ビクトリア＆アルバート博物館

167. 柿右衛門色絵獅子2匹　1670〜1685年　高さ16cm　バーリーハウス

168. 柿右衛門色絵虎2匹　1670〜1700年　高さ23.5cm/24cm　ドレイトンハウス

169. 柿右衛門色絵雄鶏　1670〜1700年　高さ28cm　バーリーハウス

170. 柿右衛門色絵極楽鳥　17世紀後期　高さ42.5cm　ペットワースハウス・エグルモント公

171. 柿右衛門色絵おしどり　オルモル台付　1670〜1690年　長さ20.4cm　クランドン-パーク・ナショナルトラスト

172. 褐釉台鷲2羽　1680〜1700年　高さ55cm/56cm　グリムスソーン＆ドラモンド城トラスト

173. 伊万里風色絵鷹　18世紀初期　高さ23cm　大英博物館

174. 伊万里風染付色絵役者（?）　18世紀初期　高さ53cm　フロニンゲン・フロニンゲル博物館

175. 犬　部分色絵　1670〜1690年　長さ24cm　バーリーハウス

176. 染付色絵馬　1720～1740年　長さ18cm　フロニンゲン・フロニンゲル博物館

177. 雄鶏雌鶏　色絵　18世紀初期　高さ25cm/23.5cm　ケンブリッジ・フィッツウィリアム博物館

178. 染付色絵金箔鯉　18世紀初期　高さ31.5cm　ケンブリッジ・フィッツウィリアム博物館

179. 波上の鯉2匹　色絵　17世紀後期　高さ24cm

Ⅷ　ヨーロッパの日本様式

180. 染付山水瓢壺　陶器　オランダ・デルフト　1660～1680年　高さ38.5cm　ケンブリッジ・フィッツウィリアム博物館

181. 染付柿右衛門色絵花文壺　陶器　オランダ・デルフト　1680～1700年　高さ32.2cm

182. 染付山水壺　陶器　オランダ・デルフト　1670～1680年　高さ33.2cm　レディー・ビクトリア・リーサム

183. 中国製釉裏紅瓶　磁器　1700～1720年　オランダで後絵付（およそ1710～1725年）　高さ21.5cm　大英博物館

184. 柿右衛門色絵深鉢複製品　磁器　ドイツ・マイセン　1730年頃　口径24.1cm　ロンドン・ビクトリア＆アルバート博物館

185. 柿右衛門＝伊万里風皿　磁器　ドイツ・マイセン　1735年頃　口径57.2cm　ロンドン・ビクトリア＆アルバート博物館

186. 有田風壺　花文色絵　ドイツ・マイセン　1730～1733年頃　高さ34.6cm　銘：AR（オーガスタス王の意）　大英博物館

187. 蓋付タリーン・セット　柿右衛門風色絵磁器　フランス・シャンティ　1730～1751年　台長23.4cm　ロンドン・ビクトリア＆アルバート博物館

188. 柿右衛門風色絵唐人図壺　フランス・シャンティ　1735～1745年　高さ25.5cm

189. 人形　柿右衛門仙人像（No.162）倣製品　フランス・メネシー　1740～1750年　高さ9.5cm　ケンブリッジ・フィッツウィリアム博物館

190. 柿右衛門風色絵雄鹿型燭台　オルモル台付　ドイツ・マイセン　1730年頃　台はフランス製(?)1730～1750年　高さ18cm　ミュンヘン・宮殿博物館

191. 有田風（No.172）鷲　ドイツ・マイセン　1730年頃　高さ49cm　ドレスデン・磁器博物館

192. 司馬温公物語図八角皿　ドイツ・マイセン　1730年頃　口径25.2cm　大英博物館

193. 司馬温公物語図八角皿　英国チェルシー　1755年頃　口径22cm　大英博物館

194. 柿右衛門風色絵皿　英国チェルシー　1753～1755年頃　口径17.5cm　ロンドン・ビクトリア＆アルバート博物館

195. 六角蓋物　柿右衛門（No.155）倣製品　ドイツ・マイセン　1730年頃　高さ30.9cm　大英博物館

196. 柿右衛門風色絵鳳凰花文六角壺　英国チェルシー　1753～1755年頃　高さ23.5cm　ロンドン・ビクトリア＆アルバート博物館

197. 色絵六角壺　英国チェルシー　1752～1755年頃　高さ24cm

198. 柿右衛門風色絵松竹梅文六角蓋物　1752～1755年頃　高さ26.5cm　大英博物館

199. 花文六角蓋物　英国チェルシー　1752～1755年頃　高さ16.5cm

200. 柿右衛門風花鳥図六角蓋物　英国ウスター　1775年頃　高さ28.8cm　大英博物館

201. 柿右衛門風文様六角蓋物　英国ウスター　1775年頃
　　　高さ37.9cm　大英博物館

IX　伊万里焼

202. ヨーロッパ製金属台付マスタードポットと塩入2点
　　　色絵花文　1670〜1690年　高さ12.3cm/6.6cm/3.9cm
　　　ロンドン・ビクトリア&アルバート博物館

203. 柿牡丹文八角瓶　1670〜1690年　高さ23.8cm　オッ
　　　クスフォード・アシュモリアン博物館

204. 水注　1690〜1710年　高さ14.5cm　大英博物館

205. 花文皿　1700〜1720年　口径12.6cm　オックス
　　　フォード・アシュモリアン博物館

206. 色絵銚子　1690〜1710年　高さ16.5cm　オックス
　　　フォード・アシュモリアン博物館

207. 色絵菊文銚子　1690年頃　高さ16cm

208. 貼付花文香炉2点　1690〜1710年　高さ7.5cm/7.1cm
　　　ドレスデン・磁器博物館

209. 貼付花文ゴブレット　1690〜1710年　高さ約15cm
　　　ドレスデン・磁器博物館

210. 貼付花文水注　1690〜1710年　高さ11.5cm　ドレス
　　　デン・磁器博物館

211. 獅子文香炉2点　1690〜1710年　高さ15.5cm　大英博
　　　物館

212. 花文四方鉢　1700年頃　18.2cm　オックスフォー
　　　ド・アシュモリアン博物館

213. 青磁皿　18世紀初期　口径21.2cm　オックスフォー
　　　ド・アシュモリアン博物館

214. メロン型壁掛け青磁花瓶2点　18世紀初期　長さ
　　　16.8cm

215. 松梅牡丹文皿　1700年頃　幅27cm

216. 献上伊万里風筒瓶2本　1710〜1725年　高さ24.6cm
　　　ドレスデン・磁器博物館

217. 蓋付深鉢　1700〜1720年　口径24cm　ドレスデン・
　　　磁器博物館

218. オランダ風コーヒーポット　1710〜1725年　高さ
　　　31cm　フロニンゲン・フロニンゲル博物館

219. 染付色絵花文皿　1710〜1730年　口径28cm　ケンブ
　　　リッジ・フィッツウィリアム博物館

220. 窓絵深鉢　1700〜1720年　口径20cm　バーリーハウ
　　　ス

221. 花文深鉢　1700〜1720年　口径24.6cm　英国女王陛
　　　下

222. 花文角瓶2本　1700〜1720年　高さ22.8cm　ロンド
　　　ン・ビクトリア＆アルバート博物館

223. 染付壺　1700〜1720年　高さ51.5cm　ロンドン・ビ
　　　クトリア＆アルバート博物館

224. 染付藤文深鉢　1700〜1720年　口径37.2cm　ロンド
　　　ン・ビクトリア＆アルバート博物館

225. 染付蓋付八角鉢　1710〜1730年　高さ44.5cm　ゼッ
　　　トランド侯爵

226. 菊牡丹文蓋物　1680〜1700年　高さ67cm

227. 菊牡丹文壺3点と同じく筒瓶2点　18世紀初期　高さ
　　　29cm/17.3cm

228. 蓋付大甕2点　18世紀初期　高さ89.5cm　ナショナル
　　　トラスト・アーディグ

229. 大皿　1700〜1720年　口径54cm

230. 大皿　17世紀後期〜18世紀初期　口径54.5cm　フロ
　　　ニンゲン・フロニンゲル博物館

231. ファン・ブレン家紋章皿　1702〜1720年頃　口径
36cm　フロニンゲン・フロニンゲル博物館

232. 欧風紋章大皿　1710〜1725年　口径55cm

233. 色絵大皿　1710〜1730年　口径55cm　レディー・ビ
クトリア・リーサム

234. 色絵竜文大皿　1680〜1700年　口径49.5cm　大英博
物館

235. 鶴文大皿　1690〜1720年　口径54.6cm　英国女王陛
下

236. 大皿　1690〜1720年　口径53.5cm　英国女王陛下

237. 深皿　1710〜1730年　口径24.5cm　大英博物館

238. 芙蓉手皿　嘉靖銘（明朝）　1720〜1740年　口径26cm
ロンドン・ビクトリア＆アルバート博物館

239. 色絵花文鉢と同皿　銘：大根の図　1730年頃　高さ
7.3cm　口径17.8cm

240. 欧風ゴブレット　1710〜1730年　高さ9.9cm

241. 調味料入セット（水注5点・塩入1点）　1700〜1725年
口径28.5cm

242. 欧風ソース入　1710〜1730年　長さ24cm

243. オランダ製銀型風水注　1720〜1740年　高さ29.9cm
オックスフォード・アシュモリアン博物館

244. 献上伊万里風鳳凰菊文深鉢　1700〜1720年　フラン
ス製銀台付（1710〜1725年）　高さ11cm　ミュンヘ
ン・国立バイエルン博物館

245. 宝石箱　伊万里の瓶を切断後ウィーン製（?）銀台に装
着　1725年頃　長さ37.5cm　ウィーン・ホフシル
バー＆タフェルカメール

246. センターピース（伊万里茶碗5点・同水注4点）　1700
〜1730年　英国製銀台に装着（1755〜1756年）　オラ

ンダで後絵付（1766〜1767年）　幅60cm　ウィーン・
ホフシルバー＆タフェルカメール

247. 卓上噴水（日本製と中国製磁器付）　1700〜1730年
オランダ製銀台に装着（1772年）　高さ45cm　ウィー
ン・ホフシルバー＆タフェルカメール

248. 伊万里人形と鉢付燭台　1690〜1720年　オランダ製
銀台に装着（18世紀中期）　高さ約30cm　ウィーン・
ホフシルバー＆タフェルカメール

249. 角瓶2本　1700〜1720年　フランス製オルモル台に装
着（1740〜1750年）　高さ29.5cm　英国女王陛下

250. ポプリ入と噴水（蓋物付）　1700〜1730年　フランス
製（?）オルモル台に装着（1810〜1815年）　高さ43cm
英国女王陛下

251. 伊万里焼大皿2枚　1700年頃　木製脚に装着（19世紀
初期）　口径57cm/32cm　コーシャム・メシュエンコ
レクション

X　日本風中国磁器

252. 柿右衛門色絵風メロン型水注　景徳鎮　1690〜1700
年　高さ16cm　英国女王陛下

253. 伊万里風花文壺　景徳鎮　1710〜1720年　高さ
38.4cm　ロンドン・ビクトリア＆アルバート博物館

254. 伊万里風菊牡丹文深鉢　景徳鎮　1710〜1725年　口
径27cm　ナショナルトラスト・ベルトンハウス

255. 伊万里風皿　景徳鎮　1710〜1725年　口径27cm　ロ
ンドン・ビクトリア＆アルバート博物館

256. 伊万里風菊文蓋付鉢　景徳鎮　1710〜1725年　口径
22.2cm　ロンドン・ビクトリア＆アルバート博物館

257. 伊万里風皿　景徳鎮　1720〜1730年　口径54cm　ロ
ンドン・ビクトリア＆アルバート博物館

258. 卓上アーン　景徳鎮　1715〜1730年　フランス製オルモル台（1720〜1730年頃）　高さ33.7cm　ロンドン・ビクトリア＆アルバート博物館

259. Ⅲ　景徳鎮　1710〜1720年　口径33.4cm　オックスフォード・アシュモリアン博物館

260. 柿右衛門風染付Ⅲ　底にウォルポール家紋章　景徳鎮　1752年頃　口径31.5cm

261. 英国製銀型風マグカップ　伊万里風色絵　景徳鎮　1730〜1740年　高さ15.3cm　ロンドン・ビクトリア＆アルバート博物館

ⅩⅠ　ヨーロッパで装飾された磁器

262. 薬瓶　日本　18世紀初期　オランダで一部伊万里風色絵付（1710〜1725年）　高さ48cm　オックスフォード・アシュモリアン博物館

263. 染付徳利　日本　18世紀初期　オランダで柿右衛門風色絵付（1730〜1740年）　高さ20.3cm　オックスフォード・アシュモリアン博物館

264. 色絵渦文瓶　景徳鎮　1710〜1725年　オランダで獅子と子の色絵付（1725〜1735年）　高さ26.3cm　ロンドン・ビクトリア＆アルバート博物館

265. Ⅲ　景徳鎮　1710〜1725年　オランダで柿右衛門風色絵付（1725〜1735年）　口径21cm　ロンドン・ビクトリア＆アルバート博物館

266. 水注と受けⅢ　ドイツ・マイセン　1720〜1725年　オランダで柿右衛門風色絵付（1725〜1735年）　口径10cm　オックスフォード・アシュモリアン博物館

267. 角瓶　ドイツ・マイセン　1720年頃　オランダで柿右衛門風色絵付（1730〜1740年）　高さ21cm

268. 筒瓶　景徳鎮　1720年頃　オランダで柿右衛門風色絵付（1730〜1740年）　高さ27.3cm

269. 猿とオランダ商人　中国徳化窯　1700年頃　オランダで伊万里風色絵付　高さ30.5cm　ロンドン・ビクトリア＆アルバート博物館

270. カップ　中国徳化窯　1700〜1720年　ヨーロッパで柿右衛門風竜文色絵付　高さ6.8cm　オックスフォード・アシュモリアン博物館

ⅩⅡ　デルフト焼とファイアンス（錫釉土器）

271. 明末風染付壺　オランダ・デルフト　1660〜1670年　高さ24.5cm　ケンブリッジ・フィッツウィリアム博物館

272. 染付深鉢　オランダ・デルフト　1665年　高さ15cm　ハーグ市立博物館

273. 染付蓋物　オランダ・デルフト　1670〜1680年　高さ40.3cm　アルンヘム市立博物館

274. 有田風染付水注　オランダ・デルフト　1670〜1680年　高さ22cm　アルンヘム市立博物館

275. 藍釉マグカップ　英国ランベス　17世紀後期　高さ8cm　ケンブリッジ・フィッツウィリアム博物館

276. 大Ⅲ　フランス・ヌヴェール　1670〜1690年　口径41cm　ケンブリッジ・フィッツウィリアム博物館

277. 柿右衛門風色絵花鳥文飾り板　オランダ・デルフト　18世紀初期　高さ36.8cm　ロンドン・ビクトリア＆アルバート博物館

278. 柿右衛門風色絵花鳥文バターケース　オランダ・デルフト　1730〜1740年　口径10cm　デルフト・プリンセンホフ博物館

279. 伊万里風蓋物　オランダ・デルフト（「ギリシャA」窯）　1701〜1722年　高さ48.2cm　ロンドン・ビクトリア＆アルバート博物館

280. 伊万里風香辛料入　オランダ・デルフト（「ギリシャA」窯）　1701〜1722年　幅10.8cm　ロンドン・ビクトリア＆アルバート博物館

281. 伊万里風虎文皿　オランダ・デルフト　18世紀初期　口径22.5cm　ロンドン・ビクトリア＆アルバート博物館

282. 伊万里風皿　オランダ・デルフト　18世紀初期　口径22.5cm　ハーグ市立博物館

283. 蓋付深鉢　伊万里香炉倣製品　オランダ・デルフト（「ギリシャA」窯）　1701〜1722年　口径16cm　ハーグ市立博物館

284. 皿　伊万里倣製品　オランダ・デルフト　18世紀初期　口径35.5cm　大英博物館

285. 皿　伊万里（または中国磁器）倣製品　トルコ語銘入　ポーランド・ワルシャワ　1776年頃　口径28.5cm　ロンドン・ビクトリア＆アルバート博物館

286. 色絵山水皿　ドイツ・アンスバッハ　18世紀前半　口径37.9cm　ロンドン・ビクトリア＆アルバート博物館

287. 伊万里風鯉型タリーン　ドイツ・フルダ　1740〜1743年　高さ30.5cm　ロンドン・ビクトリア＆アルバート博物館

288. 伊万里風色絵皿　フランス・サンセニまたはルーアン　1740〜1750年　口径38.6cm　ロンドン・ビクトリア＆アルバート博物館

289. 柿右衛門風深鉢　英国ランベス　1730〜1740年　口径34.3cm　ロンドン・ビクトリア＆アルバート博物館

ⅩⅢ　ヨーロッパ大陸の磁器

290. 日本風染付瓶　ドイツ・マイセン　1720〜1725年　高さ16cm　ロンドン・ビクトリア＆アルバート博物館

291. 有田風花鳥文染付ジョッキ　ドイツ・マイセン　1730年頃　高さ18.3cm　大英博物館

292. 竹梅文八角鉢　柿右衛門倣製品　ドイツ・マイセン　1730年頃　口径18cm　大英博物館

293. 柿右衛門風扁壺　ドイツ・マイセン　1730年頃　高さ22.5cm　ブリュッセル・王立美術歴史博物館

294. 柿右衛門風色絵チョコレートポット　ドイツ・マイセン　1740年頃　高さ16.5cm　ベッドフォード・セシル・ヒギンズ博物館

295. 柿右衛門風牡丹文食器　ドイツ・マイセン　1735〜1740年　高さ18cm　ブリュッセル・王立美術歴史博物館

296. 赤絵竜文チョコレートカップ　ドイツ・マイセン　1734〜1739年　幅11cm

297. ポーランド王室紋皿　ドイツ・マイセン　1731年頃　口径23.4cm　大英博物館

298. 柿右衛門風色絵八角鉢　ドイツ・マイセン　1735年頃　口径25.8cm　大英博物館

299. 壺　柿右衛門倣製品　ドイツ・マイセン　1730年頃　高さ30.2cm　大英博物館

300. 柿右衛門風色絵バターケース　ドイツ・マイセン　1738〜1740年　口径12.1cm

301. 深鉢　ドイツ・マイセン　1730年頃　口径21.4cm　大英博物館

302. 柿右衛門風色絵盆　ドイツ・マイセン　1735年頃　長さ44.4cm　ロンドン・ビクトリア＆アルバート博物館

303. 柿右衛門風色絵水注　ドイツ・マイセン　1735年頃　高さ11.8cm　ロンドン・ビクトリア＆アルバート博物館

304. 柿右衛門風色絵カップと受け皿　ドイツ・マイセン　1730〜1740年　口径10.5cm　オックスフォード・アシュモリアン博物館

305. 柿右衛門香炉風スープボール　ドイツ・マイセン
1730年頃　幅18cm　オックスフォード・アシュモリ
アン博物館

306. 伊万里風色絵花文箱　ドイツ・マイセン　1735年頃
幅16.5cm　ロンドン・ビクトリア＆アルバート博物
館

307. 鳥文皿　伊万里倣製品　ドイツ・マイセン　1740年頃
口径23.7cm　大英博物館

308. 伊万里風唐人花文皿　ドイツ・マイセン　1735年頃
口径15.5cm

309. 鳳凰牡丹文鉢　オーストリア(?)・ウィーン（ドゥパキ
エ窯）　1735～1740年　口径24.1cm　ロンドン・ビク
トリア＆アルバート博物館

310. 絵皿　伊万里倣製品　オーストリア・ウィーン　1750
年頃　口径21cm　ブリュッセル・王立美術歴史博物
館

311. 卓上酒樽　一部有田風花文色絵　オーストリア・
ウィーン　1735年頃　高さ27.6cm　ケンブリッジ・
フィッツウィリアム博物館

312. タリーン　フランス・サンクルー　1730～1740年頃
口径24.8cm　ロンドン・ビクトリア＆アルバート博
物館

313. 柿右衛門風松竹梅文カップと受け皿　フランス・サン
クルー　1735年頃　口径12.6cm　大英博物館

314. 柿右衛門風獅子文溲瓶　フランス・シャンティ　1730
～1751年　長さ19cm

315. 柿右衛門草文ワインクーラー　フランス・サンティ
1730～1751年　幅20cm

316. ステッキ柄　フランス・サンクルー　1730～1740年
長さ14.9cm　ロンドン・ビクトリア＆アルバート博
物館

317. ステッキ柄（磁器）　フランス・サンクルー　1730～
1751年　長さ4.7cm

318. フォーク2本とナイフ1本　A：フランス・シャンティ
1730～1751年　B：フランス・ヴィルロワ　1740年頃
C：ドイツ・マイセン　1740年頃　長さ22.3cm

319. 柿右衛門型色絵皿　フランス・おそらくバンサンヌ
1745～1750年　口径12.7cm　ロンドン・ビクトリア
＆アルバート博物館

320. 花文小鉢2点　フランス・バンサンヌ　1745～1750年
口径7.9cm

321. 伊万里釉唐風文タリーン　イタリア・ベネチア（コジ
窯）　1770年頃　幅28cm　ケンブリッジ・フィッツ
ウィリアム博物館

322. 花文皿　ドイツ・ルドヴィグスブルグ　1760～1770
年　幅36.5cm　ケンブリッジ・フィッツウィリアム博
物館

323. 伊万里風絵皿　オランダ・ローズドレヒト　1778～
1782年　幅40cm　フロニンゲン・フロニンゲル博物
館

324. 藤松文皿　伊万里倣製品　オランダ・アムステル
1785～1800年　口径25.3cm　フロニンゲン・フロニ
ンゲル博物館

ⅩⅣ　英国磁器

325. 赤竜文カップと受け皿　チェルシー　1750～1752年
口径10.8cm　ロンドン・ビクトリア＆アルバート博
物館

326. 柿右衛門風竹虎文八角皿　チェルシー　1755年頃　口
径22.2cm　大英博物館

327. 十角皿　ボウ　1756～1758年　口径14cm　ロンド
ン・ビクトリア＆アルバート博物館

328. カップと受け皿　チェルシー　1750〜1753年　幅14.8cm

329. 梅鳥文十角皿　チェルシー　1752〜1754年　口径16.5cm　ロンドン・ビクトリア＆アルバート博物館

330. 十角深鉢　チェルシー　1752〜1755年　口径19cm　大英博物館

331. 八宝唐草文砂糖入　チェルシー　1752〜1755年　高さ11.5cm　ロンドン・ビクトリア＆アルバート博物館

332. 銀器風竜虎文皿　チェルシー　1752〜1755年　長さ23cm　大英博物館

333. 鶴文皿　チェルシー　1755年頃　口径20cm

334. 柿右衛門風蝶文皿　チェルシー　1752〜1755年　口径22cm

335. マグカップ　ヴォクスホール　1755〜1760年　高さ12.5cm

336. カップと受け皿　ロングトンホール（?）　1755〜1760年　幅13cm

337. 中国風壺　ボウ　1755年頃　高さ26.5cm

338. 葉型皿　ボウ　1760年頃　長さ30cm

339. 深鉢　トーマス・クラフトを意味する「TC」のモノグラム入り　ボウ　1760年頃　口径22cm　大英博物館

340. 水注　プリマス　1768〜1770年　高さ14cm　ロンドン・ビクトリア＆アルバート博物館

341. 伊万里風鯉型壺　チェルシー　1760〜1765年　高さ17.1cm　大英博物館

342. 有田風食塩釉鷹　スタッフォードシャー　18世紀中期　高さ18.7cm　大英博物館

343. 食塩釉水注　スタッフォードシャー　1750〜1760年　高さ13.3cm　大英博物館

344. 柿右衛門風花鳥文染付皿　チェルシー　1755年頃　口径22.8cm　大英博物館

345. 皿　伊万里錦手花文倣製品　チェルシー　1760年頃　口径20.8cm　大英博物館

346. 染付柿右衛門色絵皿　ボウ　1755年頃　口径18.4cm　ロンドン・ビクトリア＆アルバート博物館

347. 花文四方鉢　ウスター　1765〜1770年　幅23.5cm　オックスフォード・アシュモリアン博物館

348. 四方鉢　ウスター　1765〜1770年　高さ11.5cm

349. 柿右衛門風花鳥文花器　ウスター　1765〜1770年　幅21.7cm　大英博物館

350. 伊万里錦手風色絵皿　ウスター　1765〜1770年　口径24.8cm　ロンドン・ビクトリア＆アルバート博物館

351. 伊万里風深鉢　ウスター　1770年頃　口径19.6cm　オックスフォード・アシュモリアン博物館

352. 渦扇文バターケース　ウスター　1770年頃　幅11.7cm　ロンドン・ビクトリア＆アルバート博物館

353. 菊文パンチポット　ウスター　1775年頃　高さ22.5cm　大英博物館

354. 伊万里風鯉文皿　ウスター　1770年頃　口径22.3cm　オックスフォード・アシュモリアン博物館

355. 伊万里風色絵深鉢　ダービー　1765年頃　口径11.5cm　大英博物館

356. 伊万里風皿　ダービー　1775年頃　口径17.8cm　オックスフォード・アシュモリアン博物館

357. 染付紅茶セット　ダビ

XV 鶉文様

358. 掛軸「黍と鶉」 土佐派 17世紀後期〜18世紀初期
77.7cm x 28.6cm 大英博物館

359. 柿右衛門色絵八角皿 日本 1700年頃 幅25.5cm
オックスフォード・アシュモリアン博物館

360. 柿右衛門色絵小皿 日本 18世紀初期 口径12cm
オックスフォード・アシュモリアン博物館

361. 染付鶉文皿 日本 18世紀初期 口径14.7cm バー
リーハウス

362. 筒瓶 中国徳化窯 17世紀後期 ヨーロッパで後絵付
（18世紀初期） 高さ16cm

363. 錫釉色絵皿（土器） オランダ・デルフト 1720〜
1735年 口径22.4cm 大英博物館

364. 八角砂糖入 ドイツ・マイセン 1730〜1740年 口
径9.5cm ロンドン・ビクトリア＆アルバート博物館

365. タリーン フランス・シャンティ 1735〜1745年
口径30.5cm オックスフォード・アシュモリアン博物
館

366. メロン型鳥文水注 フランス・シャンティ 1735年頃
高さ10cm ベッドフォード・セシル・ヒギンズ美術
館

367. 色絵八角水注 英国チェルシー 1752年頃 高さ
13.7cm ベッドフォード・セシル・ヒギンズ美術館

368. 色絵八角皿 英国チェルシー 1753〜1755年 口径
26.2cm 大英博物館

369. 色絵センターピース（イルカと貝） 英国ボウ 1755〜
1760年 口径18.4cm ロンドン・ビクトリア＆アル
バート博物館

370. 色絵瓶 英国ボウ 1755〜1760年 高さ20.3cm 大
英博物館

371. 色絵水注 英国ウスター 1765年頃 高さ17.5cm
大英博物館

372. 色絵砂糖入 英国ウスター 1765〜1775年 スタン
ド口径18.4cm ロンドン・ビクトリア＆アルバート
博物館

Index